Occupational & Industrial Safety Health Management and Engineering

Taken from:

Industrial Safety and Health Management, Fifth Edition
by C. Ray Asfahl

Occupational Safety Management and Engineering, Fifth Edition
by Willie Hammer and Dennis Price

**Second Custom Edition for
Columbia Southern University**

Custom Publishing

New York   Boston   San Francisco
London   Toronto   Sydney   Tokyo   Singapore   Madrid
Mexico City   Munich   Paris   Cape Town   Hong Kong   Montreal

Taken from:

Industrial Safety and Health Management, Fifth Edition
by C. Ray Asfahl
Copyright © 2004 by Pearson Education, Inc.
Published by Prentice Hall
Upper Saddle River, NJ 07458

Occupational Safety Management and Engineering, Fifth Edition
by Willie Hammer and Dennis Price
Copyright © 2001, 1989, 1985, 1981, 1975 by Prentice Hall
A Pearson Education Company

This special edition published in cooperation with Pearson Custom Publishing.

Printed in the United States of America

10 9 8 7 6 5 4 3 2 1

ISBN 0-536-18536-0

2008160004

RG

Please visit our web site at *www.pearsoncustom.com*

PEARSON CUSTOM PUBLISHING
501 Boylston Street, Suite 900, Boston, MA 02116
A Pearson Education Company

Contents

Taken from: *Occupational Safety Management and Engineering*, Fifth Edition by Willie Hammer and Dennis Price

CHAPTER 4   *APPRAISING PLANT SAFETY*   42

CHAPTER 5   *ACCIDENT INVESTIGATIONS*   60

Taken from: *Industrial Safety and Health Management,* Fifth Edition by C. Ray Asfahl

CHAPTER 6   *CONCEPTS OF HAZARD AVOIDANCE*   71

Taken from: *Occupational Safety Management and Engineering*, Fifth Edition by Willie Hammer and Dennis Price

CHAPTER 7   HAZARDS AND THEIR CONTROL   103

Taken from: *OSHA, Job Hazard Analysis*, U.S. Department of Labor

CHAPTER 8   JOB HAZARD ANALYSIS   129

Taken from: *Occupational Safety Management and Engineering*, Fifth Edition by Willie Hammer and Dennis Price

CHAPTER 9   SAFETY ANALYSIS   153

Taken from: *Industrial Safety and Health Management,* Fifth Edition by C. Ray Asfahl

Taken from: *Occupational Safety Management and Engineering,* Fifth Edition by Willie Hammer and Dennis Price

Taken from: *Industrial Safety and Health Management,* Fifth Edition by C. Ray Asfahl

CHAPTER 17   *ENVIRONMENTAL CONTROL AND NOISE*   361

CHAPTER 18   *CONSTRUCTION*   390

C H A P T E R   1

Management and Its Responsibilities

Active participation by all managers of any industrial organization, especially those at the top, in carrying out accident prevention programs is so vital that the safety engineer who is not given effective support should (1) begin looking for a job elsewhere and (2) keep a "Pearl Harbor" file.

Without management support the conscientious safety engineer will be in a constant state of frustration; his or her efforts to accomplish the job successfully will be hampered from the start. Avoidance of accidents requires a sustained integrated effort by managers of all departments, supervisors, and other employees at all levels and in all activities. The safety engineer may indicate of what this effort should consist and may determine whether it is being carried out properly and adequately. Only the managers, however, can ensure that it is a properly integrated and coordinated activity.

SAFETY POLICIES

The influence of management must be apparent in the safety policies it sets, the degree to which those policies are observed, and the concern with which it treats any violation. Managers must leave no doubts in the minds of employees that they are concerned about accident prevention. This concern to prevent injury and damage must be sustained continually, rather than intermittently or only temporarily being presented with an accident report.

Unless management can provide this support, accidents will take place, perhaps repeatedly. A safety engineer working under such unfortunate conditions will do well to document all efforts to carry out a successful accident prevention program. Changing legal attitudes are leading more and more toward holding managers and safety engineers, especially managers, responsible for workers' safety. If the manager of the organization is not providing adequate support, the safety engineer must be able to demonstrate he or she was not at fault if an accident should occur.

Such a file can have beneficial results other than simply safeguarding the safety engineer against any managerial recriminations or claims of deficient job performance. It will tend to protect him or her in case there is an injury to an employee or costly damage, which might lead to criminal or personal charges or liability. Putting all affecting factors, conditions, and actions on paper in a logical sequence will make for an orderly presentation of any situation. Managers will respond more readily to presentations of all pertinent facts, in a foresighted, coherent, and well-thought-out manner, than they would to unsubstantiated, rambling dissertations.

Other than for normal routines, safety engineers generally have to request management approval for any safety actions or expenditures—modifying or replacing equipment or authorizing a new safety rule or procedure. In addition to having all pertinent facts regarding the situation that brought about the request, the safety manager should be aware of the possible answers to questions or directions by the manager. When the recommended corrective action would require expenditure of funds, the manager's comment, action, or question probably would be among those listed in Fig. 1-1. This list provides forewarnings so the safety engineer can make cogent presentations and be prepared for the manager's decision. The list was arranged in order of increasing costs. For example, if there is no violation of a mandatory standard or code, managers will usually attempt the least costly solution that will resolve the problem. Actions recommended or requested by the safety engineer could best be achieved with the same aim—lowest cost. Decisions by managers become matters to be acted on. Where actions are to be undertaken by others, the file becomes a means by which their progress can be monitored.

1. If the cost of correction is minor, approve with no quibbling.
2. If the cost of correction is high, the manager will ask the engineer to determine whether
    a. such a problem actually exists.
    b. it is mandatory in a standard, code, or regulation.
    c. the seller of the hazardous part of the equipment is contractually obligated to pay for the correction or for a safer item.
    d. more detailed studies can be made, including determination of the probability an accident might occur, with and without correction.
    e. a risk/cost/benefit analysis had been made.
    f. any liability resulting from the injury or damage caused by an accident would be covered.
    g. if a safeguard or correction must be made, what would it cost? Could the correction or safeguard be:
        • procedural: providing warnings and cautions about the hazards to operators.
        • an "add-on" device: low-cost item that would not be of great expense.
        • partial replacement: a redesign or add-on for only the portion of the equipment or operation that is legally required.
        • total replacement: replacing the entire equipment or operation with one which is safe.
        • abandonment: shutting down the equipment or operation because correction is too costly.

FIGURE 1–1 Managerial Decisions and Comments on Safety Measures

Managers will come to realize that if the safety engineer is concerned enough to make a problem a matter of record, it should be given greater consideration.

OSHAct AND MANAGEMENT

The OSHAct places the responsibility for employee safety principally on the employers. When a business is owned by one person, it is easy to determine who the responsible "employer" is. When the organization is a corporation, there may be a problem determining who can be held responsible for any violation of the OSHAct. It bears repeating here that under the California Cal-OSHA this may be any "employee having direction, management, control, or custody of any employment, place of employment, or other employee."

A monetary penalty, such as a fine, can be paid by a corporation; a penalty, such as imprisonment indicated in paragraph (e), can be imposed only on an officer of the company. It therefore becomes a matter of determining which corporate officer had the responsibility for ensuring that the OSHAct and OSHA standards were observed and not violated. This may require judicial review in a federal court in states that have not assumed responsibility for administration of the OSHAct or in the courts of states which have been granted authority to undertake this administration. In either case the legal proceedings may cost more, in terms of dollars, than the fine imposed.

Previously, managers were willing to invest in accident prevention programs when they were forced to, and to the degree to which they believed the savings realized would at least counterbalance any costs. The interest in accident prevention also depends to a large extent on the opinions of the individual managers regarding what they considered the risks their companies take. Generally the fines applied by OSHA or the states against firms have been far less than accident-generated costs to workers killed or injured, their families, the states, or the federal government.

Theoretically, if firms fail to react suitably and favorably by providing workplaces free from recognized hazards, and consequently accidents do occur, penalties may become extremely personal as managers are imprisoned. This would undoubtedly alert other managers that the government is adamant in its desire to make workplaces safe. Soon after the OSHAct and OSHA came to pass, it was believed that fines and penalties would be great enough to act as deterrents. Unfortunately, OSHA or state fines and penalties generally have been regarded more as threats to company managers to force adherence to standards than as actual economic losses to fear. Further, any managerial apprehension about personal losses was lessened by the protective corporate structure and insurance coverage.

ACTIONS AGAINST MANAGERS

In *United States v Park*, the Supreme Court pointed out that a top manager can delegate tasks to be accomplished but, in effect, cannot delegate the responsibility for ensuring that those tasks have been done. In that case, the Food and Drug Administration charged that Acme Markets and its president, Park, had violated the Federal Food, Drug, and Cosmetic Act by permitting food held in a warehouse to be contaminated by rodents. Acme pleaded guilty, but Park would not. He admitted responsibility for seeing that sanitary conditions were maintained but argued he had assigned the responsibility to "dependable subordinates." The case was first tried in a federal court, where Park was found guilty; the decision was reversed in a Court of Appeals and reversed again in the Supreme Court. In 1975 the Court indicated that companies may assign responsibilities but they must follow up on such assignments.

The Court's opinion made clear that all officers who have the power and authority to ensure compliance with the law (in this case, the Food and Drug Act) have a duty to do so. An executive with the responsibility and authority to prevent a violation but who fails to do so may be held criminally liable. Although this precedent was set in a case involving food, a violation of a safety law could result in similar decisions by other courts in similar situations. When a government agency searches for a target because of accidents or violations of a health or safety law, managers are sitting on the bullseye.

Managers are increasingly being held responsible for accidents and the existence of unsafe work places. An accident took place before the advent of OSHA. Although the responsible manager was initially sentenced to 20 years and 6 months in jail after seventeen men were killed in an accident, after a retrial his sentence was reduced to probation for three years and a fine of $6,875.

After an accident in the nuclear power plant at Three Mile Island in Pennsylvania in 1979, there were demands for the removal and jailing of three top executives. Although findings laid the blame for the accident on the designers of the system, who failed to incorporate proper human engineering, and on the operators, one manager was relieved of his job.

After repeated failures to observe Cal-OSHA standards, two men were killed in an accident because of the presence of toxic gases after entering a manhole. The plant manager was convicted of involuntary manslaughter and initially sentenced to a year in the county jail. The sentence was reduced later to a fine of $500 and 300 hours of community service as conditions of probation.

In July 1985, three former executives of a silver recycling plant in Maywood, Illinois, were sentenced to 25 years in prison and each fined $10,000. The state prosecutor in the case claimed the death was neither involuntary manslaughter nor an accident, but murder. The conviction of the three men was the first in the country of such job-related deaths. In a plant used to recover silver on photographic film, a worker had died because he had not been directed, taught, or otherwise safeguarded so as to prevent his inhaling the cyanide fumes. It was claimed that the three company officers had clearly been aware of hazardous conditions in the plant but did nothing to warn the workers of the dangers of the cyanide. The court held that directors, officers, and high managerial personnel in a corporation act both for the benefit of the corporation and for themselves. The prosecutor in this case contended, and evidently the court accepted, that corporate responsibility is applicable in civil cases. In this instance, the charge had been murder and therefore one of criminality.

There had been other indictments of corporate officers for criminally negligent homicide when persons were killed in the workplace, but the case in Illinois was the first one in which corporate officials were charged with murder and convicted of killing an employee. It was part of the growing effort to fix individual responsibility for accidents and their prevention.

Numerous examples of managerial deficiencies can be cited. Fine[1] listed these as shown in Fig. 1-2. The results ensuing from accidents under both good and ineffective managerial control are described in Fig. 1-3. As Price stated in 1985, "Don't accidents in the work environment fall outside of management's control? And don't these accidents occur because of random events? How can management be held accountable? Yet, repeatedly the justice system is placing responsibility at management's door. . . . The courts have developed two important tests to determine management's responsibility: foreseeability and prudence." These dual tests will be examined carefully in the chapter on safety analysis. The answers to Price's questions are: (1) management bears a responsibility, and (2) occurrence of accidents can be modified by systematic factors subject to good management. Accidents are not simply random events.

Safety cannot escape legal issues, and legal/regulatory knowledge and skill are required for the practice of safety.[2] The questions that companies and their management face in court are: (1) whether or not a reasonable effort was made to anticipate undesirable events (foreseeability), and (2) whether or not the action taken by management was reasonable and prudent. The emphasis is upon *reasonable*. A reasonable manager will analyze or have analysis performed. Good safety analysis is the job of the safety engineer. In many cases, the manager will delegate safety analysis to a properly educated safety engineer or safety engineering consultant. For one major professional certification in safety there are specialty areas of examination.

Thus, managers bear the ultimate responsibility for all activities under their control, although the faults may be those of subordinates. On the other hand, "A factor which is being recognized more and more by operations managers is that they, in the past, have borne the brunt of criticism due to inadequately designed systems. That is to say, when a badly designed system reaches the field and the inevitable operator error happens, the operator or the operational management supervisory system was blamed for carelessness or laxity . . . . It is becoming more and more important that the designer must design and defend her/his designs . . . [to a greater degree than has been necessary in the past]."[3] Thus in a company with a product that is deficiently designed so that injury, death, or monetary loss takes place, it is not the designer against whom any legal action is taken; it is the manager (although the designer may receive reprimand or be fired).

MANAGEMENT ATTITUDES TOWARD SAFETY

Fortune magazine stated[4]

Many corporate managers continue to believe that careless workers are really to blame for accidents. But a 1967 survey of industrial injuries in Pennsylvania concluded that only 26 percent were the result of employees' carelessness. Even that figure does not tell the whole story. As a General Motors pamphlet on safety notes: "It is impossible to have an accident without the presence of a hazard." The pamphlet goes on to say that "carelessness" is not a good word to use in connection with analyzing the cause of an accident—it is human nature for people to make mistakes, to take short cuts. Even if "accidents will happen" in other words, it is management's responsibility to eliminate—as much as possible— the conditions that bring accidents about. Beyond that, workers have almost no control over the health hazards of dust or toxic gases whose effects they do not understand and whose presence they may not even be able to detect.

ACCIDENT CAUSES TRACED BACK TO MANAGEMENT RESPONSIBILITIES

IMMEDIATE CAUSE	EXAMPLE	POSSIBLE UNDERLYING CAUSES	POSSIBLE MANAGEMENT FAILURES
1. Poor housekeeping	An employee trips and falls over equipment left in an aisle Material poorly piled on a high shelf falls off	Hazards not recognized Facilities inadequate	INADEQUATE: Supervisory training Supervisory safety indoctrination Planning, layout
2. Improper use of tools, equipment, facilities	Using the side of a grinding wheel instead of the face and the wheel breaks Someone using forklift truck to elevate people–person falls of Someone using compressed air to clean dust off clothes–eye injury	Lack of skill, knowledge Lack of proper procedures Lack of Motivation	Employee training Established operational procedure Enforcement of proper procedure Supervisory safety indoctrination Employee training Employee safety
3. Unsafe or defective equipment, facilities	Portable electric drill without ground wire Axe or hammer with loose head Car with defective brakes, steering	Not recognized as unsafe Poor design or selection Poor maintenance	Supervisory safety indoctrination Employee training Employee safety consciousness Planning, layout, design Supervisory safety indoctrination Equipment, materials, tools Maintenance, repair system
4. Lack of proper procedures	No requirement to check for gas fumes before starting engine–explosion No definite instructions requiring power to be locked out before maintenance is done	Omissions Errors by designer Errors by supervisor	Operational procedures Planning, layout, design Supervisory proficiency
5. Improvising unsafe procedures	"Rube Goldberg" haphazard temporary expedients, without proper planning	Inadequate training Inadequate supervision	Established operational procedure Enforcement of proper procedure Supervisory safety indoctrination Employee training Employee safety consciousness Supervisory safety indoctrination Employee selection, placement
6. Failure to follow prescribed procedures	Short-cuts bypassing safety precautions Operation will only be done once; take a chance	Need not emphasized Procedures unclear	Enforcement of proper procedures Supervisory safety indoctrination Operational procedures

FIGURE 1–2 Accident Causes Traced Back to Management Responsibilities Continued on next page

✗ 7. Job not understood	Employee uses wrong method, doesn't follow instructions	Instructions complex Inadequate comprehension	Operational procedures Planning, layout, design Employee selection, placement
✗ 8. Lack of awareness of hazards involved	Not realizing rotating shaft was dangerous Not realizing fumes were dangerous Not realizing that hydrogen from battery-charging operation could explode	Inadequate instructions Inadequate warnings	Supervisory safety indoctrination Employee training Employee safety consciousness Planning, layout, design Safety rules, measures, equipment Operational procedures
✗ 9. Lack of proper tools, equipment, facilities	Cart too small for hauling large items Auto maintenance done without proper wrenches—cut knuckles	Need not recognized Inadequate supply Deliberate	Planning, layout, design Supervisory safety indoctrination Equipment, materials, tools Morale, discipline
10. Lack of guards, safety devices	Machine has exposed belt and gear—severe cut No warning horn on vehicle—pedestrian hit No guard rail on a scaffold 10 feet high	Need not recognized Inadequate availability Deliberate	Planning, layout, design Safety rules, measures, equipment Supervisory safety indoctrination Employee safety consciousness Equipment, materials, tools Operational procedures Morale, discipline, laziness

FIGURE 1–2   Continued

Prior to the passage of the Railway Safety Act in 1893 most managers blamed accidents on the unsafe acts of the personnel involved. (Railroad statistics still reflect this attitude. Bureau of Railroad Safety reports still list "negligence of employees" as the cause of more than half the railroad accidents that occur every year.) The number of trainmen involved in accidents increased, yet the number killed or injured in coupling accidents dropped substantially. Installation of the mechanical safety device was undoubtedly the principal factor.

Each manager endeavors to achieve the organizational mission most economically and effectively. Few will accept without objection any restraints or added requirements that could adversely affect that endeavor. A common attitude is that safety requirements will do just that. In most cases this is a misconception; generally, improvements in working conditions will increase productivity and improve employer-employee relations. Workers have to spend less time thinking of their own safety.

On May 23, 1939, during a trial dive in a series of acceptance tests, the American submarine *U.S.S. Squalus* sank to the bottom in 240 feet of water off the New Hampshire coast. A later investigation reported that according to the indicator lights in the submarine, the main air induction valves were closed as it submerged, but the valves were actually open. Twenty-six men of the 59 aboard were drowned as she sank.

The admiral in command had prescribed procedures for all test-dive operations and any emergencies that might arise. When, within the specified time, no surfacing report had been received that the test-dive had been successful, he became concerned. The admiral ordered another sub, about to start a long voyage, to proceed through the area of the missing boat, directing it to look for any signs of the *Squalus*. The *Squalus* was found and its predicament determined within hours.

Although the submarine was equipped with Momsen lungs for escape (which, like similar British and German designs, were found after the war to be and were declared ineffective), their use was considered inadvisable by the commander because of the water depth and temperature, except as a last resort. The admiral had rescue operations initiated immediately. Distant highly trained and specialized personnel, suitable rescue ships, and equipment were brought hurriedly to the site and in action within 24 hours; all of the trapped men who had not been drowned immediately were rescued 16 hours later.

Eight days after the *Squalus* accident, a similar acceptance test-dive of the British *H.M.S. Thetis* took place. The bow of the *Thetis* flooded when a torpedo tube was inadvertently opened and she sank to the bottom of the Irish Sea. There the water was only 130 feet deep, and because the craft sank at an angle, 18 feet of her 275-foot length remained above the surface. Unfortunately, although the regular crew normally consisted of 53 men, 103 persons were in the sub. The manager of the operation had permitted aboard other supervisors, observers, technicians, and seemingly almost anyone who had a desire to go, including even to waiters to feed the horde.

When a small escorting ship failed to find out what happened to the sub, it attempted to get a message to its headquarters. Receipt of the message was delayed when the messenger boy blew a tire, which he then had to repair. Divers on a tug sent to provide assistance proved to be ill-equipped to do the rescue work. The only other support ships available were a flotilla of destroyers under a commander who knew little about submarines. Each new rescue attempt was developed only after the previous one had failed.

The lack of managerial control cost 99 men their lives (seven men tried to use the escape apparatus, but only four reached the surface alive). All the others died of suffocation. The overcrowding had reduced the survival time available for a successful rescue. In addition, lack of planning for possible emergencies and the use of hurriedly improvised procedures (that failed) increased the time it took to reach the trapped men.

Thus, differences in management control can have different end effects.

FIGURE 1–3 The *Squalus* and the *Thetis*

The Survey of Working Conditions conducted by the University of Michigan found that of 18 areas of concern investigated, 86.7 percent of all workers interviewed considered that "becoming ill or injured because of my job" was foremost on the list. In addition, 80.7 percent were concerned about "physical dangers or unhealthy conditions on my job." Minimization of such concerns will undoubtedly improve employee morale and productivity. In addition, an employee who has to pay less attention to protecting himself or herself against an imminent danger can work more effectively and efficiently. Experience has shown that an employee will work much faster in a safe, compatible environment than in one in which he or she feels endangered. It has also been found that any safeguard engineered into any piece of equipment is outstandingly more beneficial than any warning or caution to be careful.

MIDDLE MANAGERS

Top executive managers often create safety problems for middle managers. These lower-echelon managers are often pressed for production that is hazardous to their personnel. Top executives often make a decision and then tell middle managers to get it done "and I don't care how you do it." The result is often increased production at unsafe rates of work or supervision, or reduction in expenditures for necessary safety equipment.

In March 1987, newspapers published comments that great increases in producitvity requirements by managers had greatly increased stresses and accidents to workers. To reduce costs, managers were requiring workers to do the same work as three or four had previously done. Federal statistics for 1984 and 1985 show that injuries increased 12 percent over those in 1982. In one industry, from 1982 to 1985, workdays lost because of injuries increased from 77.7 to 97.7 per 100 workers while employment dropped from 394,300 to 304,900 workers. Management-generated stresses on workers are also indicated by manufacturing output that rose over 30 percent while worker employment increased only 0.5 percent.

Another contention is that, in their desire to reduce costs, managers are making unsafe cutbacks that increase accidents. They have reduced equipment maintenance and worker training programs. The deterioration of maintenance so that more accidents occurred, first noted with railroads, has spread to industrial plant activities. Training has deteriorated as workers laid off from one job are transferred to another where the work and required skills are different.

In the early 1990s, many companies trimmed management, staff, and work force in downsizing efforts to meet the challenge of a global economy. Often, middle management was the target, thus increasing stress on the management and workers remaining in the "streamlined" organization. Attention to safety can be easily lost when personnel see their jobs in jeopardy or the management personnel who cared for safety are eliminated. Some companies moved activities "offshore" to foreign countries where standards of safety and health are less developed. Workplace safety, at the beginning of a new millenium, is now a global concern, drastically in need of international voices.

FOREMEN/FOREWOMEN AND SAFETY

A prime requisite for any successful accident prevention program is to leave no doubt in the mind of employees that supervisors are concerned about their safety. Supervisors such as low-level managers and forewomen or foremen have close contact with workers and can provide the closest control of all activities, including safe operations. Similarly, the supervisor is often at the receiving end when there are recriminations because of accidents. Unfortunately, foremen/forewomen have so many duties and schedules to carry out that they are often overworked, and certain duties are not accomplished adequately. Neglect of accident prevention, which often occurs, can have the most serious consequences.

Although it is frequently and truly said that safety is everyone's responsibility, many people have a tendency to ignore or forget this. The supervisor, manager, or foreperson must ensure that such ignoring or forgetting does not happen. Where designed safeguards are lacking, failing to address hazards by the use of procedures and warnings can lead to disastrous results. Sometimes, when safety is everybody's business, it becomes nobody's business. The supervisor, manager, or foreperson is key to ensuring that this does not happen.

For the worker, a foreperson represents management. This person has to exert his personal authority and influence and has to see that the intentions and orders of the management are carried out. If the foreperson does not take safety seriously, those under her or him will not either. On the other hand, if the foreperson is convinced of the importance of safety, shows that safety has to be considered all the time, and personally does everything that reasonably can be done to prevent accidents, workers will follow his or her example.[5]

PROCEDURAL SAFEGUARDS

Use of procedural safeguards is a less satisfactory means to avoid accidents than is a well-designed safeguard in the equipment or operation. (As indicated previously, when tested by court decisions, procedural safeguards may not be acceptable.) Procedures or safety work rules issued by managers depend on workers to observe them and on foremen to ensure they are observed. Managers evaluating a procedural safeguard must also consider the effects of the added load on the front-line supervisor.

Prior to passage of the OSHAct, management decisions to provide safety devices or equipment were to some extent predicated on one or more of four factors: economic considerations (including added cost of insurance if adequate built-in safeguards were not provided), local codes, past or potential litigation, and employee (union) relations.

With the enactment of the OSHAct and the stricture that places of employment be free from "recognized hazards," the question of cost becomes largely academic. The issue is no longer whether the cost for safety can be justified economically. Many managers have said that standards and safety measures should be imposed only when they are economically justified as computed by risk/cost/benefit/effectivity analyses (see previous chapters). However, both because the costs of lives of persons can never be calculated definitely before an accidental fatality and because costs analyses differ so greatly from later actualities, managerial calculations are never accepted by OSHA or courts. In 1987 this was definitively ruled out, the indication being that when safety of personnel is at stake, cost cannot be considered.

MANAGEMENT AND SUPERVISION

Above all, managers must maintain an active, effective interest in the safety effort. Some means by which a manager responsible for any operation can have an effective program are to:

1. Establish in writing and disseminate specific and firm safety policies for the organization, and then ensure they are carried out.

2. Provide a coordinated effort, integrating the safety efforts of all organizations concerned. Many of these functions are described in the following paragraphs.

3. Direct the participation of all subordinate organization heads in the safety effort, with specific responsibilities assigned to each. Ensure that each manager passes on suitable guidance to personnel under his or her jurisdiction.

4. Establish a safety element that reports directly to the manager to be sure the safety program is carried out properly and effectively. This safety element should ensure that all organizations are familiar with OSHA standards pertinent to their operations; should be responsible for seeing that the standards are observed or action is taken to ensure compliance (such as making higher-level managers aware of any deficiencies); and should be the designated party to accompany any OSHA compliance officer or other safety inspector who may visit the plant.

5. Issue work rules or operating procedures to guide the safe conduct of all employees, including having:

   a. Detailed emergency procedures specifying when a dangerous condition exists or a critical failure or accident occurs. In addition to work rules, these procedures should include preestablished warning signals or alarms, safe areas and evacuation routes, communications to notify support activities (such as a firefighting unit), and availability and use of protective clothing and rescue equipment. These procedures should be familiar to all personnel participating in plant activities.

   b. Each potentially hazardous operation reviewed and analyzed to ensure that suitable procedures and safeguards are provided.

   c. Each dangerous operation conducted and controlled according to procedures developed and approved for that operation.

   d. A procedure requiring permission permits and safety surveillance for any hazardous operation.

   e. The buddy system to be used for tasks that involve considerable danger. These tasks include such work as operations on high-voltage equipment, where toxic gases or fumes might be present, cleaning or repairing the insides of tanks or cisterns, or similar situations. When the buddy system is used, constant communication must be maintained between the persons involved. A person in a hazardous situation must remain within sight of his or her buddy at all times or otherwise maintain evidence of well-being or a sign of need for assistance.

6. Carry out safety training on a continuing basis for all supervisors and workers, especially those newly employed or transferred. No supervisor should assume

that any new employee has received adequate safety training but should check each individual's knowledge and work habits. Managers should be sure that:

a. Workers have had at least the minimum training necessary to be aware of any hazards before they are assigned to their jobs.

b. Workers are taught the nature of possible hazards, how to avoid exposure, and the actions necessary if a mishap occurs.

c. Periodic safety training is conducted for all workers.

d. No worker is permitted to continue in any hazardous work if he or she is found unqualified, unsuitable, or incapable or performs unsafely.

e. Training drills are held to ensure high proficiency of personnel during emergencies. Designated items of protective and emergency clothing normally used should be used during the drills.

7. Ensure:

a. Good housekeeping practices are maintained at all times.

b. Every piece of plant, vehicle, or other item of equipment is operated within the limitations for which it was designed.

c. New equipment is inspected on receipt to ensure that all desirable safety features and devices have been incorporated or provided. The safety engineer should ensure that the equipment meets OSHA standards. Any deviations from the operating procedure considered unsafe, or any obvious safety deficiency, should be corrected before the equipment is accepted. Appropriate procedural safeguards should have been established for any hazard that could not be eliminated by design.

d. Access to equipment components during operation, maintenance, repair, or adjustment should not expose personnel to hazards such as electrical charges, moving parts, radiation burns, extremes of heat and temperature, chemical burns, toxic gas, cutting edges, sharp points, or any other hazard unless a suitable safeguard has been provided.

e. Persons involved in any hazardous operation should be instructed to report promptly any unusual condition or malfunction that would place them in or indicate that they are in jeopardy, such as an unusual odor or irritating substance.

f. Personnel are directed to report any device, control, equipment, or protective clothing that does not work properly.

g. Any piece of safety equipment that adversely affects performance is reported.

8. Check that every reported dangerous condition or accident is investigated.

9. Establish a program to monitor and audit operational activities for their safety aspects. A personal visit, even if short, is a highly effective use of time for all managers. Ensure that all subordinates or subordinate organizations are participating effectively in the safety program.

10. Establish a safety review board to evaluate, discuss, and take action on safety problems. The board should review mishap records, hazard and failure reports, and safety studies and analyses to establish that improvements are necessary or desirable. Whenever possible, a manager should act as chairman of the board or delegate the duty to a subordinate high-level manager.

11. Provide budgets adequate for achievement of all safety objectives.

12. Ensure that all OSHA record-keeping requirements are being observed.

SAFETY EFFORTS OF OTHER MANAGERS

Management structures and titles vary from company to company, but no matter the actual titles, some of the organizations involved in the safety program, and their contributions, may be:

- *Personnel:* ensures that workers are trained and physically capable of conducting their duties.

- *Medical:* ensures that prospective employees physically or mentally incapable of the work or questionable in those respects are denied employment. Conducts examinations for workers at time of hiring and then periodically after employment. Provides first aid and emergency treatments.

- *Production:* ensures that unsafe practices are not permitted, even at the expense of increased output.

- *Plant engineering:* ensures that no equipment that could affect health or safety is selected or installed which might adversely affect personnel unless potential hazards are adequately safeguarded. Ensures that safeguards are maintained properly and repaired where necessary.

- *Research and development:* ensures that when new products involve use or testing of materials, any hazards will be brought to the attention of managerial personnel.

- *Plant maintenance:* ensures that good housekeeping is maintained at all times.

- *Security:* ensures that emergency accesses are not blocked, unauthorized persons do not use company equipment, and all vehicles on company property are operated with due care and within safe speed limits. Figure 1-4 indicates checks involving safety that security personnel can make during conduct of their duties.

- *Purchasing:* ensures that safety equipment and materials are procured expeditiously. Materials, parts, and equipment that could be hazardous are obtained using specifications with applicable safety requirements.

- *Legal:* ensures that all managers are aware of the latest laws and judicial interpretations of laws that could affect the company. Takes necessary action if there is any citation for a violation or any litigation because of an accident.

- *Employee relations:* ensures that employee suggestions and complaints regarding safety are evaluated; that needs for use of safe practices are continually indicated in company newspapers, on bulletin boards, and through other media; and that employer-employee-union relationships are maintained at the best level possible. Assists workers in compensation insurance claims.

- *Records:* ensures that all data regarding safety are recorded, collated, and analyzed to spot adverse trends in accident occurrences.

Often there are several management systems within a business management system. These systems overlap and intersect so that they are not mutually exclusive.

SECURITY PERSONNEL SAFETY CHECKS

Plant security personnel can assist safety engineers by reporting hazards which they detect during duty periods. Following are some of the hazards that should be watched for:
- Obstructed lanes for emergency vehicles.
- Obstructed emergency exits and passages to the exits.
- Fire doors blocked or opened.
- Unlocked doors or gates to enclosed hazardous areas, such as electric transformer banks.
- Accesses blocked to fire fighting or other emergency equipment.
- Boxes, bales, cartons, or other items piled so high they destroy the effectiveness of sprinkler systems.
- Boxes, crates, bales, drums, cartons, or other packages piled so high that they may fall over and injure someone in the vicinity.
- Loose wires, piping, metal, tools, or other material, equipment, or supplies over which personnel can trip or fall.
- Wet, oily, or heavily waxed floors on which persons can slip and fall.
- Obstructions or loose objects on stairs or at the head of stairs; or poorly lighted stairs.
- Missing or inoperative egress or exit lights.
- Loose or broken stair treads, hand rails, or guard rails.
- Barriers, lights, and other protective devices missing at excavations, manholes, ditches, or other openings into which a person or vehicle could fall.
- The presence of oily rags, excelsior, or other highly flammable materials outside proper containers.
- Uncovered containers of solvent, fuels, or other flammable liquids.
- Cigarette butts, matches, or other evidence of smoking in nonsmoking areas.
- Failure of welders to have fire extinguishers close at hand.
- Missing fire extinguishers or evidence that they have been used, are not in their assigned locations, or due or past due for inspection.
- Steam, oil, water, fuel, or chemical leaks.
- Unusual odors or fumes.
- Improperly stored or inadequately secured gas cylinders.
- Broken electrical fittings, outlets, plugs, or other devices.
- Broken glass or other sharp, unprotected edges, points, or surfaces.

FIGURE 1–4   Security Personnel Safety Checks

Health and Safety Management is an integral part of each. The intersection of these systems forms the company's Core Management Systems. Figure 1-5 illustrates this concept. Each system in the figure intersects with the Health and Safety Management System, often in vital ways. Core management balances risks. If attention is paid only to safety and environmental issues, for example, then quality, productivity, and costs might suffer too much.

Two management systems are receiving a great deal of attention because they are addressed by International Standards Organization (ISO) standards. The first, Quality Management System, is supported by the ISO 9000 series; the second, Environmental Management System, by the ISO 14000 series. Because of their safety implications, the safety professional should become familiar with these standards; however, their contents are too extensive to be covered here. Many nations and regional jurisdictions have adopted these standards. They provide a basis for the core management of integrated business systems, including safety.

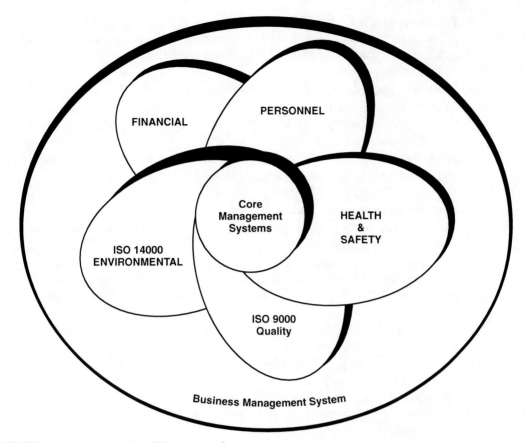

FINANCIAL

PERSONNEL

Core
Management
Systems

HEALTH
&
SAFETY

ISO 14000
ENVIRONMENTAL

ISO 9000
Quality

Business Management System

FIGURE 1–5   Interrelationship of Management Systems

Source: Modified from I. Fredericks and D. McCallum, "International Standards for Environmental Management Systems: ISO 14000," *Canadian Environmental Protection*, August, 1995.[6]

HAZARDOUS OPERATIONS

The safety person generally is immediately responsible for accident prevention in all hazardous operations. Each safety person should have the authority to stop any operation considered so unsafe that an imminent danger exists. In addition, safety engineers should be delegated by managers to ensure that:

1. Each operation is monitored to comply with OSHA standards and other established criteria.
2. Each operation considered hazardous is conducted strictly in accordance with procedures and checklists included in approved publications or approved by authorized agencies, using only designated equipment.
3. Each operation the safety person considers to be hazardous and to require surveillance is provided with suitable personnel to permit adequate surveillance.

4. Permit systems are instituted for operations requiring special care. Permits are required for operations that have to be controlled closely, such as for blasting or welding other than those industrial operations carried out automatically or semi-automatically.

5. Hazardous operations are conducted only in designated and approved areas.

6. Controls are instituted limiting access to areas where hazardous operations are to be conducted, with the number of permitted personnel posted conspicuously at each entrance.

7. Personnel permitted to remain at one time in a controlled area are limited to the number that could be evacuated safely in an emergency or supplied with necessary protective equipment to safeguard them.

8. Where advisable, guards are used to control entrances.

9. All personnel and organizations concerned or affected are notified before any hazardous operation is begun.

10. Exits, stairways, and escape routes are marked clearly, with provisions for emergency lighting. Evacuation procedures are posted conspicuously and tested periodically by drills to ensure designated equipment is in place, available, and operable.

11. Operations are forbidden while winds or other meteorological conditions could endanger personnel.

12. Open flames or unprotected electrical equipment are not permitted in areas where flammable or explosive materials are permitted. Welding or flame-cutting operations are permitted only in areas and at times approved by the responsible safety engineer. Persons smoking in locations other than designated areas are recommended for disciplinary action.

PERSONNEL

Managers and safety engineers must ensure that:

1. Undue exposure of personnel to physiological, psychological, or physical stresses is avoided where conditions are unsafe due to inadequate design, improper operating instructions, faulty equipment, or lack of suitable protective equipment.

2. No person is required to perform an operation that could result in injury to himself or herself or to any other person because of close proximity or incompatibility of their tasks.

3. Only qualified and certified personnel are permitted to undertake any hazardous duties or operations such as handling toxic, explosive, or highly flammable materials; to maintain, service, or repair any dangerous equipment; or to transport or operate any vehicle or mobile equipment or its component assemblies.

4. Programs are instituted to quality and certify workers for their duties. Qualified personnel are indicated as certified by suitable identification issued after proficiency examinations and demonstrations.

5. Certification programs include training and testing on safety subjects such as: hazards involved in the operation for which the worker is being certified; practices and procedures required to safeguard themselves and others; remedial actions to be taken in any contingency; safety devices; possible malfunctions that could cause an accident; color coding and other means of identification and markings of wiring, piping, and equipment; and meaning of warnings, sound alerts, or any other emergency signal; and any other information the safety manager considers advisable.

PERSONAL PROTECTIVE EQUIPMENT

Some operations require equipment to be worn by workers (1) to avoid injurious effects on the body and (2) to safeguard workers in the event of accidents. Here again, managers must ensure that certain rules are observed:

1. For normal operations, first choice will be given to eliminating the hazard in the environment rather than using personal protective equipment.

2. Approved protective equipment and devices must be made available and used to guard against specific hazards that cannot be eliminated but should be controlled when encountered during the operation

3. No supervisor will permit an operation to be conducted unless such equipment and devices are in proper working order and used as stipulated by the safety engineer.

4. Only protective and rescue equipment approved for the purpose by responsible agencies and in accordance with OSHA or other mandatory standards will be used. Managers will ensure that procedures are available for the supply, maintenance, and operation of such equipment, and that personnel are proficient in their operation and upkeep.

5. Locations of personal protective, emergency, and first aid equipment must be easily accessible and readily distinguishable. Equipment should be stored as close as practicable to the possible point of use. Operating procedures should identify the equipment stored and its location. Inspections are to be made periodically to ensure that stipulated items are present. Unauthorized persons removing, tampering with, using, or damaging the equipment are to be disciplined.

6. No person will enter a hazardous environment without the prescribed protective equipment, remove it while in the hazardous environment, or use it if it is faulty or damaged. Tests to demonstrate that the equipment is operating properly will be required before a worker enters a questionable environment.

7. All workers must be familiar with the capabilities, limitations, and proper method of fitting, testing, using, and caring for protective equipment. Managers will require and ensure that courses of instruction are provided to familiarize personnel with safety equipment, especially new types. Safety engineers and supervisors will schedule practice sessions or have training units conduct sessions to maintain user proficiency.

8. Devices are available to detect, warn, and protect against an impending or existing adverse environmental condition. Such equipment will be used to evaluate

atmospheres that might be toxic, flammable, or explosive or in which excessive levels of radiation, heat, pressure, noise, or other hazard might exist. Devices will be provided to apprise personnel of the status of such conditions that might be hazardous or of the loss of control of a hazard. Equipment provided should be adequate for detecting the presence of the hazard under conditions other than normal for the operating environment.

9. Detection and warning equipment will be maintained in a state in which operations and readings are dependable and accurate. To assure this, they will be tested and calibrated periodically.

10. Detection and warning equipment will be installed, maintained, adjusted, and repaired only by personnel trained and assigned for that purpose. Warnings will be posted against other persons tampering with, inactivating, or damaging this equipment.

11. Operating procedures specify the actions personnel should take when a warning signal indicates a time of danger or an emergency.

CHECKLIST FOR MANAGERS

Figure 1-6 presents a checklist managers might use to review a few of the aspects of plant safety and to determine whether they are taking appropriate action. Both managers and safety engineers can prepare additional items they believe should be covered in any periodic safety audit.

The disaster involving the space shuttle *Challenger* caused reassignment of many of the top managers of NASA. Managers had known for years about many of the deficiencies, most of them due to bad original designs. The accident was attributed to the managerial decision to launch in cold weather, despite an engineering deficiency in the booster. It illustrated the fact that management and engineering rely on each other. In the past, putting the blame for accidents on workers or users has been management's device for transferring responsibility for errors. Today any blame must be scrutinized more carefully, especially in light of the accident causers or contributors.

No matter who is blamed for accidents to workers, management suffers a loss: increased premium costs and loss of skilled employees. A study was made in California of over 1,000 seriously injured workers who suffered a permanent impairment. One out of three had dropped entirely out of the job market, while a similar number indicated themselves as "unemployed and not looking for work." The loss to management because of workplace accidents has been substantial.

SAFETY INFORMATION SYSTEM

Management and safety professionals should institute and maintain a safety information system. The system must enable management (1) to determine if the safety program is adequate to meet stated goals and objectives, (2) to accept, eliminate, or control risks on a reasonable and prudent basis. In order to evaluate its risks and make

1. Has the chief executive issued a directive that indicates his or her policy toward worker safety?
2. Have rules of conduct to insure safe conduct of the facility been prepared?
3. Have the policy and the safe-conduct rules been widely posted in prominent locations where they can easily be read?
4. Does the policy directive indicate the functions and responsibilities of each organization as they relate to safety?
5. Is the chief executive kept informed of the progress of safety programs and any deficiencies?
6. Is the chief executive aware of the major restrictions on safety and health imposed by OSHA?
7. Does the executive's directive designate a top-level manager to be responsible for workplace safety?
8. Is the authority of this manager adequate to carry out safety functions effectively?
9. Is the person in charge of safety activities experienced and knowledgeable in those matters, or does he or she have someone to rely on who is?
10. Is the safety staff large and diverse enough to handle any problems that might arise, or will it be necessary to obtain consultant services to assist?
11. Is there a means by which progress of the workplace safety effort can be measured?
12. Is the list of accidents that have occurred in the workplace up-to-date so that it is ready and available for use by OSHA personnel?
13. Is there a method by which documents relating to workplace safety can be circulated to all concerned and then be stored and available?
14. Have budgets been prepared that include safety activities as normal functions, and have those activities been funded adequately?
15. Has a company safety committee been established, headed by someone at least at a management level and also including representatives of all workplace areas?
16. Does the committee meet regularly to hear and review presentations on plant hazards and accidents and to review employee complaints and suggestions regarding safety?
17. Is a procedure in effect to generate hazard reports, assign action to investigate the matter, and review the subsequent findings?
18. Have training courses been established for all personnel, especially new hires, to teach them of potential hazards, safeguards, warnings, and other safety matters?
19. Do contracts or purchase agreements require equipment sellers to inform the chief executive's staff of any potential hazard in the equipment?
20. Is new equipment reviewed by the plant safety engineer before it is purchased or before it is put into operation?
21. Do personnel training for operating newly purchased equipment have adequate information on safety and accident prevention?

FIGURE 1–6   Checklist for Managers

reasonable and prudent decisions to accept some risks and not others, management must have an adequate information system available. If management is to eliminate or control hazards, which otherwise present unacceptable risks, administrative, engineering, and operational factors must be in place to enable a sufficient and defensible safety program. These factors are discussed by the chapters in this text. They should be integrated into a safety information system.

Safety Technical Information System. A safety information system for management has several parts. The first part provides a detailed description of hazards under the responsibility of management. This prerequires a definition of what management's responsibility is and a systematic and iterative review of all things within the scope of that definition. The second part is a collection of codes, manuals, reference books on safety science and practice, research reports, lists of experts, accident case studies, accident history and trends, human factors reports, engineering reports, etc., which are relevant to the type of industry being managed. This part is an up-to-date and iterative collection of relevant information from *outside* the plant, grounds, or immediate jurisdiction of management. The third part consists of data and data analysis derived regularly from safety monitoring systems active *within* the jurisdiction of management. These systems produce specific, local data from sources such as the accident/incident/close-calls reporting system, safety inspections system, independent safety audits and appraisals, and reports of significant observations. These data are not useful unless coordinated with a clearly stated management safety policy and evaluated in accordance with pre-determined action triggers or action levels.

Safety Management Information System.   The heart of this system is management's policies and plans for safety and health. The general company safety policy should be an up-to-date, clearly stated commitment to providing a safe and healthful place to work. It should be broad enough in scope to address the challenges to safety of workers, property, and the environment that are likely to occur.

Where there is a line-and-staff organization model, this information system should include a clear statement of line responsibility assignments for safety. These assignments are given to line individuals, from the duties of the highest line officer, through the supervisor, to the line employee. A similar statement of the responsibility for safety by staff functions and staff personnel should be included. Specific safety functions of staff departments (such as personnel, training, maintenance, purchasing, engineering, transportation, medical, etc.) should be stated.

It should also include a specification of the safety information that management needs and how it is to be obtained and delivered. It should include all management directives used to implement safety policy. These directives should state methodologies and functions to be used in policy implementation. It should include methods for providing, implementing, and tracking safety recommendations and improvements.

Individual plans for elements in a complete safety program are located in this system. Plans might include those for accident and illness prevention, safety audits and inspections, safety training, human factors and ergonomics reviews, Job Safety Analysis programs, Confined Space Entry programs, facility occupancy use and readiness, maintenance safety, safety data collection and analysis, employee motivation for safety, emergency response, medical services and rehabilitation, environmental safety, public relations, risk assessment and risk management, safety of design, safety and engineering change management, contractor and subcontractor safety, hazard recognition-identification-control, fire prevention, hazardous waste management, etc. It is not enough to have a well-written plan that is specific and *can* be implemented. A plan must *be* implemented. The safety professional can fall into the trap of spending too much time writing plans that are never implemented.

Safety Administrative Information System.   This system includes not only budget and personnel information but also administrative interventions for accident, illness, and injury prevention, property and environmental protection. Records of budget requests (including those denied or cut back), past and present budgets, and supporting documentation should be maintained here. Personnel resumes of persons given professional safety duties, records of employees given safety training, and qualifications of personnel involved in the safety program should be maintained here.

Where there are administrative controls over hazards, these should be documented here. For example, if personnel assigned to an operation must be rotated out of that duty on a regular schedule for health and safety reasons, that requirement is recorded here. [A few examples of administrative controls are: (1) placing a time limit on a person's remaining in a noisy work area, (2) placing shelf-life deadlines on stored chemicals, (3) storing hazardous waste on-site for no longer than some specified period, and (4) limiting the manual filling of a tank to 80 percent of capacity.] Many such administrative controls are used for safety. This part of the system should have a means to track and alert management when deviations from administrative controls occur.

Regulatory and legal aspects of the safety program, such as lawsuit documentation, OSHA inspection, compliance, fines, and enforcement documents and correspondence can be placed here. Flags for deadlines for response or compliance should be maintained.

Safety Science and Engineering Information System.   Records of engineering controls for safety are included in this system. This includes not only records and drawings of the safety features of physical facilities, stores, and equipment under management's jurisdiction, but also records of the safety reviews of engineering design and engineering change documents. It should include engineering reviews, analyses, and solutions for safety. These include reviews of energy sources that have danger or accident potential, of the adequacy of barriers that contain or redirect the flow of dangerous energy, and of objects or persons that might be affected by undesirable energy flow. Physical energy sources include chemical, thermal, mechanical, electrical, kinetic, and nuclear. Where science and engineering are involved in mitigating hazards, the records are maintained in this information system. Material Safety Data Sheets could be included.

These systems contain information about elements in the safety program that are not mutually exclusive or exhaustive. Therefore, similar information may appear in one or more of the systems, and elements of the information system may be added, subtracted, or otherwise customized as necessary. The purpose is to give management information that allows them to determine the adequacy of their safety program to meet specified goals and objectives and to determine the adequacy of safety policies. Also, it should enable management to decide whether a given risk of harm is acceptable to take or whether some other risk is controlled to an acceptable, reasonable, and prudent level.

To have value, information must be communicated to appropriate persons. The safety information system must implement a plan to provide its information to appropriate targets within and outside the organization.

BIBLIOGRAPHY

[1] W. T. Fine, *A Management Approach to Accident Prevention*, White Oak TR 75-104 (AD A 014562) (Silver Springs, MD: Naval Surface Weapons Center, July 1975).

[2] Fred A. Manuele, *On the Practice of Safety* (New York: Van Nostrand Reinhold, 1993), p. 132.

[3] Aerojet Nuclear Company, *Human Factors in Design*, Idaho Falls, Idaho, Feb. 1976.

[4] Dan Cordtz, "Safety on the Job Becomes a Major Job for Management," *Fortune*, Nov. 1972, p. 112.

[5] From *Accident Prevention—A Worker's Education Manual* (Geneva, Switzerland: International Labour Office, 1961).

[6] I. Fredericks and D. McCallum, "International Standards for Environmental Management Systems: ISO 14000," *Canadian Environmental Protection*, August 1995.

EXERCISES

1.1. Why is management support necessary for a safety engineer to accomplish his or her job?

1.2. Can a manager delegate all responsibility for safety to a lesser manager, a safety engineer, consultant, or other person?

1.3. Can a manager (a) be fined for a violation of an OSHA or state standard, (b) be cited in a civil lawsuit, or (c) be cited in a criminal lawsuit because of an accident? Explain what might happen to the manager.

1.4. How can managers show they are concerned with accident prevention?

1.5. Describe what would happen if managers or supervisors were lax in prescribing or enforcing (a) safety and work rules, (b) needs to wear protective clothing or equipment, and (c) a safe environment.

1.6. Why is the foreman or first-line supervisor key to any accident prevention program?

1.7. If you were a manager or supervisor, what corrections would you make in the area of safety?

1.8. Why are procedural safeguards less satisfactory than good design as safeguards? What have the OSHA and courts to say about this?

1.9. List five ways in which a manager can have an effective safety program.

1.10. Discuss how eight submanagers of a large company might participate in its safety program.

1.11. List five operations often considered extra hazardous.

1.12. List some causes of accidents that might be traced back to managers.

1.13. Managers often blame accidents on worker carelessness or other worker fault. Do you believe this assertion to be true often, occasionally, or rarely?

1.14. Do you believe there is good or bad management control of safety in the place where you work? Why? What evidence is there?

1.15. Do any of your supervisors press for improved production to the point where your safety or that of any of your co-workers is jeopardized? If, for that reason, you caused an accident, on whom would the blame fall?

CHAPTER 2

The Changing Roles of Safety Personnel

Traditionally, fire engines were red; now many are being painted yellow. Safety personnel's roles, capabilities, and training have also changed with time, as technologies advance and needs for accident prevention increase. Technical personnel who were concerned with preventing injury and damage in early safety efforts were interested in a comparatively narrow range of problems. Sir Humphrey Davy's miner's lamp can be considered the first technical advance in accident prevention that was deliberately sought because a hazard urgently needed controlling. Since then, other inventors have turned to accident prevention and thereby have become safety personnel.

One hundred years ago, when some of the major U.S. industrial companies became concerned, most of the causes of accidents (aside from fires) were mechanical. Pictures of machine shops of those days show them crowded with equipment operated by flatbelts from overhead lineshafts. Belts and machines were generally unguarded, constant hazards to the workers. Industrial plants were dangerous places for other reasons. Rupturing boilers and disintegrating flywheels on steam engines were violent, catastrophic failures which frequently generated devastating injuries and damage in the crowded facilities.

As science, invention, and industry entered new fields, new safety problems arose. Generally these involved new hazards, which first became known as scientists and inventors created and sometimes suffered from them. But even the scientists, and later the engineers, were concerned chiefly with the utility derived from the new inventions rather than with assurance of safety. Only in rare cases did consideration of safety outweigh other benefits. Thomas Edison rightly claimed that direct current was less hazardous than alternating current and preferred it for general use. (Alternating current was selected, however, because of the greater ease with which it could be transmitted over long distances.)

The next progression came as laboratory equipment and processes of scientists were transformed into industrial equipment, where the safety problems involved became concerns of the design, process, and plant engineers. The hazards resulting from high-temperature, high-pressure reactions or toxicities of the reactants and their products in the growing chemical industry were initially handled by chemists and chemical engineers (who were also the creators of the hazards). It became necessary to have other persons responsible for accident prevention. Similarly, safety in electrical plants was handled by electrical engineers after devices had been invented by others and accidents had taken place. As usage of formerly unique equipment and processes became more common and ceased to be the exclusive province of the engineer, efforts to provide safeguards and controls in industrial plants were assigned to less specialized persons. Industrial plant managers generally found it uneconomical to employ a technical specialist in each problem area. The end result was often that newly graduated engineers or lesser trained personnel were assigned to handle day-to-day accident prevention activities. Consultant specialists were called on only when a solution to a problem was beyond the plant safety person's capabilities.

SAFETY LAWS AND SAFETY ENGINEERS

Workers' compensation supposedly would spur increased safety, but it did even less toward that end than did insurance companies and litigation of the times. The growth of the labor laws and safety codes after Franklin Delano Roosevelt assumed office increased demands for safety personnel. This demand grew with the involvement of the United States in the Second World War. Accidents affected war efforts, as many untrained persons who had never before been employed moved into hazardous industrial jobs. When accidents took place, it became necessary to address the problem.

In 1943, Blake[1] wrote: "It is obvious that since widespread knowledge of good safety practice is necessary, at least the fundamentals of accident prevention should be taught widely. It seems reasonable to predict that the inclusion of safety in collegiate curricula generally will follow. Two methods were under discussion, namely, offering courses leading to the degree 'Safety engineers,' or including in each engineering subject taught the part of safety appropriate to the subject in question." The first organized courses in safety and accident prevention were taught in 1943 at a few engineering schools to undergraduates studying industrial engineering. Even fewer four-year schools now use Blake's concept of including information on safety. In many instances, teaching of accident causes and prevention is undertaken in two-year technical schools.

The next great advance took place with the passage of the OSHAct and of the OSHA standards. The standards required employment of safety personnel in both federal and state positions. For federal employment large numbers of engineers were necessary and had to be trained in safety matters. States had had some safety engineers to ensure observance of state codes, but the new laws resulted in needs for additional trained personnel.

Although the OSHA standards in general were a tremendous boost for safety personnel, in certain aspects they worked against the creation of new ideas on accident prevention. Because the OSHA standards indicated in detail most of the precautionary measures that had to be taken, the main function of plant safety personnel, consultants, and engineers who had to incorporate safeguards was to ensure that all OSHA provisions were met. The study of equipment, operations, or processes lagged. When a new type of activity began that was not covered by OSHA, any new hazards often were not covered.

At the start of the twenty-first century, new acts and new OSHA standards, OSHA guidelines, and OSHA publications have impacted the safety professional's role. Safety professionals are already greatly affected by the Americans with Disabilities Act, Guidelines for Ergonomics, Permit Required Confined Space Entry, and the Workplace Violence Awareness and Prevention publication referred to elsewhere in this book. At the time of this writing, OSHA has many regulations in the Proposed Rule Stage, including those for Safety and Health Programs (for General Industry), Permissible Exposure Limits for Air Contaminants, Plain English Revision of Existing Standards, Flammable and Combustible Liquids, and numerous regulations for the construction industry and shipyards. The safety professional should expect this situation to continue. It is part of the safety professional's role today to track what OSHAdministration and other governmental agencies are doing in their rulemaking and publications and to provide OSHA and others with feedback to influence these processes as a stakeholder. The internet makes this very feasible, and governmental agencies maintain on-line information systems which are available to anyone. The present-day safety professional must be engaged in governmental activities which ultimately impact the profession and industry in general.

SAFETY PERSONNEL

Whoever is designated in a plant with diversified activities must be a generalist, knowledgeable in a wide range of technical, legal, and administrative activities. To some, the breadth of effort involved and knowledge required provides variety that is found in few other industrial jobs. To others, this same scope engenders mental stress. Top-level managers too often assume a safety professional is knowledgeable in depth in all areas of accident prevention and capable of solving all problems that may arise. On the other hand, practically everyone has seen or been involved in an accident, or been alerted because of some hazard, and therefore has some knowledge or opinion regarding safety matters. Because of the need for correct and certain knowledge, properly educated safety personnel are increasingly necessary. Individual safety engineers must realize their capabilities and limitations, based on their education and experience, so they can understand exactly when a specialist should be consulted.

The difference in types of industry with their attendant hazards, organizational structures, management attitudes toward safety, and governmental emphasis on accident prevention have created a wide diversity of safety positions, duties, and responsibilities in industrial plants. When other employment of safety personnel, such as in government agencies, is considered, the number of positions, titles, duties, and responsibilities grows even larger.

To a certain extent, the following order of assignment of safety personnel indicates how their responsibilities have changed over the years. Since the days when there were few laws, codes, and standards for accident prevention, workers' compensation premiums were low, and there were far fewer and lesser awards for liabilities resulting from industrial plant accidents, costs have mounted. So have needs for their prevention and control.

"SAFETY MAN"

Years ago, the person called the "safety man" in most industrial plants, even large ones, was responsible for filling out accident reports and other papers required by insurance companies and state agencies. (The plant at which one of the authors first worked had been built around the turn of the century. For a long time its original safety deficiencies remained. In the 1930s, long after passage of workers' compensation and other labor laws, which were generally ineffectual, minor corrections finally began in our plant. One of our jobs, to be accomplished when there was little else to be done, was to design guards against rotating equipment.) In some cases the "safety man" may even have been someone partially disabled in an accident who was given the job to keep him or her on the payroll. This avoided any need for workers' compensation and the increase in premiums it might entail. The safety man's education and experience may have consisted almost entirely of the accident in which the injury had taken place. In today's plants, the safety professional is not represented by such a gender-specific form of address.

SAFETY ENGINEER

The term "safety engineer" is frequently applied to the person in charge of accident prevention, who may in fact be the so-called "safety man"—a person with some technical experience, or an engineering school graduate assigned to accident prevention duties. Government regulations requiring safe designs in industrial plants frequently resulted in reassignment of engineers of other disciplines into accident prevention activities. Because of deficiencies in safety education in engineering schools, these engineers lacked the knowledge of safety laws and standards and related information they needed in order to perform competently in their new jobs.

As discussed in the chapter on engineers and safety, some persons have passed examinations as Certified Safety Professionals. Many are graduate engineers, but others have achieved this rating by having shown their knowledge in safety and accident prevention. Other safety-related certifications include those of Certified Product Safety Professional, Certified Industrial Hygienist, Certified Professional Ergonomist, and Certified Hazard Control Manager.

In the past, engineering schools rarely taught safety courses to undergraduates. This is slowly changing. In many schools, safety and accident prevention may be taught to students taking industrial engineering courses. Some safety matters may be touched on because past massive accidents made them noteworthy. Some schools have initiated postgraduate engineering degrees in safety for insurance companies. The federal government has also had courses leading to postgraduate degrees in safety. These graduate courses have responded to the inadequacy of instruction in safety and accident prevention in undergraduate schools. This educational deficiency is slowly being reduced. In 1998 approximately 125 colleges and universities in the United States offered degrees in safety management, occupational safety, environmental protection, or a related field.

In the fall of 1987 a university in Pennsylvania commented: "While the demand for well-educated safety professionals is at an all-time high, the safety profession is still one that most people have never heard of. . . . The current demand for safety professionals is not likely to be satisfied by the present number of available graduates. They continue to be sought out all around the country." To help meet this need, the National Institute for Occupational Safety and Health provides, on a competitive basis, academic grants to institutions of higher education around the nation for the provision of graduate programs in safety. These grants usually include provisions for student financial aid. In 1998 there were NIOSH-funded programs in 18 colleges of engineering and other technical departments. The educational requirements of a safety engineer are changing with changes to the profession. The site review process for NIOSH-funded programs sets standards for these programs. In addition, the Academic Accreditation Council of the American Society of Safety Engineers and the Board of Certified Safety Professionals have jointly published curriculum standards for baccalaureate and master's degrees in safety.

A 1992 survey of the 27,000 members of the American Society of Safety Engineers indicated that 30 percent majored in safety or health in college, 20 percent trained as engineers, and 19 percent have business or management degrees. Three percent hold doctorates; 25 percent, master's degrees; and more than 50 percent, at least a baccalaureate degree.[2] In the future, more and more safety engineers will have baccalaureate and graduate degrees in safety as an engineering discipline.

In addition to plant safety engineers, other safety personnel can be described. One group of consultants may be limited to reviews of plants to determine compliance with OSHA and other standards. A second group may be knowledgeable in specific areas, such as flammable gases, explosives, or mines. Both of these groups may also be concerned with investigations after an accident has taken place. System safety engineering grew because of efforts to evaluate hazards that might be present and potential accidents that might take place with advanced new products and processes, usually with new military systems, even as they are being designed. Some methodologies derived from system safety engineering have led to their adoption by other types of safety engineers.

Four states now have registration of professional engineers in a safety engineering discipline. Registration gives the registrant the right to use the title "Safety Engineer," but the enabling law has no requirement that the services of such an engineer be used. The contracting office of one military service responsible for development of advanced high-tech systems does require that certain hazard analyses and documents be signed off and approved at specific points in the designs. Such approval will be valid only under the signature of a registered safety engineer or other engineer shown to have had extensive experience in safety programs. The principal problem is that in a new advanced design project, there may be 400 engineers with no training in accident avoidance who may make critical errors and only one or two safety engineers to find them.

PRODUCTION AND PROCESSING LOSSES

Early in the Industrial Revolution, accident prevention by owners was oriented toward preventing losses to equipment and facilities such as mines, and to chattel such as horses, mules, or oxen. Gradually, preventing accidents to workers regained the importance for safeguarding lives and preventing injuries it had formerly had even in ancient and biblical times.

Thus, over the years decisions have resulted in safety engineers having to revise their priorities regarding accident prevention. While protection of personnel safety still comes first, the second priority has come to be protection of the environment. This also means protection of animals, especially in endangered species and against man-generated environmental problems such as "acid rain." The new priority includes prevention of leakage or release of liquids, oil, chemicals, or noxious gases and other deleterious substances. Safety engineers must now be almost as concerned about accidental release or unprotected use of materials that affect the environment as they are with an injury that affects persons directly and quickly. Protection against damage to the environment comes right after protection of personnel and animals and before prevention of damage to equipment. Priority for rescues of equipment and plant is last, usually following stoppage of operations.

The other new concern of safety engineers is in the area of accidental in-process damage or loss. Parts and materials being processed can sometimes be damaged or rendered unusable, so that they are as worthless as if destroyed by a catastrophe. For example, timing equipment in a metal conditioning oven may become faulty, so that the metal is as damaged as if by fire. Avoidance of such damage usually has been the responsibility of the production manager and his or her staff. However, accident prevention principles and methodologies are being applied more and more to process control. Lack of a simple feature that should have been reviewed by a safety engineer might lead to an accident and to a disaster in a large, complex plant. Protective devices and similar principles are increasingly being incorporated. Damage to a component in a production process might cause a failure in the assembled product during operation, and consequently an accident. The expertise of safety engineers for plant safety may be beneficially applied to product safety. A knowledgeable safety engineer can help greatly in such matters.

Increased realization that accident prevention is productive and gainful in all types of industrial activities may increase the standing of all safety personnel.

GROWING AREAS WITHIN SAFETY

Computer-related areas such as computer integrated manufacturing (CIM) and software safety are expanding rapidly. Product safety, environmental protection, and system safety are presently experiencing growth.

There has been much discussion about whether a major shift in safety is in progress from engineering controls to an emphasis upon psychological and social factors. Certainly behavior-based safety interests have grown through the 1990s, complementing but not diminishing the more traditional approaches to safety engineering and management.

BIBLIOGRAPHY

[1] Ronald P. Blake, *Industrial Safety* (New York: Prentice-Hall, 1943).

[2] Roger L. Brauer, "Educational Standards for Safety Professionals,"*Professional Safety*, Sept. 1992.

EXERCISES

2.1. How have the roles of safety personnel changed over the years?

2.2. List ten functions of safety personnel. Which would you consider most important? Why?

2.3. Discuss some safety aspects of building design with which a safety engineer should be concerned.

2.4. Why is it necessary that a safety engineer keep informed on the latest technical developments?

2.5. Discuss some means by which a safety engineer can keep informed.

2.6. If an accident were to take place, what priorities should be given to rescuers? How has this priority changed over the years?

2.7. Until the Railroad Safety Act was passed in 1893, was safety of equipment more highly regarded than that of personnel? Why?

CHAPTER 3

Promoting Safe Practices

In former years, any effort to promote safe practices probably would have consisted almost entirely of a campaign to alert employees to the hazards in their work and a call for them to conduct themselves safely. The modern concept is that efforts to promote safe practices must start long before this. The fact that many design deficiencies cause accidents has been pointed out. There have been other causes of accidents, of which many have been blamed unfairly on workers.

Hazards that cannot be eliminated should be controlled, first by design and then by procedural means. Procedural means consist, in effect, in relying on employees to perform properly and safely. Use of procedures is a far less desirable means of accident prevention than is good design. The preceding chapter provided a rough indication of priorities that could be used for accident minimization, and use of good procedures comes last. Although many of the deficient designs may not be correctable by workers, they can be reported so people in authority can take other corrective action. And because there will be times when hazards cannot be eliminated by design, there will be times when the safe practices of workers will have to be relied on.

A very strong interest in behavior-based safety has emerged at the close of the 90s decade. This is shown clearly by a survey conducted by the *Industrial Safety and Hygiene News* for its 1997 Annual White Paper. This survey showed an increase in the percentage of environmental, safety, and health professionals who say behavior-based safety is a training priority, from 20 percent in 1994 to 56 percent in 1997.[1] Eighty-nine percent of the professionals surveyed for the report said the behavioral assessment and coaching skills are "very important" or "somewhat important" to their career growth.

Some zealots of the regulatory approach to safety, initiated by the Occupational Safety and Health Act of 1970, react to behavior-based safety (BBS) as a frontal attack upon the regulatory approach that has brought considerable progress and punch to the safety movement. Some BBS advocates have displayed a penchant for telling derogatory anecdotes about OSHA inspectors and have shown a lack of appreciation for the safety history that brought the safety movement forward. Pronouncements that the regulatory approach is a failed approach or that the BBS movement is "frightening" are extremes that do not serve safety. There is room for the engineering-for-safety, the regulatory, and the behavioral-based motivational approaches. A complete safety program will promote safe practices and comply with regulations, while eliminating and controlling hazards through engineering.

THE BEHAVIOR-BASED SAFETY APPROACH

This approach relies heavily on classical psychology of learning and motivation through stimulus and response, response conditioning, and response generalization. Human behavior is viewed as emanating from a complex of personal and situational factors. Personal factors include long-term personal traits, as well as short-term psychological states as antecedents to immediate behavior. Situational factors include the physical, task, organizational and cultural, and immediate psychosocial environments. It has often been said that every worker is a manager. Each worker can be expected to manage her/his situation to personal advantage. That advantage varies with how the worker perceives his/her situation. That situational awareness can result in well-trained employees who, nevertheless, remove machine guards, fail to use hearing protection, or perform similar unsafe acts.

BBS has been applied in the industrial setting with success to reduce unsafe acts. It focuses intervention on observable behavior, directing and motivating managers and workers through "activators" and "consequences." One approach uses what E. Scott Geller, Professor of Psychology at Virginia Tech, calls the activator-behavior-consequence (ABC) principle.[2] "Activators" are events or conditions which tell a person what to do or when to do it. Consequences are the rewards and/or penalties that result from, or are perceived to result from, the activated behavior(s). There are competing consequences for the worker. The timing, consistency, and significance of the consequences determine which will influence behavior. More competitive consequences are those that occur immediately and consistently after the activated behavior and are positive. If long-term improvement in safety behavior on the job is to occur, it must persist whether or not external controls such as rewards and penalties are there. The worker must have internal activators and internal rewards. Therefore, workers must have a sense of ownership of this process that brings them satisfaction and pride.

The next chapter discusses the validity of the statistics often used in safety. If a company's culture is simply to provide reward when there is a reduction of a statistic and to punish if the statistic goes up, that statistic may go down, but without any improvement in safety. Behaviors may be elicited such as bringing an injured worker to the workplace to sit or lie on a couch in the nurse's office to avoid the injury counting as a lost-time injury. Behavior-based safety seeks goals that will produce safe behaviors and reduce the potential for accidents.

In BBS, both workers and management must participate actively and "buy into" the process. This process is to produce a safety culture, which involves the uniqueness of a specific work site or facility.

1. A steering committee is formed, made up of both managers and workers. The committee identifies hazardous behaviors which workers encounter regularly.

These are critical at-risk behaviors that expose the workforce to injury and equipment and facilities to harm. This inventory emerges from a careful analysis of the past few years of safety data at a work site.

2. The committee investigates the number of injuries that are related to the hazardous or unsafe behaviors to analyze why both the behaviors related to the injuries or damage and the injuries or damage occur. The goal is to change the unsafe behavior.

3. The committee, or designated observer(s), observes a particular selected job task (preferably volunteered by the employees involved) a few times and then writes up the observations. The workers are encouraged to work as they normally would without fear of retribution or disciplinary action.

4. Then the committee notes the safe and unsafe (at-risk) behaviors

5. The committee presents its findings to the work-site workers and establishes a log of safe behaviors for each task.

This approach focuses on observable behaviors, provides positive activators to motivate workers, and applies continuous interest and evaluation. Positive activators are those which provide the workers with a sense of empowerment, freedom, and control. These are said to be longer lasting than negative activators, which generally are those events that tell the worker to avoid failure (i.e., an accident).

Measurement is a key to sustained interest. Geller emphasizes that employees and management should systematically track a variety of success indicators, such as numbers of behavioral observations, percentage of employees volunteering to be observed, the number of coaching sessions conducted per week, and the percentage of safe behaviors per critical behavior category or per work area.

Geller believes that behavior and person factors represent the human dynamic of occupational safety. A Total Safety Culture includes the persons (knowledge, skills, abilities, intelligence, motives personality), the environment (equipment, tools, machines, housekeeping, temperature, physical layout), and behavior (safe/unsafe work practices, "actively caring," complying, coaching, recognizing, communicating, demonstrating). The factors should be based upon ten principles:

1. The culture, not OSHA, should drive the safety process.

2. Behavior-based and person-based factors determine success.

3. Focus on process, not outcomes (outcomes are statistics such as OSHA recordables).

4. Behavior is directed by activators and motivated by consequences.

5. Focus on achieving success, not on avoiding failure.

6. Observation and feedback lead to safe behaviors.

7. Effective feedback occurs via behavior- and person-based coaching.

8. Observing and coaching are key actively caring processes.

9. Self-esteem, belonging and empowerment increase "actively caring" for safety.

10. Shift safety from a priority to a value.

THE REGULATORY APPROACH: SAFETY RULES

Having safety rules is not a new idea. Rushbrook[3] mentions:

> Even the pirates of the early eighteenth century had fire prevention regulations, which were rigidly enforced. The articles of Captain Shaw (1723)—which incidentally were "swore to" upon a hatchet for want of a Bible!!—contained the following fire prevention clause: Article 6—"That man shall snap his arms (flintlock guns) or smoke tobacco in the hold without a cap to his pipe, or carry a lighted candle without a lanthorn, shall receive Moses's Law (forty stripes lacking one) on the bare back."

Safety rules are codes of conduct to avoid injury and damage. Under common law the employer is obligated to provide rules by which all employees can perform safely and the means to ensure that those rules are observed. Unless the employer formulates such rules and sees they are observed, he or she may be considered willfully and grossly negligent if an employee is injured because there was a lack of such rules or they were not enforced adequately.

Employers have been cited and fined under the OSHAct where employees were injured or killed because of failures to enforce safe work rules. Safety rules may have been published which state horseplay is prohibited. Joe is a high-spirited young man who likes to indulge in horseplay. If his supervisor is aware of this and fails to restrain Joe from such conduct during working hours, so that another worker is injured, the company may be open to a personal injury suit. In such an event, the other worker would be entitled to workers' compensation; and Joe could be dismissed immediately.

It is important enough to repeat: *Safety rules must be provided to govern the conduct of employees, and they must be enforced.*

Rules to cover all employees in a plant, especially a large one, can only be general in nature. In addition to these may be specific rules and orders such as those regarding occurrence of a fire or use of protective equipment. Certain rules of conduct and procedure may be more critical than others, and it may be necessary to apply two different penalty levels for nonobservance. Needs for most rules are generally apparent, so it is unnecessary to go into long, detailed explanations of why they have been imposed.

Certain criteria should be observed in the preparation of safety rules:

- The number of general rules should be kept to a minimum.
- Rules for a participating operation and for workers involved should be included in the procedures for conduct of that operation.
- Each rule should be clear and unambiguous.
- Stipulate only those rules currently required. A prohibition against smoking may be unnecessary where no combustible material is present and where no one objects to smoking.
- Stipulate only those rules that will be strictly enforced.

EMPLOYEE PARTICIPATION

After the OSHA standards went into effect in 1971, an inspection was made of an oil company's plant after the union charged that numerous "imminent" dangers existed. The subsequent three-way controversy between the company, union, and the OSHA is of little interest. One thing which is of interest is the fact that the workers had known of previous problems which they then brought to the attention of the OSHA. Very frequently the workers in any operation are the ones most aware of the existence of hazards in their work. They are the most concerned with ensuring the elimination of hazards because their own lives and health are involved. Workers (and their unions) therefore constitute excellent sources from which information on hazards, potential and imminent, can be derived. There are numerous ways by which employees can participate in any safety effort.

It has been pointed out that design deficiencies frequently generate hazardous conditions under which employees have to work. It has also been pointed out that such deficiencies should be brought immediately to the attention of supervisors and their superiors for correction. Many workers fail to do so, often because they believe the presence of hazards is usual and normal, and they accept the potentially injurious condition. Some persons may not recognize the danger; others may recognize them but will do nothing unless they are rewarded in some way.

On the other hand, some workers frequently object to design changes that merely change the mode and rate of operation without affecting safety.

CRITICAL INCIDENT TECHNIQUE

The simplest way to find from employees if they are aware of any hazards in their work is to ask them. The Critical Incident Technique developed by Tarrants[4] is a means of doing this most effectively. The method is based on collecting information on hazards, near misses, and unsafe conditions and practices from operationally experienced personnel. It can be used beneficially to investigate human-machine-operational relations and apply the information learned to improve equipment, procedures, and operations.

The technique consists of a capable reviewer interviewing personnel regarding involvement in accidents or near accidents; difficulties, errors, and mistakes in performance; and conditions that might cause mishaps. The surveyer first explains to a group of experienced workers what is to be done. Then each worker is interviewed individually and asked to answer a series of questions individually on safety matters.

Also requested of the interviewee are any other pertinent comments regarding safety aspects of other occurrences they have observed, even though they themselves had not been involved. The worker is asked to describe all hazards, mishaps, or near misses he or she can recall.

In effect, the Critical Incident Technique accomplishes the same result as a review of a series of accident investigations: identification through personal involvement of hazards that could result in injury or damage. Tarrant states, "Studies have shown that people are more willing to talk about 'close calls' than about injurious accidents in which they were personally involved, the implication being that if no loss ensued, no blame for the accident would be forthcoming."

It has been estimated that for every mishap there are at least 400 near misses. When the witnesses who observed mishaps or near misses, but were not participants, are added to those who were involved, an extremely large population is available from which information on possible accident causes can be derived.

When more than two or three interviewees report similar difficulties, hazards, or near misses with similar types of equipment or operations, the area can be accepted as one that should be investigated. The results of the investigation will determine whether corrective action is necessary or advantageous.

OTHER METHODS

Attempts have also been made to obtain safety information through the use of questionnaires to be filled in by selected personnel. This method has generally proved to be unsatisfactory for a number of reasons. Many plant workers and numerous other persons hate to write anything lengthy. Much information on hazards, accidents, or near misses may be extensive, so that written worker reports are often incomplete. Where a question is answered by a true-or-false notation or multiple choice, much pertinent information may be omitted. If this method is used, one fundamental problem is the need for extreme care in selecting and phrasing the questions. Too often the person completing a questionnaire would give the questions interpretations neither considered nor intended by the person who prepared them. Any question should be avoided whose answer requires involved reasoning that is not immediately apparent to the reader.

Much information is also submitted to control and action agencies in the form of hazard or trouble reports. However, such reporting itself generates discrepancies that can be avoided through use of the Critical Incident Technique. Reports may require entries in narrative or checklist form or both. Personnel find it time consuming and difficult to prepare narratives. Even conscientious writers tend to select the easiest and most rapid means of accomplishing reports, which therefore usually lack detailed and precise expression that could indicate the source of the problem. Checkoff items can be completed more rapidly, but these, too, result in omissions of information that may be critical. In both types, entries may include information on the immediate or principal cause of an accident but neglect other contributory causes and factors.

Taped oral reports are often helpful, but they may omit useful information unless someone else is present to keep the reporting person on the subject in question and from wandering too much. Thus, the Critical Incident Technique appears to be the most eminently satisfactory.

SUGGESTION PROGRAMS

A prime concern of industrial workers is in avoiding accidents and ensuring that any potentially hazardous situation they may note is corrected. Suggestion programs are therefore to the employees' benefit. There are generally a number of ways an employee can participate. The employee can report orally a suggestion to his or her supervisor, safety office, union representative, an OSHA office, or the representative on a safety committee, or submit it in writing by dropping it into a collection box.

Submitting suggestions in writing is an excellent idea, especially if there is a reward for any idea accepted. The disadvantage is that many people heartily dislike writing. Suggestion programs have often been so beneficial, attempts have been made to make suggestions easier to submit. Often workers are given small awards even if none are accepted, large ones if they result in savings.

Some companies have appointed clerical workers to distribute widely the forms used and to collect periodically any submissions. The name of each suggestor is recorded and filed. The remainder of the suggestion is then routed for comment to any office that might have an interest. The comments are then collected and, if worthy, suitable action is taken. Suggestions can sometimes be stimulated by having contests to see who can submit the most within a stipulated time period.

For suggestion programs to be successful, certain facts must be recognized. The employee's effort must be acknowledged. Even if the suggestion is not adopted, it must be given careful consideration. If it is accepted, the employee should be rewarded, preferably in public, so that fellow employees are aware of the award. Such awards act as inducements for more suggestions and suggestors.

UNION PARTICIPATION

Management and unions frequently disagree on production goals, methods, rates, and work rules, work hours and conditions, and numerous other matters. However, they do cooperate when they have a common goal, and safety is generally one of these. A survey of almost 300 companies showed that, of 22 areas of mutual interest, accident prevention was the foremost area where management and unions cooperated.

Historically, a major reason for the birth of industrial unions has been the health and safety of its members. Some of the most common objections of workers to their representatives involve this concern. The safety engineer, therefore, will often find the union representative to be a strong supporter of his or her safety efforts. The safety engineer may, however, have two problems: (1) he or she may not consider some of the objections justifiable from a safety standpoint; and (2) he or she may agree, but supervisors and managers may not because of cost considerations. Conversely, a safety engineer who finds a worker performing in an unsafe manner can frequently have the situation corrected by pointing it out to the union representative. The representative may be able to correct the situation without creating any friction. Often much tact is required on the part of the safety engineer, the union representative, and management, although all three are interested in lessening the occurrence of accidents.

SAFETY TRAINING

Safety training should begin with the new employee and continue throughout the time he or she is with the company. The type of training, frequency, material presented, and by whom presented will vary with the employment. Safety training should be given to all new employees, regardless of previous experience. Items in this training should include information on and review of:

- Company safety rules and practices.
- Employees' duties and rights under the OSHAct or state safety codes.
- Necessity for strict observances of warning signs.

- Emergency signals and their meanings.
- Methods of use of emergency equipment.
- Company programs to aid employees in purchase of safety glasses, safety shoes, and hard hats.
- Means of summoning assistance in times of need.
- Location of medical office.
- Benefits under workers' compensation laws.

The new employee should be indoctrinated further by his or her immediate supervisor or by an experienced and knowledgeable fellow worker whom the supervisor may designate. This indoctrination should include safety matters such as:

- Hazards that might exist in the operations in which the new employee will participate.
- Safeguards that have been provided and precautionary measures that should be taken against those hazards.
- Locations of emergency exits, phones, fire extinguishers, first aid kits, and other emergency equipment workers might use.
- Procedures to follow in the event a specific type of emergency occurs or might occur.
- Means of reporting hazards or defective equipment.
- Need for good housekeeping.
- Recapitulation of pertinent items the new employee was told during initial training.

Even older and experienced employees can benefit from additional on-the-job safety training. One of the most effective means is by periodic safety meetings. However, such meetings should observe certain rules:

- Meetings should be only long enough to present the desired information; they should not be too lengthy.
- The attendees should be employees in approximately the same categories—that is, construction workers, drivers, office employees, or production workers—and the subject matter should be pertinent to their activities. Small meetings oriented to specific problems the attendees may encounter are effective but may be less effective than mass assemblies. Mass assemblies are often conducted because of the importance of the message or the speaker. The assemblage usually feels that if a top manager is willing to spend the funds and time required, the message must be important.
- In any case, the speaker must be capable of impressing his or her listeners with the importance of the material presented. (Any supervisor or group leader who considers the safety material unimportant and presents it only because he or she has been told to do so is wasting time. The supervisor unfamiliar with the material to be presented would do better to ask the safety engineer to conduct it.)

- Informal meetings at which attendees can contribute comments should be encouraged, since they are highly effective.
- A very effective action is to have a worker demonstrate how to use a piece of protective equipment or to describe or show the safety action to be taken in a simulated emergency.

Such meetings might include:

- Giving information on accidents with similar types of equipment or operations that have occurred previously elsewhere.
- Instructing employees on new types of equipment, their uses, capabilities, hazards, and safeguards.
- Indicating the precautionary measures that are required for any operation they will undertake.
- Pointing out (preferably without mentioning names) any unsafe practices by the workers that might have been noticed.
- Determining whether any other members of the group have any comments on unsafe equipment, conditions, or practices.
- Disseminating any pertinent safety information that may have been brought to the supervisor's attention.
- Ensuring that personal safety equipment is suitable for the activity in which the wearer will take part and is in good working order.
- Reviewing and demonstrating capabilities in first aid and emergency procedures to ensure everyone is knowledgeable and proficient in the use of equipment, CPR, and other responses to accidents.

IN-DEPTH TRAINING

Safety training can be given to a limited extent during informal meetings. Often, however, more formal and extensive training is required. For example, OSHA standards for construction require the presence near work sites of either medical personnel or persons who have valid certificates in first aid training from the U.S. Bureau of Mines or the American Red Cross. An employer may find it necessary to send employees to one of those organizations to obtain necessary certification.

The company may have volunteer fire crews to help the professional fire fighters in an emergency. Training of both the professionals and the volunteers may be undertaken by attendance at schools, by visits by members of outside fire departments, such as those of the city or county, or by consultants who may review existing capabilities and make recommendations if improvements are needed.

Training in depth may be required for personnel who must work in bulky or complicated protective equipment, such as during sandblasting or the transfer of highly toxic fluids. Or, personnel may have to be trained in the use of emergency equipment and procedures, such as resuscitation by paramedical personnel.

Representatives of companies that sell new mobile equipment will train operators in safe handling.

MAINTAINING AWARENESS

Intermittent safety efforts are generally ineffective. It is necessary to maintain an almost continual program of keeping personnel alert to safe practices. Hazardous areas must be posted with suitable warning signs; however, other means are available at other locations:

- Large billboard-type signs regarding the need to avoid and prevent accidents can be located at employee entrances to the plant or at points of entry into buildings.
- Posters for display at frequented locations are available at low cost from organizations such as the National Safety Council and National Fire Protection Association.
- Small folders or booklets from safety organizations, insurance companies, and the federal government can be given to each employee as he or she enters the plant or at other appropriate times.
- Slips with printed safety messages can be added to pay envelopes or attached to pay checks.
- Safety displays can be located at entrances to buildings, lunch rooms, or similar locations.
- Articles or photographs regarding safety matters or accidents can be posted on bulletin boards.
- Large advertisement-type displays can be included in company newspapers.
- Automatic projectors can be used for continuous showing of slides on safety subjects.
- Placemats and napkins with interesting messages on safety and accident prevention, available from the National Safety Council, can be used in lunch rooms, cafeterias, and at vending machines.
- Members of departments of other work units that have been accident free for a certain length of time or number of work-hours can be presented with green rosettes and ribbons, buttons, or pins; coffee or milk and a doughnut during a work break; or ballpoint pens inscribed with a safety message.
- Accident prevention competitions can be held between departments and plants based on low accident and injury rates.

GENERAL COMMENTS ON SAFETY COMMITTEES

Safety committees may be composed of both management and workers, of workers' representatives, of first-line supervisors, or of any mix of these. The workers' representative committee is probably the most knowledgeable of safety needs, but management backing will produce the greatest effect.

Too often, the presence of managerial personnel on such committees degrades their capabilities. Unless the managers are extremely careful, their presence alone tends to dominate the proceedings (intentionally or not); or they fail to attend, leave early because they are called away, or take part fretfully as though they had more important business elsewhere. On the other hand, a top-level manager interested in safety can be highly effective. Just the presence on a committee of such a manager indicates and raises interest, increases the committee's value, and often acts to raise the morale of all workers, because they believe managers are interested in their well-being and the roles of the workers on the committee.

Any committee, no matter how composed, should observe certain rules. The safety engineer should be a member to provide guidance and information on any matters brought up by the committee. The engineer can offer an opinion on whether a reported situation does constitute a problem, whether a proposal suggested by a worker or committee member is technically feasible, or what the standard or code requirements are regarding the matter raised. The safety engineer should not be a voting member of the committee.

A secretary should be present to take notes on matters considered and their outcomes and to prepare minutes of the meeting. Any worker who makes a suggestion, written or oral, or indicates the existence of a hazard should receive a notice regarding the outcome. If the matter requires further consideration or review, the worker should be so notified. An effective means is to forward to the worker a copy of the minutes of the meeting at which his or her suggestion or hazard report was discussed. The worker should be identified in the minutes by name, job, title, and organization.

Meetings of the safety committee should be scheduled on a periodically regular basis. Enough time should be provided to ensure that due consideration is given to each item; however, the chairman must ensure that the meetings are confined to safety matters, discussions are confined to items at hand, minimum time is wasted, and the meeting is adjourned as soon as its business is completed.

The committee should represent each area of the plant or company. If it makes the committee too large, subcommittees can be established for each major department or division. If the matter affects more than one committee, the problem under discussion can be brought to a higher-level committee. Similarly, the results at the higher level can be passed down as required. Committee members can either be elected or appointed for definite periods. Alternates should also be designated to take the places of members who cannot attend. Memberships should be on a rotating basis within specific areas; however, to maintain continuity of capability, only one or two members should be replaced on a committee at one time.

SAFETY COMMITTEE DUTIES

An effective committee can undertake numerous duties highly beneficial to the personnel of any company and the company itself. Consideration of suggestions made by employees has already been mentioned as a major function. Others include:

- Promoting accident prevention and safe performance within their own work areas.
- Assisting the safety engineer and immediate supervisor in investigating any reported safety deficiency in their own work area.
- Assisting the safety engineer, supervisor, and other investigators in determining the cause of an accident or near miss that may have occurred.
- Reviewing, as a committee, and discussing the findings of any investigating board to determine whether they appear to be reasonable, whether all pertinent facts

were considered in the investigation, the feasibility of recommended corrective action, and whether similar accidents are possible in other work areas (which should then be informed of the accident and the corrective action to be taken).

- Making inspection tours to determine whether safety rules are being observed, good housekeeping is being maintained, any dangerous conditions exist, protective devices and equipment are being used where required, and hazardous areas are posted.
- Making recommendations for additions or modifications to company safety rules.
- Assisting the safety engineer, training-office personnel, and supervisors in preparing, reviewing, or presenting safety training to fellow employees.
- Selecting those departments or employees who are to be presented with awards for safe performance.
- Assisting the safety engineer in selecting posters and other material to be used to stimulate interest in accident prevention.

BIBLIOGRAPHY

[1] *Industrial Safety & Hygiene News,* 14th Annual White Paper. Dec. 19, 1997, p. 14.

[2] E. Scott Geller, "How to Motivate Behavior for Lasting Results," www.safetyonline.net/ishn/9603/behavior.html, and in "Total Safety Culture," *Professional Safety,* Sept. 1994, pp. 18–24.

[3] Frank Rushmore, *Fire Aboard* (London: The Technical Press Ltd., 1961), p. 26.

[4] W. E. Tarrants, *Utilizing the Critical Incident Technique as a Method of Identifying Potential Accident Causes,* U.S. Department of Labor, Washington, D.C.

EXERCISES

3.1. Why are safety rules needed?

3.2. Are safety rules that are not enforced of any value?

3.3. List some of the criteria to be observed when preparing safety rules.

3.4. What is the Critical Incident Technique and how does it work?

3.5. What are some problems encountered when safety survey questions are to be answered in writing?

3.6. Describe some other types of employee participation in accident prevention programs.

3.7. Tell some of the stages of safety training that should be undertaken. Are such programs undertaken in your plant? Do you believe you have received adequate safety training?

3.8. What types of in-depth training are required? Have you ever had any? Does your company ever send personnel for such training?

3.9. What are the principal duties of safety committees? Have you ever been a member of such a committee? How were you selected? Did you find it beneficial or not? How would you improve it?

3.10. List ten ways in which the awareness of the need for safety can be maintained. Do you consider the safety engineer the principal person responsible for your safety? Do you do anything to help him or her?

3.11. What are the elements of a behavioral based safety program?

C H A P T E R   4

Appraising Plant Safety

The great English physicist J. J. Thomson said quantifying a problem is the only way to understand it. At the present time, appraising plant safety or the changes of nonaccident operations by quantitative methods with any degree of accuracy involves high degrees of uncertainty. Safety engineers will produce more accident-free plants if they raise their awareness of, and follow, effective means of accident prevention by using the material and methods described in this book. However, the quantification safety aspect has its own benefits and should be known to all safety personnel.

Managers would like to know a plant's safety posture to direct whether or where corrective action should be taken. Many personnel would like to know whether a particular action will result in improvement or degradation. Judge Learned Hand queried whether comparisons of risks can be made by means other than economic factors. However, although many quantitative studies are based on cost considerations, many are not. State safety agencies, insurance companies, and OSHA all make appraisals of plant safety using numbers of accidents, or resulting fatalities or injuries. To all of these the economic factors may be added.

Thus, while both qualitative and quantitative methods may be used, the numerical data may be indicative of where the accident causes were. The safety engineer should be concerned with any condition where there is not a zero accident rate. That such an aim is achievable is indicated annually by the National Safety Council (NSC). The NSC publishes a list of the largest number of continuous man-hours worked without a disabling injury for each of 36 major industry groups. High-safety-quality plants achieved these accident-free periods by eliminating or minimizing the existence of unsafe conditions before accidents could occur. This is opposed to the idea of taking corrective action after accidents have taken place and have become numerical data.

Almost all quantitative methods use counts of past occurrences to indicate accident numbers, frequencies, and severities. These data are often used as measures of expectable future accident occurrences and risks. Originally, safety appraisals, both qualitative and quantitative, were made of existing plants to determine where improvements could be made; and these usages are still the most common, most significant, and most useful.

NEW PLANTS AND EQUIPMENT DESIGNS

Over the years it has been found that numerous problems can be avoided in plants being built or modified if plans are reviewed for safety aspects before any construction or change was initiated. Appraisals of plant safety should begin long before construction is started. This means the safety aspects should be considered as soon as a new plant or modification is conceived or design begun.

Some companies now require their safety personnel to review drawings for new facilities and equipment to ensure they meet legal requirements and good safety practices. Too often, appraisals are made only after an accident in a similar plant elsewhere has resulted in expensive litigation. Managers may then call for appraisals of their own plants to determine when similar accidents may occur there. Company insurers, or the state safety agency in which a plant is to be located, may have to review and approve plans and specifications before construction is initiated.

In spite of preconstruction approval, it is necessary that on-site inspections be made while construction is underway, after completion and prior to the start of operations, and continually after that. The safety posture before any plant has been built or any operation started can only be uncertain and often inaccurate appraisals. A prime, costly, and far-reaching example of what might result because of any such errors is the nuclear power industry and its accidents and costs for corrective action. Assessments of plant safety, nuclear or nonnuclear, by engineering designers are generally erroneous. This is because they believe too optimistically in their own designs, are untrained by schools in aspects of accident prevention so that they lack knowledge of hazards, and are generally unduly pressed by managers to finish any project.

At one time it was common practice to consider any safety aspects after plants had been built, equipment purchased, or operations begun. Too often, knowledge and existence of any hazards was derived from accidents that devastated plants, destroyed equipment, killed or injured operators, and halted operations. Actuaries found that the lack of accident experience data on newly designed plants caused them to add a substantial uncertainty factor that resulted in high insurance premiums. Theoretically, new plants and equipment would be built or created in accordance with regulations, codes, and standards for the intended localities and usages.

However, sometimes there are errors in their creation, the requirements change, or they are not observed properly. These deviations from legally stipulated safety measures might require expensive corrective actions. It therefore behooves employers to make safety appraisals of their plants, equipment, and operations to ensure that the possibility of accidents is minimized.

EXISTING PLANTS AND EQUIPMENT

Safety engineers should review plants, new or old, features of equipment, and procedures or operations to be undertaken. Often, safety engineers first are made aware of how safe a plant is when they are designated safety personnel after plants are put into operation. Whether they are old or new, the safety person should ensure:

- Plants include the egresses and exits and their markings required by OSHA standards and local codes and are properly maintained so.

- Electrical systems, especially for hazardous locations, comply with the provisions of the National Electrical Code and other designated codes.
- Pressure vessels are designed according to the provisions of the American Society of Mechanical Engineers (ASME) Code. The vessels should be stress-tested prior to use and at required designated intervals.
- Firefighting equipment is installed and maintained as required.
- Newly purchased equipment or equipment manufactured in-house has been installed and will meet prescribed OSHA and local standards.
- High-energy process vessels are separated by the greatest distance possible to prevent damage to other equipment in the event of a violent failure.
- Fire lanes and other routes to locations where other emergencies could occur are provided, marked, and maintained so that passages are not impeded or blocked.
- Emergency equipment and locations for their emplacements or storage are provided in readily accessible locations and checked periodically.
- Ventilating equipment is kept clean. Hoods, ducts, blowers, filters, and scrubbers are provided and adequate to remove air contaminants from the plant and to keep them from contaminating the environment. Ventilating equipment should be kept clean.
- Adequate work spaces are provided between pieces of equipment so that employees can have free passage and so there will be no physical interference to create errors and cause accidents.
- Hazardous operations are isolated so they do not constitute dangers to other personnel or activities. Welding shops should never be located close to paint spray activities, fuel locations, or where personnel can be affected by welding-arc radiation.

INDICATING PLANT HAZARDS

Certain areas are always more hazardous than others. Safety engineers should know where these places are and should devote time commensurate with the degree of hazard. A common practice to study the problem is to color-code a map of the plant showing areas as high-hazard, moderate-hazard, or low-hazard. Hazardous areas would be considered places where fuels, explosives, or highly toxic or reactive chemicals are handled or stored; wood-processing plants with large amounts of sawdust or other highly flammable materials; high-energy process reactors; and high-voltage and power-distribution stations. For example, paint spray or paint storage areas can be considered high-hazard locations. Certain of these high-hazard locations may be in the middle of less hazardous areas.

Inspections where safety engineers, supervisors, insurance personnel, and others can easily recognize highly hazardous areas can be highlighted. The colors can be used to indicate the periodicity of visits to be made. The most frequent visits would be, of course, to high-hazard locations. Moderately hazardous locations would include areas where there might possibly be high-noise-exposure levels; contaminated, but not highly toxic, atmospheres; locations where accesses to egresses and exits might be blocked by materials or equipment; areas where crates, boxes, pallets, or other containers might be stacked too high; or equipment where workers have a history of inactivating, bypassing, or removing safety devices, such as guards, that interfere with their work.

Even low-hazard locations sometimes have conditions that should be corrected. A very common one involves the use of coffee-making or other electrical cooking equipment in offices. Some of these devices, especially when more than one is in use, draw large amounts of current for which the circuitry was not designed. Frayed cords, "Christmas-tree" arrangements on plugs, and extensions resting on floors where rollered equipment passes over them constitute a few items in otherwise low-hazard areas.

All conditions that are hazardous to any degree should be appraised periodically.

SAFETY INSPECTIONS

Another form of appraisal is by safety inspections, which can be either informal or formal. An informal inspection can be conducted by a supervisor who ensures every morning that the facilities and equipment are in proper and safe condition and working order prior to the start of operations. Supervisors can observe and appraise workers to determine they are in condition to conduct themselves suitably and safely. Similar inspections can also be conducted by higher-level supervisors and managers, safety personnel, safety committee members, and even members of the security force as they make their rounds. Any discrepancies noted at such times should be brought to the attention of the supervisor. A written report is not necessary for an informal report. In some instances security personnel have taken photographs of unsafe conditions with Polaroid cameras and then left the photographs with the supervisor.

More formal inspections can be conducted by plant safety personnel; safety committee members; plant or department managers; fire prevention personnel; insurance company engineers; elevator, boiler, and pressure-vessel inspectors; or municipal, state, or federal agency representatives. Personnel in the last three categories are highly experienced and trained professionals and use proved methodologies to appraise the safety of the areas they cover. Procedures they follow are beneficial to anyone making a formal inspection:

- An inspection checklist and record of findings is used to indicate the conditions of equipment and operations they inspected.
- High-risk operations and activities noted on the checklists are given special attention, but others are not ignored.
- Findings during previous inspections are reviewed to determine whether any discrepancies have been found, and if so, whether they were corrected.
- Personnel making inspections note whether workers are suitably equipped with hard hats, safety shoes, safety glasses, or other protective equipment prescribed for the areas visited.
- A report of inspection is prepared and presented to the responsible supervisors and managers. A preliminary report may be given verbally, followed later by a written report.

- Findings in the report should be specific and not vague generalities. Any report should name locations, equipment, and operations and cite pertinent discrepancies. (*Note:* Stating that housekeeping was generally poor in a described location is a specific finding.)
- The report, oral or written, may present recommendations for corrective action that should be taken.
- If a discrepancy violates any governmental standard, code, or regulation, the specific document, paragraph, and requirement should be cited.

CHECKLISTS

Checklists are often used to evaluate many of the safety features (or their lack) in industrial plants. Checklists are provided at the ends of many of these chapters to assist personnel in evaluations. Some checklist questions may not be applicable to the specific plant being appraised, and their answers can be omitted. In other cases, the person making the survey may add other items to be reviewed, especially if such reviews are made periodically and it is desirable to compare answers on different occasions.

Checklists can be prepared from numerous sources. Even persons new to safety matters can prepare them simply by asking themselves what they would like to know. One item will usually lead to another.

To determine whether or not a plant complies with the OSHA standards, the specific requirements in the standards can be presented as questions. Other sources might be items in the text of this book, articles from magazines, educational brochures used by the National Safety Council or government agencies, or newspaper notices of accidents or litigation.

The questions asked in checklists are usually very broad in scope, requiring more details. For example, a question on a checklist might be whether a pressure vessel had been proof-pressure tested. The plant might have 20 or 30 pressure vessels; therefore a simple yes or no answer would probably not suffice. In this case, asking whether or not each test had been made, whether each had been satisfactory, and by whom the test had been would require multiple answers. (A common checklist of this type might be one for fire extinguishers for which there are generally a great number in a large plant. If a checklist item questions whether fire extinguishers have been checked or refilled, a complete answer would require an extensive survey.)

The National Institute of Occupational Safety and Health (NIOSH)[1] has issued an excellent document which permits a manager or safety engineer to appraise the effectiveness of workplace safety programs. In one chapter are listed many of the activities that should be reviewed and evaluated. Standards are given by which ratings should be assigned as poor, fair, good, or excellent. The chapter also presents a rating form by which a numerical relative risk assessment can be developed if it is desirable to make comparisons.

For the safety engineer, the use of accident statistics is less productive in appraising plant safety than is knowledge of hazards, controls, checklists, and similar information. Statistical data are usually indicative of accidents after they have occurred. Zero accident- and injury-frequency rates are the only ones with which the safety engineer can be satisfied. Any accident is a profound disappointment to a safety engineer.

QUANTITATIVE APPRAISALS

To determine the safety level of any plant or industry by quantitative means by use of after-the-fact data, accident statistics and frequency and severity rates are employed. The data may be indicative only after there has been a sizable accumulation of past numerical accident information. These data generally provide limited answers about relationships between causes and effects, so only broad accident preventive measures can be taken. Checklists and analyses are more suitable, detailed, and effective for safety accomplishments.

PROBLEMS WITH VALIDITY OF STATISTICS

Probabilities are based on past performance; the longer the record the better will be the estimate of future performance if there have been no changes. To be statistically valid, quantitative data must have been collected either over long periods or from a large number of similar activities. When they must be collected over a long period, by the time statistical validity has been established, many persons may have been killed or injured before corrective action is taken. If any action has been taken, the past numerical data no longer apply until after long and exactly similar performance. For example, a number of accidents occurred in a plant within a specific period of time, so it appeared that because of unguarded rotating equipment they were at a rate of 3 mishaps per 1,000,000 man-hours. As a result, guards were emplaced. The previous accident rate was no longer valid for estimating or predicting future accident-occurrence rates in that shop. (A good safety engineer would have had guards installed before or immediately after the first accident and not waited until such mishap data accumulated.)

Accident statistics do provide valuable information to regulatory agencies and insurance companies which identify causative factors and whether additional safety measures are needed to lessen future accidents. Insurance company actuaries can use accident data to establish costs of future premiums for employers. These actuarial determinations constitute a good deal of educated guesswork for new operations and equipment where there is no or little accident experience, such as for new and untried plants or aircraft. Because of the uncertainty, insurers will charge as much as the traffic will bear to cover all financial risk losses. After there has been experience, rates can be adjusted to reflect the experience: down if there have been few or no accidents, up if there have been losses or there is knowledge that the risks of losses will increase. The very threat of increased premiums has forced some companies out of business. This has occurred because of accidents, or the threat of accidents, with zeppelins, nuclear power plants, machinery manufacturers, plant operators, and surgeons. The means of calculating accident and injury frequency and severity rates is indicated in Fig. 4-1.

Some safety engineers use accident and injury frequency and severity rates for comparative purposes to determine:

FREQUENCY AND SEVERITY RATES

Frequency rates: rates can be computed in various ways to determine the frequency of accidents or injuries, or the severity of injuries. The methodologies by which rates are computed are similar in all cases: however, the bases used may be different. If *A* is the event for which the frequency rate is to be computed, *B* the numerical base, and *C* the exposure, then

$$\text{frequency rate} = \frac{A \times B}{C}$$

If 1,000,000 man-hours is used as the base, an accident frequency rate can be computed by:

$$\text{accident frequency rate} = \frac{\text{number of accidents} \times 1,000,000}{\text{man-hours of employee exposure}}$$

Thus for a plant that had 18 accidents in a year during which employees worked a total of 1,200,000 man-hours,

$$\text{accident frequency rate} = \frac{18 \times 1,000,000}{1,200,000} = 15.0 \text{ per million man-hours}$$

If during the same time there were 6 disabling injuries at that plant, the injury frequency rate would be

$$\text{injury frequency rate} = \frac{6 \times 1,000,000}{1,200,000} = 5.0 \text{ per million man-hours}$$

The Bureau of Labor Statistics uses a base of 100 full-time employees as opposed to the 1 million man-hours used by the American National Standards Institute (ANSI Standard Z16.1). It is assumed that 100 full-time employees would work 200,000 hours per year (40 hours per week per worker, 50 weeks per year). Computed on this basis, the injury frequency rate for the plant mentioned would be:

$$\text{injury frequency rate (BLS)} = \frac{6 \times 200,000}{1,200,000} = 1.0 \text{ per 200,000 man-hours}$$

It is therefore evident that when rates are cited, it is necessary to know the bases on which they were calculated.

Injury severity rate: certain industries may show high injury frequency rates, but the injuries may be minor. Other industries may have few injuries and an extremely low injury frequency rate, but when injuries do occur they are severe. The American National Standards Institute has therefore established a means of measuring severities through use of time charges. With this method fatalities and injuries are assigned time charges to be used in determining the rates. These charges are based on average experience. For example, each fatality or permanent total disability is assigned a time charge of 6,000 days. This was based on the life expectancy of the average worker times the number of working days per year. (The Bureau of Labor Statistics does not include a fixed charge for a fatality.) Time charges for permanent partial disabilities are tabulated in ANSI Standard Z16.1: loss of an arm above the elbow, 4,500 days; loss of an eye (or sight), 1,800 days; loss of both eyes (or sight) in one accident, 6,000 days; complete loss of hearing in one ear, 600 hours; and in both ears (one accident), 3,000 days. Injuries resulting in temporary disabilities are charged the number of calendar days lost for computations by ANSI methods. With the Bureau of Labor Statistics method, only actual work days lost are changed. The Bureau of Labor Statistics method requires time charges be included even if an employee is assigned another job; any change in occupation resulting from a work accident or illness is recordable. Therefore, by ANSI Z16.1:

$$\text{disabling injury severity rate (BLS)} = \frac{\text{total days charged} \times 1,000,000}{\text{employees hours of exposure}}$$

FIGURE 4–1   Frequency and Severity Rates   Continued on next page

If the six disabling injuries indicated above resulted in 240 days lost, the disabling severity rate would be:

$$\text{disabling injury severity rate (BLS)} = \frac{240 \times 1,000,000}{1,200,000}$$

$$= 200 \text{ days per million man-hours}$$

The average severity per injury can also be determined. This can be done in either of two ways:

$$\text{average days charged} = \frac{\text{total days lost or charged}}{\text{total number of disabling injuries}} = \frac{240}{6} = 40$$

OR

$$\text{average days charged} = \frac{\text{injury severity rate}}{\text{injury frequency rate}} = \frac{200}{\textcircled{5}} = 40$$

FIGURE 4–1   Continued

- How rates for his or her plant or company compare with the averages for the industry. Rates for various industries are computed by the National Safety Council[2] and the Bureau of Labor Statistics. Companies that are members of the National Safety Council are generally more safety oriented than are nonmember companies.
- How accidents, injuries, and severity compare from period to period and whether they are improving or deteriorating.
- How different types of hazardous operations compare.
- How well different departments are doing regarding safety. An increase in rates may indicate a lack of supervisory emphasis. The data can also be used to determine which department or plant had the best or worst performance if an accident prevention competition is held. In such cases the safety professional must ensure that all the organizations being compared observe the same rules for reporting. The rates may also have to be adjusted to compensate for the difference in magnitude of hazards between different types of operations. Average industry rates might be used to provide such adjustments for the units being compared. Comparisons can also be made between specific plants and for the entire industry.

PROBLEMS WITH QUANTITATIVE RATES

Unfortunately, even where accident and injury statistics can be useful, they are often so incomplete that they can lead to inaccuracies. For example, to reduce reportable injuries and lost work days, some companies reassign injured workers to temporary jobs less strenuous than the regular ones. Workers often receive pay which is not reported as lost because of injuries. Because no time was listed as lost, it appeared that no injury had taken place. OSHA reporting requirements have attempted to correct and eliminate such schemes by trying to ensure all injuries are reported. Failures to do so make quantitative safety data unreliable.

In 1986, the Bureau of Labor Statistics expressed concern over the validity of accident record keeping on injuries. Lack of proper reporting by industrial companies was distorting and undermining the use of statistics. A worker's union stated that the exemptions that OSHA had been forced into "made injury rate figures a fairly useless measure of plant safety."

There have also been differences between recordable and reportable injuries as defined in the American National Standards Institute (ANSI) Standard Z16.1, according to which reports are made to the National Safety Council, and the BLS/OSHA definitions and criteria. The result is that NSC injury rates differ and are less than those of the BLS and OSHA.

In 1941 Heinrich stated that 88 percent of all accidents were caused by "unsafe acts" of persons involved. *Fortune* indicated that a 1967 survey in Pennsylvania had concluded that this figure should be only 26 percent. Even in 1910, Eastman pointed out that managers had contended that 95 percent of the fatal accidents in the Pittsburgh area were due to "carelessness," while her own studies indicated that only 22.5 percent were caused wholly or in part by employee's negligence. The latter is more in line with a study she cited regarding workers in Germany. That study indicated that 29 percent of all work accidents were attributable to the workers themselves.

The data used by Heinrich (and the opinions expressed by the managers in the Pittsburgh area) had evidently been biased by employers themselves, so any appraisal was faulty. Heinrich had made his analysis from reports submitted to insurers by the managers of the companies at which the accidents had happened. However, no manager would want to indicate to the insurer, or to any safety agency having jurisdiction over the locale where the accident had take place, that the company had been at fault, or that hazards existed or had not been suitably controlled in the workplace under his or her own authority. It is also doubtful whether any safety person would want to indicate that any accident was due to a hazard he or she had not detected or corrected. Further, any manager would be reluctant to make such an admission, especially in writing and to an insurer or safety agency.

VALIDITY OF STATISTICAL COMPARISONS

A common problem in the use of statistics is that the person preparing them may present only one slanted aspect of the data, so readers receive erroneous impressions. In some instances this is unintentional, in others it is done to prove a point the analyst wants to prove, to impress the readers, or simply to avoid running contrary to accepted opinion. An example involving safety statistics can be cited regarding automobile accidents. A speaker quoted in the newspapers pointing out that "in the United States in 1898 one American was killed in a car accident. In 1972, more than 4 million Americans were involved in traffic accidents and 56,300 of them died."

In 1912, the first year in which the National Safety Council published statistics on automobile accidents, there were 33 fatalities for every 10,000 registered vehicles in the United States. The actual rate in 1898 was probably much higher, although the total number of fatalities was lower. The current rate is far less than 5 deaths for every 10,000 vehicles. It is evident that the two statistical statements provide far different views on whether automobiles are becoming more or less safe. The value of the statistical comparison is that often the sheer magnitudes of accidents, fatalities, and injuries will induce corrective actions.

Many statistics are quoted which leave out any measure of exposure. For example, suppose in a hypothetical case a company reports that 15 percent of persons aged 20 to 35 suffered lost-time injuries, and only 1 percent of persons aged 50–65 suffered lost-time injuries. This leaves the impression that those aged 20–35 are unsafe workers as compared with those 50–65. However, a review of the job assignments indicates that the dangerous jobs are handled by the younger group. The older group is not exposed to the same risks of injury; therefore, such simple comparisons are not valid. Statistics should be adjusted for exposure to accident potential, before they are used as a basis for comparisons.

Consideration must also be given to type of exposure. Risks are not comparable across types of industry. This is illustrated by Fig. 4-2. Neither are risks comparable within a type of industry. This is illustrated by Fig. 4-3.

RISK ASSESSMENTS

When funds are requested for correction of safety deficiencies not required by law, managers would like to know the risks involved so they can make suitable decisions. The theory is that the computed economic risk of an accident should justify any expenditure for the proposed safeguard. Managers would also like to know how greatly this improvement would increase the safety of their plant or activity. Even before plants are built, such estimates are often made by cost/risk/benefit/effectivity analyses.

Two numerical methods of risk indication are frequently used: those involving relative methods and those using probabilities of occurrence.

The relative method of indicating risks because of hazards is simpler, more widely used, and has many different forms. A task, the toxicity of gas, or the accident potential of a piece of equipment is rated by a group of knowledgeable personnel according to a numerical scale. The scale adopted may range from 1 to 10, 1 to 6, and so on to indicate degrees of hazard. A gas whose toxicity or flammability is rated at 5 may be more toxic than one rated at 3. A liquid with a flash point of 225°F may be more fire-safe than one that has a flash point of 150°F. With the relative method, doubling the number in the scale would not necessarily double the hazard involved.

Probabilities of future occurrences can frequently be estimated from past experience. However, to acheive any accuracy, the experience has to have been over a long period and comparatively large populations. The expected events to be assessed must occur under conditions similar to those under which the data were derived. The National Safety Council may predict that, based on experience during a specific holiday, a certain number of persons will die in traffic accidents. If the weather or the desirability of watching a ball game creates a situation different from that of the NSC past

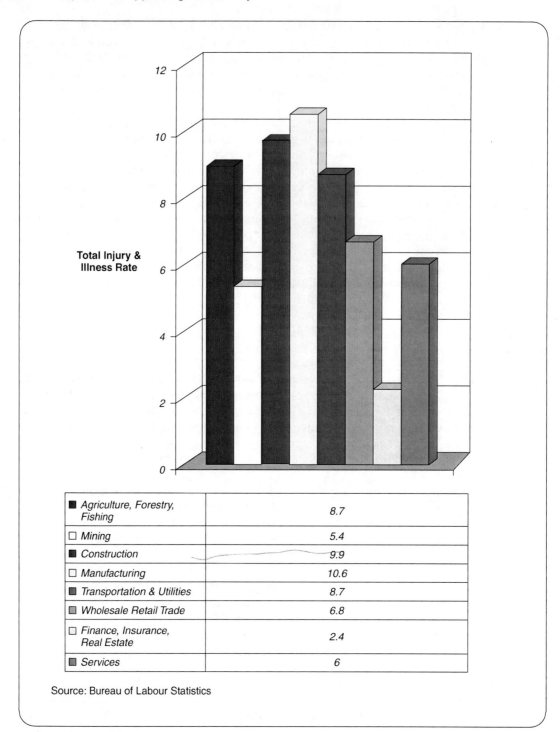

■ Agriculture, Forestry, Fishing	8.7
☐ Mining	5.4
■ Construction	9.9
☐ Manufacturing	10.6
■ Transportation & Utilities	8.7
■ Wholesale Retail Trade	6.8
☐ Finance, Insurance, Real Estate	2.4
■ Services	6

Source: Bureau of Labour Statistics

FIGURE 4–2   Total Injury and Illness Rate by Industry, 1996
Source: Bureau of Labor Statistics

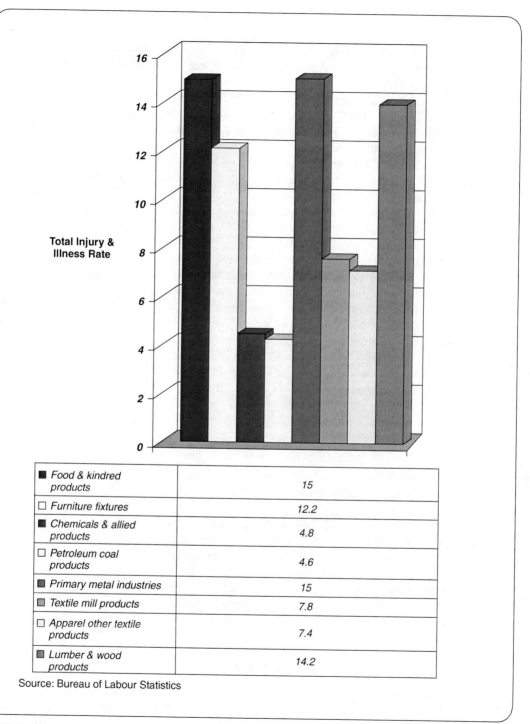

■ Food & kindred products	15
□ Furniture fixtures	12.2
■ Chemicals & allied products	4.8
□ Petroleum coal products	4.6
■ Primary metal industries	15
▦ Textile mill products	7.8
□ Apparel other textile products	7.4
▦ Lumber & wood products	14.2

Source: Bureau of Labour Statistics

FIGURE 4–3   Total Injury and Illness Rate by Manufacturing, 1996

Source: Bureau of Labor Statistics

data, the actual number of accidents, fatalities, and injuries will differ from the prediction.

Probabilities of accidents can sometimes be developed for new operations by suitably combining the probabilities of occurrence of subordinate events for which data are available. Unfortunately, because too often there is a lack of dependable input data, overall probabilities derived by these methods are rarely accurate to a highly dependable degree. Further, there is no way to prove by test the correctness of any of the computed estimates. Thus, although the theory of the methodology is acceptable, practice leaves much to be desired.

Another problem arising with risk-cost-benefit analyses involving probabilities to compute economic justifications for accident prevention measures is that estimated probabilities of accidents and losses are generally too low. The result is that employers will rarely show before-the-fact calculations of economic justifications for expenditures for safeguards. In 1987 the Supreme Court ruled that safety superseded other considerations such as any risk analysis.

A highly theoretical example would be if the operators of the *Titanic* had had to determine the economic justification for more lifeboat spaces before its initial, final, and sole voyage. The ship had been considered "unsinkable," that is, it had a zero probability of going under. If the probability of a catastrophic accident during any ship voyage was taken at the same value as that of an individual being struck by lightning (5×10^{-7}), and the ship made 50 voyages a year, such an accident would occur on the average of once every million years. The cost of additional lifeboats could never have been justified, based on the original estimate of the Titanic's announced safety features.

The risks an organization takes in any enterprise may be written as:

$$\text{risk} = P_A \times L_A$$

where P_A = probability of an accident;
          L_A = probable loss resulting from the accident.

Figure 4-4 lists the probabilities of an individual having a fatal accident during a year because of various hazardous activities. The values shown were derived by dividing the total number of fatalities in the United States in 1969 from that specific cause by the total population of that year. On that basis, since 160 persons were killed in hang-gliding accidents that year, the risk of death from that cause would be as small as that of being hit by a lightning bolt, a relatively safe operation. However, because there were only about 20,000 hang-gliding enthusiasts who exposed themselves to the risk of being killed, the actual probability of one being killed is 8×10^{-3}.

Therefore, risk calculations must include factors for exposure of the persons or activities being considered. The risk equation then becomes:

$$\text{risk} = P_A \times E_A \times L_A$$

where E_A = exposure of a person or object to an accident.

The probability loss also requires careful consideration and inclusion in any appraisal of risk. An accident loss could vary from a negligible amount to a complete wipeout. It may therefore be necessary not only to estimate the probability of an accident in increments of different amounts over the entire range of foreseeable pos-

INDIVIDUAL RISK OF ACUTE FATALITY BY VARIOUS CAUSES*

(U.S Population Average 1969)

Accident type	Total number for 1969	Approximate individual risk acute fatality probability/yr[1]
Motor vehicle	55,791	3×10^{-4}
Falls	17,827	9×10^{-5}
Fires and hot substances	7,451	4×10^{-5}
Drowning	6,181	3×10^{-5}
Poison	4,516	2×10^{-5}
Firearms	2,309	1×10^{-5}
Machinery (1968)	2,054	1×10^{-5}
Water transport	1,748	9×10^{-6}
Air travel	1,778	9×10^{-6}
Falling objects	1,271	6×10^{-6}
Electrocution	1,143	6×10^{-6}
Railway	884	4×10^{-6}
Lightning	160	5×10^{-7}
Tornadoes	91	4×10^{-7}
Hurricanes	93	4×10^{-7}
All others	8,695	4×10^{-5}
All accidents		6×10^{-4}

[1]Based on total U.S. population.

*WASH-1400-D, *Reactor Safety Study-An Assessment of Accident Risks in U.S. Commercial Nuclear Power Plants*, Atomic Energy Commission, August 1974.

FIGURE 4–4   Individual Risk of Acute Fatality by Various Causes

sible losses, but to put against each average probability increment the possible severity or estimated loss. A total of all computed averages would, in theory, give the potential loss.

Rather than use this complex type of appraisal, most companies simply use their listed assets, apply an estimated loss, and add whatever insurers might agree to permit. Here again, accident predictions are often underestimated, and actual claims are generally overstated.

ACCEPTANCE OF RISK

The risks that persons will accept vary with the benefits expected. Starr[3] commented on the risk-benefit relationship; first he categorized risks as being "voluntary" and "involuntary." A voluntary risk is one freely accepted by an individual on the basis of

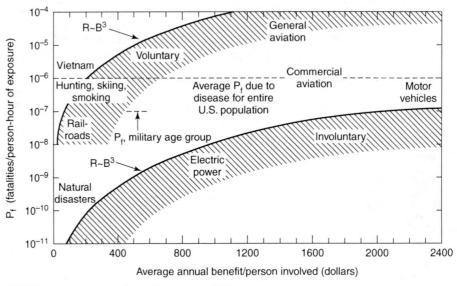

FIGURE 4–5   Starr's Benefits vs. Technological Risk

the individual's own values and experience. An involuntary risk is one by which an individual subjects himself or herself to another person's (or other persons') judgment. For example, a passenger on a bus, train, or airliner relies on the judgment of the operator and accepts risks over which he or she has no control (other than the decision to take a bus, train, or airliner). Starr prepared the chart shown in Fig. 4-5 (its derivation is presented cited in the article) and also presented the following comments:

- The indications are that the public is willing to accept "voluntary" risks roughly 1,000 times greater than "involuntary" risks.
- The statistical risk of death from disease appears to be a physiological yardstick for establishing the level of acceptance of other risks.
- The acceptability of risk appears to be crudely proportional to the third power of the benefits (real or imagined).
- The social acceptance of risk is directly influenced by public awareness of the benefits of an activity, as determined by advertising, usefulness, and the number of people participating.
- In a sample application of these criteria to atomic power plant safety, it appears that an engineering design objective determined by economic criteria would result in a design target risk level very much lower than the socially accepted risk for electric power plants. (*Note:* The accidents at Three Mile Island and Chornobyl have substantially affected that comment.)

The study that produced the table in Fig. 4-4 also produced the following comments:

- Types of accidents with a death risk in the range of 10^{-3} (one in a thousand) persons per year to the general public are difficult to find. Such high risks are not uncommon in some sports and in some industrial activities, when measured for limited groups at risk (that is exposed to the hazards involved). Evidently this level of risk is generally unacceptable, and when it occurs, immediate action is taken to reduce it.

- At an accident risk level of 10^{-4} (one in 10,000) deaths per person per year, people are less inclined to concerted action but are willing to spend money to reduce the hazard.

- Risks of accidental death at a level of 10^{-5} (one in 100,000) per person per year are recognized in an active sense.

- Accidents with a probability of death of 10^{-6} (one in a million) or less per person per year are evidently not of great concern to the average person.

The last statement is a disputable generalization. Figure 4-4 indicates that fatality probabilities in the tornado and hurricane zones are less than 10^{-6} per person per year. Yet the average person in those zones is very concerned with the effects of these phenomena. Also it appears that even though the total number of fatalities in either case might be the same, an accident that causes a great number of deaths at one time, even at rare intervals, is of more concern than are accidents involving a few persons on each of many occasions over an extended period. Thus, while there is much concern over the possibility, with very low probability, of a nuclear accident which might cause thousands of deaths, there is far less concern that 50,000 might be killed in traffic.

Quantitative appraisals of plant and operation safety, the probabilities of accidents, and risk estimates have always been considered questionable. There was much outcry against the authors of the study whose values are shown in Fig. 4-4. Appraisals of safety and risks in existing have to be readjusted with the advent of accidents as they were at industrial plants, Three Mile Island, and then Chornobyl.

RISK COMMUNICATION

It is not enough to simply appraise plant safety and risks and to "manage" plant risks. Risks must be communicated to the workers in the plant and to persons in the community. Regulations such as OSHA's Hazard Communication Standard of 1988 and the Environmental Protection Agency's The Emergency Planning and Community Right-to-Know Act of 1986 place requirements on the employer to know plant risks, appraise them, and communicate them to employees and employers. More than 30 million U.S. workers are potentially exposed to one or more chemical hazards. There are an estimated 650,000 existing hazardous chemical products, and new ones being introduced almost daily. These acts cover both physical hazards, such as flammability and explosivity, and health hazards. The acts are discussed briefly in the next chapter.

It is important to recognize that risk communication is part of the process of appraising plant safety. In 1989 a National Academy of Sciences Committee on Risk Perception and Communication defined risk communication as "an interactive process of exchange of information and opinion among individuals, groups, and institutions. It involves multiple messages about the nature of risk and other messages, not strictly about risk, that express concerns, opinions, or reactions to risk messages or to legal and institutional arrangements for risk management."[4] Behavior based safety (BBS) is a format that can be used to accomplish this interactive exchange of information and opinion.

It is possible for risks to be misunderstood and exaggerated by workers. Attention can be inappropriately invested by employees and employers on some risks, because of misunderstanding and false rumors in the community or among the workers. This phenomenon has been called by some "The Social Amplification of Risk." Similarly, insufficient attention to some risks can be given for the same reason. Risk appraisal should provide correct information about hazards within the plant and community. This information then can be provided in interactive exchange to all concerned parties. The Academy of Sciences report states, "Preparing risk messages can involve choosing between a message that is so extensive and complex that only experts can understand it and a message that is more easily understood by nonexperts but that is selective and thus subject to challenge as being inaccurate or manipulative." The interactive exchange format is important to having a culture of trust among all concerned that contributes to clarification where needed. Clarification occurs best when all persons concerned are able to listen to one another.

BIBLIOGRAPHY

[1] National Institute of Occupational Safety and Health, "Self Evaluation of Safety and Health Programs," U.S. Government Printing Office, Washington, D.C.

[2] "Accident Facts," National Safety Council, Chicago, Ill.

[3] Chauncey Starr, "Social Benefit versus Technological Risk," *Science*, Vol. 164, Sept. 19, 1969, pp. 1232–1238.

[4] National Research Council, *Improving Risk Communication* (Washington, D.C: National Academy Press, 1989).

EXERCISES

4.1. What organizations make plant safety inspections and appraisals?

4.2. How soon should considerations of plant safety and appraisals begin?

4.3. Cite some features of an individual plant that a safety engineer should review during the design stage.

4.4. What are the benefits of quantitative appraisals? How are they compared to qualitative appraisals? Can either be made without the other?

4.5. Describe how a safety inspection should be made to appraise the status of a plant's safety.

4.6. How can safety be measured?

4.7. Why would various organizations want different statistical information on accidents? What types of information would each organization want?

4.8. In what type of statistical information should an industrial plant safety engineer be interested?

4.9. Describe how statistical information on accidents and losses can be distorted unintentionally.

4.10. Why do the BLS/OSHA data differ from those of the National Safety Council?

4.11. How are accident frequency rates determined?

4.12. Do you feel that any specific probability of being injured should be set at a reasonable level of safety and that a person should not be able to sue any employer, operator, or product manufacturer who had met that level, based on prior analyses of possible risks?

4.13. What level of risk would you be willing to accept if you were told you might be injured or killed?

4.14. How does degree of risk affect insurance premiums?

4.15. Do you believe a risk-cost-benefit analysis is a good way to determine whether to undertake a proposed safety measure not required by law?

4.16. What is social amplification of risk?

4.17. What is the relationship between plant appraisals and risk communication?

C H A P T E R   5

Accident Investigations

The findings of accident investigations have long been used to identify factors that affected safe operations of industrial activities. Processes, equipment, and safeguards have become more complex, and so have the causes and effects of failures and other factors that lead to accidents. Thus accident investigations and the methods involved in determining causes have also become more complex.

For example, guards at one time were simple devices. Now even many of the mechanical ones are highly sophisticated. Electronic safety devices often consist of networks and components designed in accordance with Boolean logic as applied to switching circuits. A failure of such a safeguard would probably have to be investigated by someone knowledgeable in circuit analysis. A failure of this type occurred in 1973 with a train of the Bay Area Rapid Transit system in the San Francisco area. The accident that resulted was less severe than many that have occurred to trains since railroads were first built, but it is apparent that accidents will take place in spite of designs based on the latest technology. In January 1987 a railroad accident resulted in the deaths of 15 persons and injury to 176, although the rail line had had complex electronic systems installed. The capabilities of investigating personnel to determine the causes of these accidents had to be far greater than those required only a few years ago.

The Reason for Investigations

Many accidents are still of a nature which appear to have simple, easily determinable causes; but even here, changes in legal aspects may require investigative abilities never before required. For example, an accident occurs in which a chain breaks under a load: the load drops and hits a worker, who is killed. At one time the report of investigation may have described it in fairly simple terms and indicated that a contributory cause of the worker's death was an unsafe act on his part: he put himself in a dangerous position. Reports of a later period might also include as a contributory cause supervisory error: the supervisor should not have permitted the worker to put himself in danger. An attorney for the worker's dependents might have shown the supervisor knew the worker was in the dangerous position or knew the chain was bad and permitted the worker to continue with the operation and so was guilty of gross negligence. The attorney might also bring suit for the dependents against the manufacturer of the chain, claiming negligence in its manufacture. For this, analysis of the chain and the part where it broke might be required. The chain manufacturer might claim as a defense that the chain had been damaged through long use (if it was an old one), had been used improperly in that it was too small for the intended load or there had been a warning the load should not exceed a specific weight. It is apparent that in such cases there may be investigations by representatives of organizations with different interests, each attempting to ensure that whomever it represented is not held to be at fault. Groups with such interests might include, but not be limited to:

- The union that represents the worker, to ensure that blame is not attributed to the worker unless it is very evident he or she was the cause. The Airline Pilot's Association frequently objects to findings of the Federal Aviation Agency (FAA) that the blame for an aircraft accident was pilot error.
- The employer, who would be against any finding which indicated he or she had not maintained a safe place to work, or had been grossly negligent in any respect. It has sometimes been said that the person in charge of an investigation should be a supervisor of the operation where the accident occurred. However, because charges of supervisory error could be levied, a supervisor might be somewhat biased. The supervisor would be the suspect, the judge, and the jury. Also suspect because of possible bias would be the safety engineer, who, it might be contended, had properly failed to safeguard the plant. It therefore appears the best investigator in any company is a top-level manager from elsewhere in the organization. (*Note:* The head and most of the members of the team that investigated the accidental loss of the booster and space vehicle *Challenger* were mostly nonastronauts, although the astronauts were represented.)
- The employer's workers' compensation insurer, who might not be obligated to pay full benefits if it could be shown that the worker's negligence had contributed to the accident. The insurer might have to pay nothing if a third party could be shown to be at fault and liable for damages.
- The insurer of the third party (the chain manufacturer), who would endeavor to show that the accident could not be attributed to negligence on the manufacturer's part in producing the product which failed.
- State agencies, whose personnel would endeavor to determine whether any state regulations or codes had been violated.

OSHA, which would also try to determine whether any of its standards had been violated. Figure 5-1 shows an accident report form utilized in the past by the Department of Labor. Other federal agencies might also have investigations for matters under their jurisdiction. The National Transportation Safety Board might have someone to investigate accidents, especially major ones, which occurred to interstate carriers.

		1. CSMO NO.	2. OSMA-1 NO.
U.S. DEPARTMENT OF LABOR Occupational Safety and Health Administration		3. AREA	4. REGION
		5. DATE	

ACCIDENT INVESTIGATION REPORT

SECTION I

EMPLOYER INFORMATION

6. EMPLOYER'S NAME		7. EMPLOYER CONTACT	8. TELEPHONE
3. ADDRESS	10. CITY	11. STATE	12. ZIP
13. TYPE OF BUSINESS	14. SIC NO.	15. PROCESS INTERRUPTION COST *(Est.)*	16. PROPERTY DAMAGE COST *(Est.)*

SECTION II

ACCIDENT FACTS

17. NAME OF INJURED ☐ M ☐ F	18. BADGE NO.	19. AGE	20. TIME OF ACCIDENT	21. DATE OF ACCIDENT	22. EXACT LOCATION OF ACCIDENT SITE
23. WORK ASSIGNMENT WHEN ACCIDENT OCCURRED			24. OPERATION INVOLVED		25. EXACT LOCATION OF ACCIDENT AT SITE
26. REGULAR OCCUPATION OF INJURED			27. EQUIPMENT INVOLVED		28. NAME OF SUPERVISOR AT TIME OF ACCIDENT
29. FATAL	30. TOTAL DAYS LOST	31. NO LOST TIME	32. NO INJURY	30. OTHER FACTS	34. FIRST NOTIFICATION OF ACCIDENT *(Phone, Radio, Paper, Other)*

35. BRIEFLY DESCRIBE ACCIDENT

SECTION III

CORRECTIVE ACTIONS

36. 1. What has been done to correct condition causing accident? If nothing, explain.

37. 2. What remains to be done? *(Investigator's comment)*

SECTION IV

STANDARDS INVOLVED

38. 1. Did a violation of a standard cause or contribute to the accident?

Check one ☐ Yes ☐ No If "yes," cite standard.

39. 2. Does the standard adequately cover the cause? ☐ Yes ☐ No

If "no," complete and submit OSHA-9.

SECTION V

40. WITNESSES

NAMES	ADDRESS	CITY	STATE	TELEPHONE

CSHO's Signature _____

From OSHA-4
Aug. 1971

FIGURE 5–1 Department of Labor Accident Investigation Form

INVESTIGATING BOARD CHAIRMAN'S RESPONSIBILITIES

Figure 5-2 lists the duties and responsibilities of the chairman of the board named to conduct the investigation if the accident has been considered great enough. In some companies there are standing boards of members that can be called immediately should an accident happen. Rosters should be kept up to date, with a number more than might be required, including personnel who possess capabilities that might be needed. This is because members leave, change positions, retire, or die. Thought as to possible memberships should be given before an accident takes place, because as little time as possible should be lost before the investigation is begun.

CONTRIBUTING PERSONNEL

In any accident investigation chaired by a board, there will be other plant personnel who probably can contribute knowledge of what took place. Figure 5-3 indicates briefly how an investigation is to be conducted.

The safety professional must investigate each accident or near accident, but may be asked to provide information pertinent to an accident. Insurers, manufacturers, and government agencies may undertake their own investigations, participate in any being conducted by plant personnel, or review findings (with which they may not agree).

---

(1)   Direct and manage the investigation.
(2)   Assign tasks to members; establish deadlines.
(3)   Use the abilities of a trained investigator to outline and expedite the work.
(4)   Establish a "command post." Do not use your office or even your building. If feasible, separate the investigation office from regular work.
(5)   Assure that the scene is safe and that investigation does not compound the event or interfere with emergency operations.
(6)   Assure that the scene is secured until all evidence has been recorded or collected.
(7)   Release the scene to management for rehabilitation and operation when possible.
(8)   Handle requests for information, witnesses, technical specialists, laboratory tests, or administrative support with a liaison member of management.
(9)   Handle all communications with the field organization and public officials. Remember, the field organization is responsible for public news releases.
(10) Keep the appointing official informed.
(11) Assure that the investigation does not function in ways which relieve line management of operational responsibility.
(12) Call and preside over meetings.
(13) Assure that all potential causal factors are studied.
(14) When the board has determined its findings, conclusions, and recommendations, supervise preparation of the report.
(15) Do not release the board until the report has been completed.
(16) Unless otherwise instructed in the appointment, before leaving the site, brief management on the facts determined (not conclusions and recommendations). Receive additional factual evidence, if offered by management, but revise the factual section of the report only as the evidence warrants.

FIGURE 5–2   Chairman's Responsibilities for Accident Investigations

(1) Initial actions. Getting started properly is very important; otherwise, evidence can be lost while the board is trying to organize itself. Following these sequential steps should assist in beginning an orderly investigation:

    (a) Assemble the board for field organization briefing on synopsis of the occurrence and scope of investigation.

    (b) When possible, assign tasks to board members then or while enroute to the accident scene. (If board members travel by different means or from different locations, do this as soon as possible after arrival.)

    (c) Get a short briefing from the individual who has been controlling the accident prior to your arrival. Get local organization charts.

    (d) Establish formal liaison with management.

    (e) Go to the accident scene.

    (f) Perform a general survey of the accident scene to get a "feel" for the accident.

    (g) Prevent unnecessary handling or moving of evidence. Review security provisions.

    (h) If personnel are readily available, find out what each witness might be able to contribute. Alert him or her to a possible follow-up interview.

    (i) Photograph evidence and the scene.

    (j) When needed, give the board a briefing on investigation methods.

    (k) Establish command post and arrange for other needed resources.

    (l) Finalize board organization and plan.

    (m) Assign additional initial tasks or revise previous instructions based on the briefings you have received.

(2) Continuing tasks.

    (a) Collect and preserve evidence.

    (b) Interview witnesses.

    (c) Prepare diagrams.

    (d) Secure as-built drawings; copies of procedures, manuals, and instructions; maintenance records; inspection and monitoring records; alteration or change records; design data; material records; and personal histories.

    (e) Conduct reenactment, where necessary or useful.

    (f) Arrange for laboratory tests, where necessary or useful.

(3) The board should meet at least once daily to exchange information and coordinate results.

(4) An analysis of the accident goes forward simultaneously, both in the minds of board members and in analytics prepared by the trained investigator or consultants. The analytics help determine what additional information to seek and later help determine causes and recommendations.

(5) Prepare an outline, and start writing as soon as feasible.

FIGURE 5–3   Conduct of an Investigation

Each accident which involves any injury or in which there is damage greater than a specific amount (to be set by the plant manager) should be investigated. Besides members of the investigating board, there should be:

- The safety professional.
- The supervisor of the unit or area where the accident occurred.
- Any workers who saw or were involved in the accident.
- An employees' representative, such as a union committee member or the safety committee member from that unit or area.
- A representative from the plant engineering staff, if plant equipment or facilities were involved or damaged.

- And, if advisable, a specialist in investigating accidents of the type that caused the injury or damage. The services of the specialist or technical expert should be employed if the injury was serious, the damage level was high, or there might be litigation because of the accident. The exact number and type of personnel involved should depend on the severity of the injury or damage. In case of a near miss, investigations by the safety engineer, supervisor, and worker's representative, all of whom may be biased to some degree, would probably be adequate. If a fatality or very extensive damage has occurred, the inquiry should be conducted by the investigating board.

In no case should a plant manager attempt to put the blame for the accident on the workers, until and unless the causes have been determined through an investigation done adequately and properly.

CONDUCTING THE INVESTIGATION

Investigations require that certain equipment be available. Each member should have a copy of an accident report form to use as a checklist. Since the form must be completed for submission to the state and to the insurer, using it will also ensure that all minimum necessary information is obtained. Not only will insurers supply those forms on request, but other forms such as Fig. 5-1 are also available. This form indicates only that an accident has taken place, and it must be submitted rapidly. A proper investigation of a serious accident will take longer.

Investigators should also have on hand a notebook or paper on which to record any notes, comments, or information that might be pertinent. A measuring tape or rule is usually needed. A tape recorder is useful to record the comments of any person involved in the accident, witnesses, or any other person knowledgeable of factors pertaining to the accident. A video recorder would be helpful to record and show any pertinent objects, equipment, facilities, or other items. If such a record had been made before the accident, the postaccident film could be used to point out losses.

The investigation should be initiated as soon as possible after notification of occurrence. The investigator should attempt to avoid prejudging what may have happened. Prejudgments may lead to investigator failures to make proper use of witnesses' statements. Even where a statement contains highly significant information, it may be ignored if it does not meet an investigator's preconceived ideas.

Similarly, the investigator should not place total reliance on statements of only one witness or even of a person involved in an accident unless the statements are supported by physical facts or by other persons. Statements can be valuable. However, experience has shown that they can often be unreliable, increasingly so as time passes. This is due to a number of facts: persons have a tendency to see what they expect to see and to believe what they theorized had happened. In addition, accidents generally occur so rapidly there are often gaps in the witnesses' accounts, if they did not fill them in with events they believe took place.

There is a fair probability that when independent statements of fact from different witnesses are consistent, the fact is true. Here again, if there was much discussion between witnesses of the accident before their statements were taken, there was probably an unconscious influence of one person on another. Such discussions may have occurred with a person (or persons) involved in the accident. Fellow workers or witnesses with only a partial, incomplete knowledge may modify their recollections, since they would probably believe the person (or persons) involved knew more about what was going on than they. Yet, the workers (or persons) involved may have been in such a state of shock, events may have occurred so rapidly, or both, that they may not have actually known what happened.

Methods of Accident Investigation

A great deal of information, sometimes conflicting, may be gathered which must be sorted out in an orderly fashion. There is always at least one established, incontrovertible fact: an accident occurred. When, where, to whom it happened, and the results are known. The how and why it occurred are often more obscure and difficult to determine. A logical method of approaching the problem is to put down on paper a short phrase which indicates the final outcome: for example, "John Jones killed by falling load." Then, working backward, below this can be listed information that contributed to the cause of the accident. The information can then be separated into pertinent statements or facts which relate to each contributing cause: "Chain broke" and "Jones in dangerous position." The investigators may then want to know whether the chain broke from any readily apparent causes: was the load jerked or was any other unusual stress put on the chain; was Jones in the dangerous position for any reason? The depth to which the investigation should proceed may depend on the severity of the accident. Thus, if it had had serious effects, and the reason the chain broke is of interest, a laboratory analysis would be required. The investigators can indicate in their report that the chain's failure was unknown, and, if the matter was to be pursued further, that a laboratory analysis was to be undertaken.

Figure 5-4 is a diagram assembled from all the available facts about an accident investigated by the National Traffic Safety Board. The diagram indicates the relationship of events and causal factors after a tank truck partially filled with liquid oxygen (LOX) exploded. The same report also says: "Strict adherence to the rules for developing the diagrams is not necessary. Common sense works as well."

Management Oversight Risk Tree (MORT), another method for investigating accidents, is described in Chapter 9. The general technique, fault-tree analysis, is also given in Chapter 9.

ACCIDENT REPORTS

In a very high percentage of plants, accident reports are prepared by the supervisor concerned. In many instances the pertinent facts are then transcribed to forms which must be submitted to government safety agencies and to the insurer. As mentioned earlier, Heinrich estimated that 88 percent of all accidents were due to unsafe acts of the workers involved. The figures were probably due to a built-in bias. A supervisor or manager probably prepared the report and would be reluctant to indicate it was his or

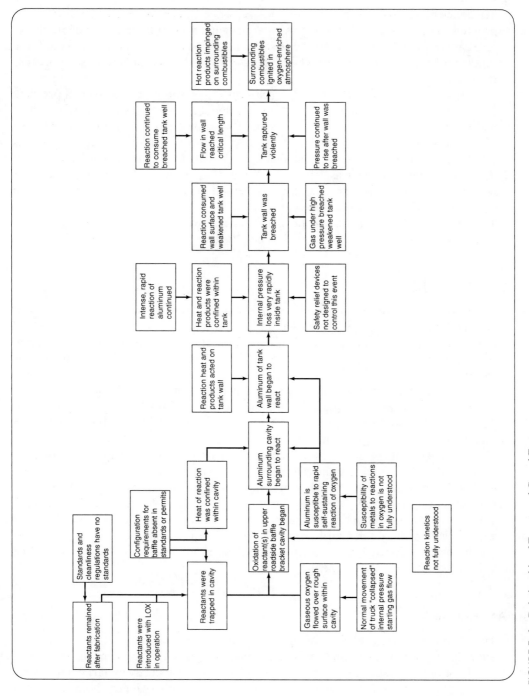

FIGURE 5–4   Relationship of Events and Casual Factors

her deficient actions that had caused the accidents. The accident investigation would probably also be oriented that way. A safety engineer might be less biased and therefore a more suitable person to evaluate and report the facts. Best, of course, would be a report prepared by a committee whose members would impartially represent all areas of interest.

How lengthy and detailed a final accident report should be has been a problem for a long time. (The initial report to the government agency or insurer is usually short and is used only to indicate that an accident has taken place.) Although the report should be kept as short as possible, it should be long enough to provide all the facts which contributed to the accident, so that corrective action can be taken. If any person involved in the accident was injured and is available, he or she should review the report to determine whether there is any objection to its contents. With the increase in claims and litigation because of accidents, attorneys may call for sworn depositions. The attorneys, often with technical experts to assist, will then proceed to pick apart in minute detail any claims or facts that will help further their cases.

CORRECTIVE ACTIONS

Here also concepts are changing. When supervisors fill out reports of accidents or accident investigations, they are often required to indicate the actions they have taken to prevent recurrences or occurrences of a similar nature. Generally, the corrective action stated is that the employee had been given a warning or additional instructions on how to carry out the work.

Two major aspects of accident prevention are usually omitted. The first is eliminating or controlling the hazard. Each accident (or near miss) must be evaluated to determine whether it would be possible to incorporate a suitable safeguard. Such a safeguard should either prevent a worker from performing incorrectly or else prevent an injury even if the person did act wrongly. Supervisors may not be qualified to assess such possibilities adequately and therefore will require assistance from a person who is technically qualified to do so: the safety engineer or a plant engineer. The safety engineer should be required to indicate whether a plant engineer can provide the safeguard, whether the company that supplied the deficient equipment should do so, or whether a procedural safeguard is the only solution. The second aspect of accident prevention usually omitted is "corrective action" by changing the procedures, including behaviors that led to the accident.

INSURANCE CLAIMS

The report submitted to the government agency or insurer may relate to either an injury (or fatality) to personnel, property damage, or both. The company may have suffered not only damage to equipment and facilities but also costly material and operational losses. In some instances there might have been no injury because of the accident, but only damage and other economic losses.

In either case it is necessary that all costs be certified and evaluated so suitable claims can be submitted to the company's insurer. The need for prompt and effective action is especially critical when a large loss has occurred to a moderate-sized company, especially one which has only one plant. Insurers may be especially critical if the company's financial posture is not the best and there is even a slight suspicion of possible arson. The regular company managers would probably be fully occupied with the problem of keeping the plant and company operational. It may therefore devolve on the investigating board, safety engineer, or fire investigators to determine what the losses had been. This job cannot be left to the insurance company's adjusters; their jobs are to minimize the size of claims against the insurance company.

Any person who attempts this job of preparing a loss claim will require assistance. The effort must be an integrated one, because no one person in the plant will be completely familiar with all the details or information which must be collected and recorded.

Equipment and facilities that were damaged or destroyed must be identified and evaluated. Supervisors and plant engineering personnel may have to determine whether equipment has been totally destroyed or is repairable, and if so, the extent of the repairs that will be required to restore it to its former capabilities. The plant engineering department may have to provide exact data on the type, size, and manufacture of the equipment; when it was purchased and at what cost; whether replacement parts are available; and the labor cost to make repairs.

Losses of raw materials, materials in process, and completed products may have to be determined from records or from estimates. It may be necessary to obtain information from suppliers, plant storekeepers, supervisors, or other personnel in many departments. Material that could be salvaged must be separated from that damaged beyond use and the degree of damage determined. The cost of the salvage operation itself must be computed.

Erection or use of temporary facilities to keep the company operating must be undertaken to replace damaged or destroyed facilities, equipment, or material before restoration work is begun.

If the investigation showed that the accident was due to faulty equipment or to a safeguard that failed that had been provided by a third party, the remains should be isolated and conserved. This would permit a closer search, more detailed examination, and possible identification and determination of the cause.

The labor costs in combating the emergency and in preventing any subsequent losses must be determined. Records of expenditures of material, such as medical and fire extinguishing supplies, must be collected. Each cost must be made available or prepared by the company accountant, or one hired by the company, to compute overhead charges for activities to which these apply. Knowledge of cost data is so necessary that companies often rent storage facilities in safe places, such as former salt mines, to maintain duplicate data in case of major catastrophes.

If an insurance adjuster is immediately available, he or she may be able to make a joint survey with plant personnel. Items on which there is agreement or disagreement can be identified immediately. However, under no circumstances should the matter be left entirely in the hands of the adjuster.

Insurance company officials have commented that, because of rising costs of labor and materials, losses due to accidents may be far higher than the original costs of the facilities, equipment, and materials. Current restoration costs must be known even before an accident takes place to ensure that coverage is adequate for potential losses, and they must be known after an accident to ensure that suitable and substantiable claims are made.

OTHER ASPECTS OF ACCIDENT INVESTIGATIONS

Any accident is an indication that the accident prevention program may not have been as good as it should have been. Safety engineers would do well to realize that this could reflect on their capabilities and efforts. It has sometimes been said that accident investigations are not undertaken to fix blame but to determine corrective actions to be taken. However, to determine corrective actions to be taken requires that blame for an accident be fixed. A proper accident investigation, though, will unearth its root causes. Rarely will blame lie at one place or person. For example, the root causes might lie in a cultural milieu into which many actors have bought. Whether disciplinary action should be taken if blame is fixed on an individual is beyond the duties of safety engineers, but those involved in an accident investigation should be careful not to engage in finding an easy target, a scapegoat. They are obligated to find out who was or may have been responsible for the accident—whether it was the worker(s), supervisor, manager, other third party(ies), or any or all of these. Finding the responsible party or parties is only the first step. The next step is to find out why she/he/they are responsible—then, to find out what corrective measures should be taken.

Although accident investigation does have its uses, it must be considered that the hardest way to learn about hazards and accident prevention is through accidents.

EXERCISES

5.1. What are the uses and needs for accident investigations? Who might call for an investigation? Should that person participate in the investigation?

5.2. Describe the various groups that might have an interest in an accident investigation. Why would some of these groups be interested? Which would you exclude because of their partiality?

5.3. The most publicized accident investigation took place after the explosion of the space shuttle *Challenger.* Was the membership of the board well constituted, or would you have eliminated or added anyone else?

5.4. Describe some facts to be considered in each investigation to be conducted. Give some methods of investigation analyses that have come into use.

5.5. Could an accident or any findings of an investigation be subject to litigation? What might happen if the findings were inadequate, attempted to hide facts, or were otherwise incomplete?

5.6. Why is it necessary that investigators have no preconceived ideas regarding the cause of the accident?

5.7. Why must witnesses' accounts be checked carefully? Why might they be erroneous?

5.8. What is a major reason a supervisor should not be the one to fill out the part of the accident report that indicates the possible cause?

5.9. Who is responsible for taking action to correct the condition that caused the accident?

5.10. Why is it not the best policy to simply accept any figures of cost of losses indicated by a claims adjuster? Cite the objections to such a practice.

C H A P T E R   6

Concepts of Hazard Avoidance

Hazards involve risk or chance, and these words deal with the unknown. As soon as the unknown element is eliminated, the problem is no longer one of safety or health. For example, everyone knows what would happen if he or she jumped off a 10-story building. Immediate death would be virtually a certainty, and such an act is not properly described as unsafe; it is described as suicidal. But to work on the roof of a 10-story building with no intention of falling off becomes a matter of safety. Workers without fall protection on an unguarded rooftop of a building are exposed to a recognized hazard. This is not to say that such workers will be killed or even to say that they will come to any harm whatsoever, but there is that chance, that unknown element.

Dealing with the unknown makes the job of the safety and health manager a difficult one. If the safety and health manager pushes for a capital investment to enhance safety or health, who is able to *prove* later that the investment was worthwhile? Improved injury and illness statistics help and may look impressive, but they do not actually prove that the capital investment was worthwhile because no one really knows what the statistics would have shown had the investment *not* been made. It is in the realm of the unknown.

Since safety and health deal with the unknown, there is no step-by-step recipe for eliminating hazards within the workplace. Instead, there are merely concepts or approaches to take to whittle away at the problem. All of the approaches have merit, but none is a panacea. Drawing on their own strengths, different safety and health managers tend to concentrate on certain favorite approaches familiar to them. The objective of this chapter is to present various approaches so that the safety and health manager will have a variety of tools, not just one or two, to deal with the unknown elements of worker safety and health. Both the good and the bad will be discussed for each approach. The good is often obvious or taken for granted. But the drawbacks of each approach must be squarely faced, too, so that safety and health managers can see the limitations and draw on the strengths of each approach to accomplish their missions.

THE ENFORCEMENT APPROACH

This is the approach initially taken by OSHA, but OSHA was certainly not the first to use it. Safety rules with penalties for breaking them have existed almost since people first began to deal with risks. The pure enforcement approach says that, since people neither assess hazards properly nor make prudent precautions, they should be given rules to follow and be subject to penalties for breaking those rules.

The enforcement approach is simple and direct; there is no question that it has an impact. The enforcement must be swift and sure and the penalties sufficiently severe. If these conditions are met, people will follow rules to some extent. Using the enforcement approach, OSHA has without doubt forced thousands of industries to comply with regulations that have changed workplaces and made millions of jobs safer and more healthful. The preceding statement sounds like a glowing success story for OSHA, but the reader should know that the enforcement approach has failed to do the whole job. It is difficult to see any general improvement in injury and illness statistics as a result of enforcement, although some categories—such as trenching and excavation cave-ins—have shown marked improvement. Despite its advantages, there are some basic weaknesses in the enforcement approach, as the statistics suggest. These weaknesses will now be examined.

At the foundation of any enforcement approach lies a set of mandatory standards. Mandatory standards must be worded in absolutes, such as "always do this" or "never do that." The wording of complicated exceptions can alleviate the problem somewhat, but requires the anticipation of every circumstance to be encountered. Within the framework of the stated scope of the standard, recognizing all exempt situations, each rule must be absolutely mandatory to be enforceable. But mandatory language employing the words *always* and *never* is really inappropriate when dealing with the uncertainties of safety and health hazards. To see how this is true, consider Case Study 6.1.

CASE STUDY 6.1

Suppose that a properly grounded electrical appliance used for the resuscitation of injured employees is equipped with a three-prong plug. But in the midst of an emergency, it is discovered that the wall receptacle is the old, ungrounded, two-hole variety. With no adapter in sight and an employee in desperate need of the appliance, who would not bend back or cut off the grounding plug and proceed to save the employee's life?

Of course, this example states an extreme case, and we must be "reasonable" and use our "professional judgment," but in the arena of enforcement and mandatory standards, who is going to say what is "reasonable"? Everyone knows what is reasonable in such an extreme case, but countless borderline cases occur every day in which it is not certain whether the proper course of action is to violate or not to violate the rule. Consider Case Study 6.2.

CASE STUDY 6.2

A dangerous fire was in progress as flammable liquids were burning in tanks. To shut off the source of fuel, a thinking employee quickly turned off the adjacent tank valves to avert a more dangerous fire that could have cost many lives, not to speak of property damage. Did the employee receive a medal for his meritorious act? The answer is no. Instead, the company received an OSHA citation because the employee was not wearing gloves! The valves were hot, and because the employee went ahead and closed the valves, burning his hands, the company was issued a citation.

If a government agency will issue a citation for failure to wear gloves while closing a valve in an emergency, who will have the courage to "be reasonable" and to go ahead and act even if a violation is the consequence? A strikingly similar case is described in Case Study 6.3.

CASE STUDY 6.3

In a trench cave-in accident in Boise, Idaho, a worker was buried and coworkers, "Good Samaritans," bravely jumped into the trench in the emergency to attempt to free the buried worker. OSHA responded by fining the company $8000 because of the humanitarian response of the rescue workers to the emergency. This action was ridiculed by some U.S. Senators, who awarded OSHA the infamous "Red Tape Award" for issuing the citation (ref. OSHA, 1993).

Although OSHA later rescinded the fines in the Idaho trench rescue case, one can see that the enforcement approach leads to problems when it is the only response to dealing with a safety or health hazard. Sometimes a fine is a negative and inappropriate response in a vain attempt to place blame after the fact when an accident has occurred. In the face of a pure enforcement approach, many industry employees and employers alike will gradually retreat to a defensive position, failing to produce, and blaming their lack of productivity on the government.

As stated earlier, OSHA did not invent the enforcement approach for dealing with hazards. Other mandatory safety rules and laws are familiar to everyone. Sometimes overzealous and oppressive rules can destroy themselves by alienating the very persons they are intended to protect. A notorious example is the mandatory helmet law for motorcycle riders. The helmet manufacturers can present impressive statistics that show how helmets save lives, at least in some accidents. Such statistics should be a strong motivation to motorcyclists to wear helmets. But in certain situations, the use of a helmet has disadvantages that may cause motorcyclists to hate the law that requires them *always* to wear a helmet. Thus, it is illegal to give a friend a trial ride around the block without obtaining an extra helmet for the passenger for that one ride. If a temporary skin rash or scalp treatment prevents an operator from wearing the helmet for a day or two, he or she must not ride, even if the motorcycle is the sole means of transportation. Where to put the helmet during a brief stop can also become extremely awkward in some situations. One motorcyclist in Houston became so frustrated that he complied with the letter of the law while he defied its spirit by riding his motorcycle around and about the city wearing his helmet on his elbow!

THE PSYCHOLOGICAL APPROACH

Contrasted with the enforcement approach is an approach that attempts to reward safe behaviors. This is the approach employed by many safety and health managers and may be identified as the psychological approach. The familiar elements of the psychological approach are posters and signs reminding employees to work safely. A large sign may be at the front gate of the plant displaying the number of days since a lost-time injury. Safety meetings, departmental awards, drawings, prizes, and picnics can be used to recognize and reward safe behaviors.

Religion versus Science

The psychological approach emphasizes the religion versus the science of safety and health. Safety meetings at which the psychological approach is used are typified by attempts at persuasion, sometimes called "pep talks." The idea is that employees can be rewarded into wanting to have safe work habits. Peer pressure can be brought to bear on an employee when the entire department may suffer if one person has an injury or an illness.

Top Management Support

The psychological approach is very sensitive to the support of top management. If such support is absent, the approach is very vulnerable. Recognition pins, certificates, and even monetary prizes are small reward if workers feel that to win these rewards they are not pursuing the real goals of top management.

Workers are able to sense the extent of management's commitment to safety by the day-to-day decisions it makes, not by written proclamations that everyone should "be safe." A rule requiring safety glasses to be worn in the production area is undermined when top management does not wear safety glasses when visiting the production floor. If safe practices are ordered to be cast aside when production must be expedited to fill an order on time, workers find out just how much worker safety and health mean to top management. Most safety and health managers will want to get a written endorsement of the plant safety program from top management. However, unless top management really understands and believes in the safety and health program, the written endorsement is not very valuable. The true orientation of top management will soon show through. Safety and health managers should beware of this pitfall when seeking such a written endorsement.

Worker Age

New workers, especially new young workers, are particularly influenced by the psychological approach to safety and health. Workers in their late teens or early twenties enter the workplace having recently emerged from a social structure that places a great deal of importance on daring and risk taking. These new workers are watching supervisors and more experienced coworkers to determine what kind of behavior or work habits earn respect in the industrial setting. If their older, more experienced peers wear respirators or ear protection, the young workers may also adopt safe habits. If highly respected coworkers laugh at or ignore safety principles, young workers may get off to a very bad start, never taking safety and health seriously.

In fairness to young workers, there is a complacency factor in older, more experienced workers that sometimes leads to tragic accidents at the end of the older worker's career. Case Study 6.4 tells the sad story of a worker who took an extra shift before a vacation prior to his retirement.

CASE STUDY 6.4

EXPERIENCED WORKER KILLED

On an extra weekend shift, a steel mill worker was removing a five-ton piece of equipment using a crane. The equipment was attached to the overhead crane, but did not lift properly because one of the equipment "hold-downs" was still attached. This caused the equipment to cock to one side. The worker saw the problem and went into the mill to detach the hold-down. Since the lift was under crane tension, the release of the hold-down caused the load to swing unexpectedly. The worker was crushed in a pinch point between the mill stand and the hold-down. The employee was 62 years old and had been employed in the industry for 33 years. Tragically, he did not quite make it to retirement.

Accident reports confirm that a large percentage of injuries are caused by unsafe acts by workers. This fact emphasizes the importance of the psychological approach in developing good worker attitudes toward safety and health. This approach can be bolstered by training in the hazards of specific operations. Once the subtle hazards are made known to workers who otherwise would not know about these hazards, the development of safe attitudes becomes less difficult.

THE ENGINEERING APPROACH

For decades, safety engineers have attributed most workplace injuries to unsafe worker acts, not unsafe conditions. The origin of this thinking has been traced to the great pioneering work in the field by the late H. W. Heinrich (ref. Heinrich), the first safety engineer so recognized. Heinrich's studies resulted in the widely known ratio 88:10:2.

Unsafe acts	88%
Unsafe conditions	10%
Unsafe causes	2%
Total causes of workplace accidents	100%

Recently, Heinrich's ratios have been questioned, and efforts to recover Heinrich's original research data have produced sketchy results. The current trend is to give increasing emphasis to the workplace machinery, environment, guards, and protective systems (i.e., the *conditions* of the workplace). Accident analyses are probing more deeply to determine whether incidents that at first appear to be caused by "worker carelessness" could have been prevented by a process redesign. This development has greatly enhanced the importance of the "engineering approach" to dealing with workplace hazards.

Three Lines of Defense

From the profession has emerged a definite preference for the engineering approach when dealing with health hazards. When a process is noisy or presents airborne exposures to toxic materials, the firm should first try to redesign or revise the process to "engineer out" the hazard. Thus, engineering controls receive first preference in what might be called *three lines of defense* against health hazards. These are identified as follows:

1. Engineering controls
2. Administrative or work-practice controls
3. Personal protective equipment

The advantages of the engineering approach are obvious. Engineering controls deal directly with the hazard by removing it, ventilating it, suppressing it, or otherwise rendering the workplace safe and healthful. This removes the necessity of living with the hazard and minimizing its effects as contrasted with the strategies of administrative controls and the use of personal protective equipment.

Safety Factors

Engineers have long recognized the chance element in safety and know that margins for variation must be provided. This basic principle of engineering design appears at various places in safety standards. For example, the safety factor for the design of scaffold components is 4:1. For overhead crane hoists, the factor is 5:1, and for scaffold *ropes*, the factor is 6:1 (i.e., scaffold ropes are designed to withstand six times the intended load).

The selection of safety factors is an important responsibility. It would be nice if all safety factors could be 10:1, but there are trade-offs that make such large safety factors unreasonable, even infeasible, in some situations. Cost is the obvious, but not the only, trade-off. Weight, supporting structure, speed, horsepower, and size are all factors that may be affected by selecting too large a safety factor. The drawbacks of large safety factors must be weighed against the consequences of system failure in order to arrive at a rational decision. There are many degrees of difference between situations when evaluating the consequences of system failures. Compare the importance of safety factors in the Kansas City hotel disaster[1] of 1981 to a failure in which the only loss is some

---

[1]Two skywalks collapsed in the crowded multistory lobby of the Hyatt Regency Hotel in Kansas City, Missouri, on July 17, 1981, killing 113 persons.

material or damaged equipment. Obviously, the former situation should employ a larger safety factor than the latter. Selection of safety factors depends on the evaluation or classification of degree of hazard, a subject that will be treated in depth later in this chapter.

Fail-Safe Principles

Besides the engineering principle of safety factors, there are additional principles of engineering design that consider the consequences of component failure within the system. These principles are labeled here as *fail-safe principles*, and three are identified:

1. General fail-safe principle
2. Fail-safe principle of redundancy
3. Principle of worst case

Each of these principles will be considered here, and their applications will appear again and again in subsequent chapters dealing with specific hazards.

General Fail-Safe Principle

The resulting status of a system, in event of failure of one of its components, shall be in a safe mode.

Systems or subsystems generally have two modes: active and inert. With most machines, the inert mode is the safer of the two. Thus, product safety engineering is usually quite simple: If you "pull the plug" on the machine, it cannot hurt you. But the inert mode is not always the safer mode. Suppose that the system is a complicated one, with subsystems built in to protect the operator and others in the area in the event of a failure within the system. In this case, pulling the plug to disconnect the machine might deactivate the safety subsystems so essential to protecting the operator and others in the area. In the case of such a system, disconnecting the power might render the system more unsafe than it was when the power was on. Design engineers need to consider the general fail-safe principle so as to ensure that a failure within the system will result in a safe mode. Thus, it may be necessary to provide backup power for the proper functioning of safety subsystems. Case Studies 6.5 and 6.6 will illustrate this concept.

CASE STUDY 6.5

An electric drill has a trigger switch that might be continuously depressed to operate the drill. The trigger switch is loaded with a spring, so that if some failure (on the part of the operator in this case) results in the release of the trigger, the machine will return to a safe mode (off, in this case). Such a switch is often called a *deadman control*. This example illustrates the common situation in which the inert state of the system is the safer one.

CASE STUDY 6.6

This example illustrates the more uncommon situation in which the inert state of the system is the more dangerous state. Consider an automobile with power steering and power brakes. When the engine dies, both steering and braking become very difficult; so at least as far as these subsystems are concerned, the inert state is more dangerous than the active one.

As will be seen in later chapters, industrial systems have characteristics similar to those described in the foregoing case studies. Sometimes safety standards specify that system failures be accommodated in such a way that subsystems for safety will continue to be operative.

The general fail-safe principle is the one that embodies the literal meaning of the term *fail safe*. However, industry and technology often associate another concept with the term *fail safe*, and that is the concept of *redundancy*.

Fail-Safe Principle of Redundancy

A critically important function of a system, subsystem, or components can be preserved by alternate parallel or standby units.

The design principle of redundancy has been widely used in the aerospace industry. When systems are so complicated and of such critical importance as a large aircraft or a space vehicle, the function is too important to allow the failure of a tiny component to bring down the entire system. Therefore, engineers back up primary subsystems with standby units. Sometimes, dual units can be specified right down at the component level. For extremely critical functions, three or four backup systems can be specified. In the field of occupational safety and health, some systems are seen as so vital as to require design redundancy. Mechanical power presses are an example.

Still another fail-safe design principle is the principle of *worst case*.

Principle of Worst Case

The design of a system should consider the worst situation to which it may be subjected in use.

This principle is really a recognition of *Murphy's law*, which states, "If anything can go wrong, it will." Murphy's law is no joke; it is a simple observation of the result of chance occurrences over a long period of time. Random events that have a constant hazard of occurrence are called *Poisson processes*. The design of a system must consider the possibility of the occurrence of some chance event that can have an adverse effect on safety and health.

An application of the principle of worst case is seen in the specification of explosionproof motors in ventilation systems for rooms in which flammable liquids are handled. Explosionproof motors are much more expensive than ordinary motors, and industries may resist the requirement to install explosionproof motors, especially in those processes in which the vapor levels of the substances mixed never even get close to the explosive range. But consider the scenario presented by a hot summer day on which a spill happens to occur. The hot weather raises the vapor level of the flammable liquid being handled. A spill at such an unfortunate time dramatically increases the liquid surface exposure, which makes the problem many times worse. At no other time would the ventilation system be more important. But if the motor is not explosionproof and is exposed to the critical concentration of vapors, a catastrophic explosion would occur as soon as the ventilation system switched on.

The concept of *defensive driving* is well known to all drivers and serves to explain the principle of worst case. Defensive drivers control their vehicles to the extent that they are prepared for the worst random event they can reasonably imagine.

Design Principles

Engineers have come to rely on a variety of approaches or "engineering design principles" to reduce or eliminate hazards. Some of these principles are listed here to stimulate thinking of the various paths that can be taken in dealing with hazards.

1. *Eliminate* the process or cause of the hazard. Often a process has been performed over so long a period that it is erroneously considered essential to the operation of the plant. After many years of operation, a process becomes institutional and plant personnel tend to accept it without question. However, it is the duty of safety and health professionals to question old and accepted ways of doing things if these ways are hazardous. Hazards that may have been considered acceptable in the days when the process was originally designed may now be considered unacceptable. New thinking may reach a different conclusion on the question of just how critical the need is for a particular process.

2. *Substitute* an alternate process or material. If a process is essential and must be retained, perhaps it can be substituted with another method or material that is not so dangerous. A good example is the substitution of less hazardous solvents for benzene, which has been found to cause leukemia. Another example is changing a machining process to perform the machining dry—that is, without the benefit of cutting fluid. Certainly many machine tool cutting operations require cutting fluid, but for some materials and processes, cutting fluid may not be absolutely necessary and the drawbacks might outweigh the benefits.

3. *Guard* personnel from exposure to the hazard. Perhaps a process is absolutely essential to the operation of the plant, and there is no substitute for it or for the hazardous materials that must be dealt with by it. In these cases, it is sometimes possible to control exposure to the hazard by guarding personnel from exposure to the hazard.

4. Install *barriers* to keep personnel out of the area. Contrasted with guards, which are attached to the machine or process, are independent barriers that are installed around the process or machine to keep personnel out of danger. Such barriers may seem more like an administrative function or an operational procedure, but the engineer who designs the process can specify in particular what barriers are needed around a process and where to place them.

5. *Warn* personnel with visible or audible alarms. In the absence of other protective design features of the system, the engineer can sometimes design the machine or process in such a way that the system warns the operator or other personnel when exposure to a significant hazard is imminent or likely. To be effective, the alarm should be used sparingly so that the personnel do not ignore the flashing light or the beeping alarm and continue operating the process despite the exposure.

6. Use *warning labels* to caution personnel to avoid the hazard. Sometimes an essential hazardous operation cannot be eliminated, substituted with a less hazardous process or material, or adequately guarded from personnel exposure. In these situations, at least it is often possible to attach a warning label to the process or device that reminds personnel of hazards that are not controlled by the machine or process itself. This design approach is not as effective as the preceding approaches, because personnel may not read or heed the warning labels. Despite the limited effectiveness of warning labels, they are better than complete disregard for the hazard in the design process.

7. Use *filters* to remove exposure to hazardous effluents. Certain hazards require a different perspective on the part of the design engineer. The exhaust of dangerous effluents is an example. The engineer can sometimes design filter systems in the machine or process itself to deal with gases or dusts that may be undesirable products of the process.

8. Design *exhaust ventilation* systems to deal with process effluents. Sometimes the undesirable products of a process are too hazardous or are impractical to filter out of the breathing air in the environment of a process. In these cases, sometimes the process or machine design itself can include features that exhaust the harmful agents as they are being produced. Again, these features may seem to be within the purview of someone else, such as a ventilation expert or plant maintenance engineer. Nevertheless, the designer of the process itself should not overlook opportunities to incorporate these features into the original design of the process or machine.

9. Consider the *human interface*. After the more straightforward engineering principles of dealing with hazards are included in the design process, it is a good idea to once again review and identify all the interfaces of the process or machine with personnel. At what points does it become necessary for persons to interact with the machine? At these points, are personnel exposed to hazards? The human interfaces so identified should include both the equipment interfaces and the material interfaces. Each interface so identified should be checked again for possible design features that can further control hazards using the other engineering design principles enumerated in this section.

Engineering Pitfalls

It is easy to get caught up in the idea that technology can solve our problems, including elimination of workplace hazards. Certainly, an inventor of a new gadget to prevent injuries or illnesses can become quickly enamored with it and present a convincing argument that the new invention should be installed in workplaces everywhere. When standards writers are persuaded by these arguments, they often require all appropriate industries to install the new device. Several things can go wrong, however.

Recalling the case against the enforcement approach, certain unusual circumstances can make the engineering solution inappropriate or even unsafe. A good example is the use of spring-loaded cutoff valves in air lines for compressed-air tools. The purpose of the cutoff valve is to prevent hose whip action by stopping the flow of air if the tool accidentally separates from the hose. The sudden flow of air overcomes the spring-loaded valve and closes it, stopping the flow. The problem comes when several tools are operated from the same main hose and flow reaches maximum even during normal use. The cutoff then becomes a nuisance and impedes production.

A second problem with the engineering approach is related to the first: Workers remove or defeat the purpose of engineering controls or safety devices. The most obvious example is the removal of guards from machines. Before faulting the worker for such behavior, take a close look at the guard design. Some guards are so awkward that they make the work nearly impossible. Some machine guards are so impractical that they conjure up doubts about the motives of the equipment manufacturer. There is a legal motivation to install an impractical guard on a new machine so that users will take the guard off before putting the machine in service. When the user modifies a machine by removing a guard, the manufacturer is absolved of guilt for any accident that later occurs, but that might reasonably have been prevented by the guard.

An irony of the engineering approach is that, if the engineered system does not do the job for which it was intended, it can do more harm than good by engendering a false sense of security.

CASE STUDY 6.7

A FALSE SENSE OF SECURITY

A printing press operator was proudly demonstrating a new printing press to his family at an open house intended to display the state-of-the-art safety devices engineered into the new equipment. One of the high-tech features was a photoelectric sensing device that was engineered to detect any object (such as the operator's hands) that had violated the danger zone at the inrunning nip point to the printing rolls. The system was designed to immediately stop the rolls whenever an object was sensed. So proud of the design feature of the system was the operator that he demonstrated by thrusting his hand repeatedly into the danger zone. Ultimately, he succeeded in beating the system, and the printing press did indeed amputate the end of one of his fingers. Incredible as this case study may seem, this incident actually happened. One could question the judgment of the operator in tempting the machine in such a foolish way, but the tendency exists to trust the engineering implicitly. Thus, workers are exposed to hazards due to the false sense of security that engineering systems sometimes engender.

Such false sense of security can even lead to new operator procedures that depend on the safety device to control the operation so that the work can be hastened. The best example that comes to mind is the hoist limit switch on an overhead crane. If the hoist load block approaches too close to the bridge, the hoist limit switch is tripped, shutting off the hoist motor. The idea sounds good, but the operator can take advantage of the device by *depending* on the switch to stop the load during normal operation. The hoist limit switch is not intended as an operating control, but workers can and do use it that way. The only defense against such use appears to be proper training and safe attitudes on the part of the operator—that is, the psychological approach.

Finally, the engineered system can sometimes cause a hazard, as illustrated in the example that follows in which a pneumatic press ram pinned an operator's hand on the *upstroke*. (See Figure 6.1.) The press was equipped with a two-hand control that was designed for safety's sake not to allow the press to be actuated except by both hands of the operator. Ironically, the two-hand control created a hazard. This press was later redesigned to place a shield in front of the ram so that the operator would be unable to reach into the area above the ram.

Foot controls for machines provide a good example of the conflicts that arise between the hazards that engineering controls are designed to prevent and the hazards that they create. Accidental tripping is a problem with foot controls, so engineers have fashioned enclosures into which the operator must insert his or her foot before stepping on the control itself. The problem with these enclosures is that they make the process of activating the foot trip more complicated. More operator attention is required to move the foot in the right ways to get it inside the enclosure and then operate the pedal. Supposedly, this is good, because then a careless motion will not accidentally actuate the machine. However, because of the sometimes awkward additional motions that the enclosure requires, some operators position their feet so that they can keep a foot on the pedal at all times, so-called "riding the pedal." Unfortunately, riding the pedal increases the likelihood that the operator will accidentally trip the machine, the very hazard that the foot pedal enclosure was intended to prevent. This problem has been studied extensively by Triodyne, Inc. (ref. Barnett).

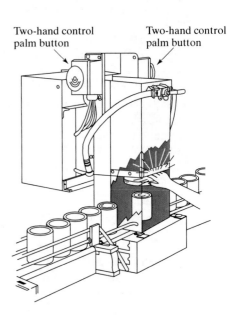

Two-hand control palm button   Two-hand control palm button

FIGURE 6.1

Pneumatic press ram pins operator's hand on the upstroke; two-hand control safety device prevents the operator from reactivating the press to release her hand.

As another example, robots are being used to work in hot, noisy environments, to lift heavy objects, and to otherwise serve in places where humans might be injured or suffer health hazards. Most industrial robots are simply mechanical arms programmed by computer to feed material to machines or to do welding. But the mindless swinging of these mechanical arms can cause injury to workers who get in the path of the robot. The irony is that a hazard is created by the robot, the very purpose of which was to reduce hazards. One solution is to make the robot more sophisticated, giving it sensors to detect when a foreign object or person is in its path. Another solution is simply to install guardrails around the robot or otherwise keep personnel out of the danger zone.

In summary, the engineering approach is a good one and deserves the recent emphasis it is receiving. However, there are pitfalls, and the safety and health manager needs a certain sophistication to see both the advantages and disadvantages in proposed capital equipment investments in safety and health systems. Upon review of the preceding examples of engineering pitfalls, it can be seen that almost every problem can be dealt with if some additional thought is given to the design of the equipment or its intended operation. The conclusion to be reached is that engineering can solve safety and health problems, but the safety and health manager should not naively assume that the solutions will be simple.

THE ANALYTICAL APPROACH

The analytical approach deals with hazards by studying their mechanisms, analyzing statistical histories, computing probabilities of accidents, conducting epidemiological and toxicological studies, and weighing costs and benefits of hazard elimination. Many, but not all, analytical methods involve computations.

Accident Analysis

Accident and incident (near miss) analysis is so important. No safety and health program within an industrial plant is complete without some form of review of mishaps that have actually occurred. The subject is mentioned again here to classify it as within the analytical approach and to show its relationship to other methods of hazard avoidance. Its only drawback is that it is *a posteriori*—that is, the analysis is performed after the fact, too late to prevent the consequences of the accident that has already happened. But the value of the analysis for future accident prevention is critical.

Accident analysis is not used nearly enough to assist in the other approaches to hazard avoidance. The enforcement approach would be much more palatable to the public if the enforcing agency would spend more time analyzing accident histories. That way, citations would be written only for the most important violations. The psychological approach could also be strengthened a great deal by substantiating persuasive appeals with actual results of accidents. The engineering approach needs accident analysis to know where the problems are and to design a solution to deal with all of the accident mechanisms.

Failure Modes and Effects Analysis

Sometimes a hazard has several origins, and a detailed analysis of potential causes must be made. Reliability engineers use a method called *failure modes and effects analysis* (FMEA) to trace the effects of individual component failures on the overall, or "catastrophic," failure of equipment. Such an analysis is equipment oriented instead of hazard oriented. In their own interest, equipment manufacturers sometimes perform an FMEA before a new product is released. Users of these products can sometimes benefit from an examination of the manufacturer's FMEA in determining what caused a particular piece of equipment to fail in use.

The FMEA becomes important to the safety and health manager when the failure of a piece of equipment can result in an industrial injury or illness. If a piece of equipment is critical to the health or safety of employees, the safety and health manager may desire to request a report of an FMEA performed by the manufacturer of, or potential bidder for, the equipment. In practice, however, FMEA is usually ignored by safety and health managers until *after* an accident has occurred. Certainly, safety and health managers should at least know what the initials FMEA represent so that they are not dazzled by the term in the courtroom should equipment manufacturers use it to defend the safety of their products.

One beneficial way of using FMEA *before* an accident occurs is in preventive maintenance. Every component of equipment has some feasible mechanism for eventual failure. To simply use equipment until it eventually fails can sometimes have tragic consequences. Consider, for example, the wire rope on a crane, or the chain links in a sling, or the brakes on a forklift truck. The FMEA can direct attention to critical components that should be set up on a preventive maintenance schedule that permits parts to be inspected and replaced *before* failure.

Fault-Tree Analysis

A very similar, but more general, method of analysis than FMEA is *fault-tree analysis*. Whereas FMEA focuses on component reliability, fault-tree analysis concentrates on the end result, which is usually an accident or some other adverse consequence. Accidents are caused at least as often by procedural errors as by equipment failures, and fault-tree analysis considers all causes—procedural or equipment. The method was developed by Bell Laboratories under contract with the U.S. Air Force in the early 1960s. The objective was to avoid a potential missile system disaster.

The term *fault tree* arises from the appearance of the logic diagram that is used to analyze the probabilities associated with the various causes and their effects. The leaves and branches of the fault tree are the myriad individual circumstances or events that can contribute to an accident. The base or trunk of the tree is the catastrophic accident or other undesirable result being studied. Figure 6.2 shows a sample fault-tree diagram of the network of causal relationships that can contribute to the electrocution of a worker using a portable electric drill.

The diagram in Figure 6.2 reveals the use of two symbols in coding causal relationships. Figure 6.3 deciphers this code. It is essential that the analyst be able to distinguish between the AND and the OR relationship for event conditions. All of the causal event conditions are required to be present to cause a result to occur when the

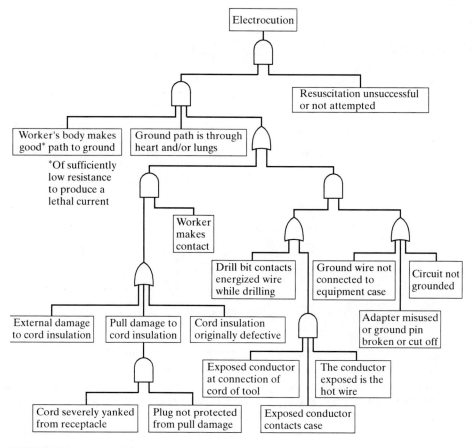

FIGURE 6.2

Fault-tree analysis of hazard origins in the electrocution of workers using portable electronic drills (not double insulated).

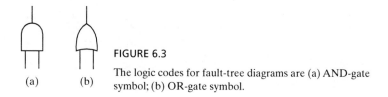

FIGURE 6.3

The logic codes for fault-tree diagrams are (a) AND-gate symbol; (b) OR-gate symbol.

conditions are connected by an AND gate. However, a single condition is sufficient to cause a result to occur when conditions are connected by an OR gate. For example, oxygen, heat, and fuel are all required to produce fire, so they are connected by an AND gate, as shown in Figure 6.4. But *either* an open flame or a static spark may be sufficient to produce ignition heat for a given substance, so these conditions are connected by an OR gate, as shown in Figure 6.5. Note that Figures 6.4 and 6.5 could be combined to start the buildup of a fault-tree branch.

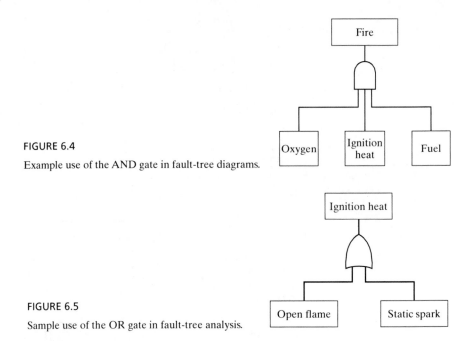

FIGURE 6.4

Example use of the AND gate in fault-tree diagrams.

FIGURE 6.5

Sample use of the OR gate in fault-tree analysis.

One difficulty with fault-tree analysis is that it requires each condition to be stated in absolute "yes/no" or "go/no-go" language. The analysis breaks down if a condition as stated may or may not cause a specified result. When the analyst is confronted with a "maybe" situation, it usually means that the cause has not been sufficiently analyzed to determine what additional conditions are also necessary to effect the result. Therefore, the difficulty in dealing with a "maybe" situation forces the analyst to look more deeply into the fault relationships, so the "difficulty" may be a benefit after all.

Fault-tree analysis permits the analyst to compute quantitative measures of the probabilities of accident occurrence. The computation is tricky, however, and is at best only as good as the estimates of the probabilities of occurrence of the causal conditions. It seems intuitive that one should add the probabilities of events leading into an OR gate and multiply the probabilities of events leading to an AND gate. This intuition is wrong in both cases and is shown for the OR gate as follows: Suppose, in the example shown in Figure 6.5, that the probabilities of occurrence of the two event causes were as given in the following table:

Event cause	Probability of occurrence (%)
Open flame	50
Static spark	50

To add these two probabilities would result in a 100% chance of reaching "ignition heat," an obviously erroneous result. A 50–50 chance of either of two possible causes is insufficient basis to find a 100% certainty of any resulting event. To make the logic even more convincing, the reader should rework the example using the following probabilities:

Event cause	Probability of occurrence (%)
Open flame	60
Static spark	70

Obviously, no result can have a probability of 130%! The correct probability computation is to subtract the "intersection," or probability that both independent causes would occur:

$$P[\text{ignition heat}] = P[\text{open flame}] + P[\text{static spark}]$$
$$- P[\text{open flame}] \times P[\text{static spark}]$$
$$= 0.6 + 0.7 - 0.6 \times 0.7$$
$$= 1.3 - 0.42 = 0.88 = 88\%$$

For OR gates in which there are several event causes, the computation becomes very complex. Adding to the complexity is the question of whether the event causes are *independent*—that is, the occurrence of one event does not affect the likelihood of the occurrence of the other event cause(s). A special case of *dependent* events are events that are *mutually exclusive*—that is, the occurrence of one event *precludes* the occurrence of the other(s). The mutually exclusive condition simplifies the computation, but event causes in fault-tree diagrams are typically not mutually exclusive.

Fully resolving the problem of fault-tree computations would require a treatise on probability theory, which is beyond the scope of this book. Suffice it to say that fault-tree probability computations are more complex than most people think they are and therefore are usually done incorrectly.

Despite the computational problems associated with fault-tree computations, the fault-tree diagram itself is a useful analytical tool. The diagramming process itself forces the analyst to think about various event causes and their relationship to the overall problem. The completed diagram permits certain logical conclusions to be reached without computation. For instance, in Figure 6.2, the event "Worker makes contact" is key because, from the diagram, it can be seen that the prevention of this event would preclude any of the five events to the lower left in the diagram from causing electrocution. Even more important is the event "Worker's body makes good path to ground." Prevention of this one single event is sufficient to prevent electrocution, according to the diagram. The reader can no doubt draw other interesting conclusions from Figure 6.2. These conclusions can result in a more sophisticated understanding of the hazard and in turn may lead to revisions to make the diagram more realistic. Such a developmental process leads to the overall goal of hazard avoidance.

Loss Incident Causation Models

Closely related to both fault-tree analysis and failure modes and effects analysis is a model that emphasizes the causes of *loss incidents*, whether or not the incident results in personal injury, as reported by Robert E. McClay (ref. McClay). McClay's model attempts to take a universal perspective in which the entire causal system is examined, including primary causes—labeled *proximal* causes—and secondary causes—labeled *distal* causes. A proximal cause would be a direct hazard in the conventional sense of the word—for example, a missing guard on a punch press. By contrast, an example of a distal cause would include a management attitude or policy that is deficient in allocating resources and attention to the elimination of hazards. Distal causes are as important as proximal causes, because, although the effect of distal causes is less direct and immediate, distal causes create and shape proximal causes.

A critical point in the progression of the loss incident causation model is the *point of irreversibility*. McClay identifies this as the point at which the various interacting proximal causes will result in a loss incident. Despite the number and variety of proximal causes, only a few select cases will result in a sequence of events in which the point of irreversibility is reached. Once this point is reached, a loss incident is unavoidable. This is still not to say that an injury will occur. A loss incident can occur, and still no personnel might be exposed, or perhaps whatever exposure does occur is not injurious. Factors such as personnel exposure in the event of a loss incident affect the severity of the effects of the incident after the point of irreversibility has been exceeded. Such factors affecting the outcome can be either negative or positive—that is, they can be *aggravating factors*, which make the outcome more severe, or they can be *mitigating factors*, which make the outcome less severe.

A diagramming convention has been proposed by McClay to assist the analyst in visualizing the universal model of causation. Figure 6.6 defines the symbols to be used in depicting the model. Note in Figure 6.6 that proximal causes are represented by three different symbols, each denoting one of three categories of hazards: physical condition,

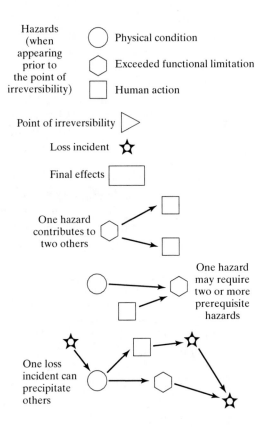

FIGURE 6.6

Symbols used in diagramming loss incidents.
(*Source*: McClay, reprinted by permission of Professional Safety, Des Plaines, IL.).

exceeded functional limitation and human action. Each of these three types of hazards can have a causal relationship with either of the other two. Further, a loss incident can in turn have a causal relationship on other proximal causes or other loss incidents, as illustrated in the examples in the diagram. Figure 6.7 summarizes the universal model of loss incident causation, revealing the relationship between distal and proximal causes and representing the region prior to the point of irreversibility as the *sphere of control*. The value in visualizing a loss incident causation system in a diagram such as the one shown in Figure 6.7 is twofold: It permits the analyst or the safety and health manager to distinguish the factors and conditions that can be controlled and allows him or her to perceive the consequences, good and bad, to be derived from applying resources to eliminate hazards or to mitigate their effects. As such, the analytical approach can be useful in assisting the safety and health manager to define and accomplish *reasonable objectives*.

Toxicology

Toxicology is the study of the nature and effects of poisons. Industrial toxicology is concerned especially with identifying what industrial materials or contaminants can harm

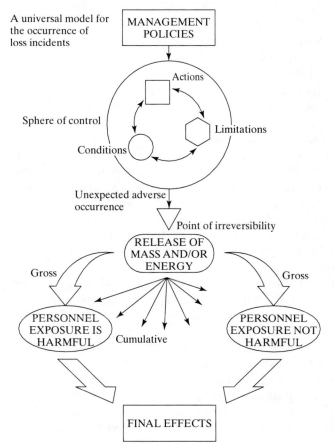

FIGURE 6.7

A universal model for the occurrence of loss incidents. (*Source*: McClay, reprinted by permission of Professional Safety, Des Plaines, IL.)

workers and what should be done to control these materials. This is really a broad state-ment because virtually every material is harmful to living organisms if the exposure rate or quantity is great enough.

Many toxicological studies are performed on animals to provide a basis for con-clusions about the hazards to humans. These animal studies are essential because most toxicological experiments would cause death or serious harm to human subjects. The disadvantage is that animal defenses to various toxic substances vary between species. The more the field of toxicology advances, however, the more various toxic materials can be classified and their effects predicted even before experiment. Rabbit–man, monkey–man, mouse–man, and guinea-pig–man comparisons of species' defenses to various agents are becoming fairly well known.

A field that relates to both pharmacology and toxicology is *pharmacokinetics*. Bischoff and Lutz (ref. Bischoff) define pharmacokinetics as follows: "Pharmacokinet-ics is a description of the absorption, disposition, metabolism, and elimination of chem-icals in the body, and is useful in both pharmacology and toxicology." It is important to the pharmacologist to understand how medical chemicals are handled within the body. In a similar way, it is important to the industrial toxicologist to understand how toxic chemicals are handled within the body.

Epidemiological Studies

Epidemiology is contrasted with toxicology in that epidemiology studies are strictly of people, not animals. The word obviously derives from the word *epidemic*, and in the lit-eral sense, epidemiology is the study of epidemics. The epidemiological approach ex-amines populations of people to associate various patterns of possible disease causes with the occurrence of the disease. It draws heavily on the analytical tools of mathe-matical statistics.

A classic epidemiological study was the association of the disease rubella (Ger-man measles) in pregnant women to birth defects in the infants born of those pregnan-cies. The study began with a curiosity observed by N. McAlister Gregg, an Australian ophthalmologist, in 1941. He observed eye cataracts among infants born of mothers who had had German measles during pregnancy in 1939 and 1940. The phenomenon might have been unnoticed except for the Australian epidemic of rubella during the World War II buildup. Years of statistical epidemiological studies later confirmed a strong relationship between rubella during pregnancy and a wide variety of birth de-fects in the infants born of those pregnancies.

Epidemics are usually thought of as attacking a general population at a specific time in a specific geographical area. Examples are the bubonic plague in Europe in the mid-14th century and the rubella epidemic in Australia in 1939–1940. But more subtle epidemics attack a specific subgroup of people who may be spread out over time and place. In other words, the victims of a particular epidemic may not live in one place or at one time, but instead have some other common characteristic, such as what they *do*. This aspect of epidemiology is what makes it important to occupational safe-ty and health. Thus, lung fibrosis may not be a very common disease in any location or at any time. But when the population of only those persons who have worked with as-bestos is examined, it can be seen that, after a long latency period, lung fibrosis can be considered an epidemic. Epidemiological studies linking lung fibrosis to asbestos have led to the identification of a type of lung fibrosis known as *asbestosis*. Other epidemiological links are *brown lung* to textile workers, *black lung* to coal miners, and angiosarcoma to vinyl chloride workers. A recent epidemiological study is examined in Case Study 6.8.

CASE STUDY 6.8

EPIDEMIOLOGICAL STUDY

This study was performed in the early 1990s by researchers at Johns Hopkins University in an investigation funded by the IBM Corporation (ref. Computer). The population studied was pregnant women who worked with diethylene glycol dimethyl ether and ethylene glycol monethyl ether acetate—chemicals used in the making of computer chips. Only 30 women were studied in the target population, but the results were seen to be significant because of the high percentage of miscarriages that occurred in this group. Of the 30 women studied, 10 had miscarriages—a rate of 33.3%! This compares with a miscarriage rate of 15.6% among women not exposed to the chemicals.

From Case Study 6.8, it can be seen that an epidemiological study can be a powerful tool to linking a potential hazard to observed occupational diseases. It becomes an excellent preliminary step to in-depth studies that pinpoint the causal relationship that underlies the observed link.

Both epidemiology and toxicology are important elements in the analytical approach to avoiding hazards, but the safety and health manager does not typically perform such studies. The studies provide the basis for mandatory standards that are subsequently used in the enforcement approach. Safety and health managers may also use the results of such analytical studies to substantiate the psychological approach or as a justification for an engineering approach to a health problem.

Cost–Benefit Analysis

Chapter 1 set the record straight on the importance of hazard costs. Like it or not, people do make cost judgments on occupational safety and health—not just management, but workers, too. In the world of reality, funds do have limitations, and cost–benefit analyses must be used to compare capital investment alternatives. Safety and health managers who feel that they can justify at any cost capital investment proposals that can be shown to have the possibility of preventing injuries and illnesses can easily appear naive. There is always more than one opportunity to improve safety and health, and cost–benefit analyses provide the basis for deciding which ones to undertake first.

The biggest difficulty with cost–benefit analysis is the estimation of the benefit side of the picture. Benefits to safety and health consist of hazard reduction, and to make the cost–benefit analysis computation, some quantitative assessment of hazard must be made. Such probabilities of injury or illness are very difficult to determine. Statistical data are being compiled at the state level. But these data are still usually of insufficient detail to permit a quantitative determination of existing risk. In addition to this determination, an estimate of expected risk *after* the improvement must also be made, since it cannot be assumed in general that every safety and health improvement will completely eliminate hazards. Case Study 6.9 illustrates the method of cost–benefit analysis.

In Case Study 6.9, the reader will perceive the large degree of speculation in the estimates of hazard costs. Such speculation casts doubt on the entire analysis, but it is better to speculate and calculate than to completely ignore the cost–benefit trade-off. This is an opportune point to lead into the next section of this chapter—hazards classification. There is a great deal to be gained from a subjective analysis of hazard costs, without resorting to overly sophisticated quantitative analysis, the credibility of which "hard" data may not support.

CASE STUDY 6.9

COST–BENEFIT ANALYSIS OF INSTALLING A PARTICULAR MACHINE GUARD

Cost

Amortization of initial investment	
Initial cost	$4000
Expected useful life	8 years
Salvage value	0
Interest cost on invested capital	20%
Annual cost = $4000 × (20% interest factor for 8 years)	
= $4000 × 0.26061 =	$1042
Expected cost of annual maintenance (if any)	0
Expected annual cost due to reduction in production rate (if any)	800
Total expected annual cost	**$1842**

Benefit

Estimated tangible costs per injury of this type	$350
Estimated intangible costs per injury of this type	2400
Total costs per injury	$2750
Average number of injuries per year on this machine due to this hazard	1.2
Expected number of injuries of this type after guarding	0.1
Expected reduction in injuries per year	1.1
Expected benefit = $2750 × 1.1 =	**$3025**

Since the total expected benefit of $3025 is more than the total expected cost of $1842, the conclusion is that it would be worthwhile to install this machine guard.

HAZARDS CLASSIFICATION SCALE

The absence of hard data to support quantitative cost–benefit analyses leaves a void of tools or benchmarks for use by the safety and health manager, safety committee, or other party on whom the decision responsibility for safety and health improvement may be thrust. Some sort of ranking or scale is needed to distinguish between serious hazards and minor ones so that rational decisions can be made to eliminate hazards on a worst-first basis.

OSHA does recognize four categories of hazards or standards violations as follows:

- Imminent danger
- Serious violations
- Nonserious violations
- De minimis violations

The categories are rather loosely defined and are distinguished chiefly by the extent of the penalty authorized for each type. The imminent danger category qualifies OSHA to seek a U.S. District Court injunction to force the employer to remove the hazard or face a court-ordered shutdown of the operation. The de minimis violations, by contrast, are merely technical violations that bear little relationship to safety or health; they typically do not carry a monetary penalty. But the designations of which violations will be recognized as falling into which category of hazard is especially unclear.

It is perhaps impossible to define clear-cut categories in every instance, but much is to be gained by some type of subjective ranking of workplace hazards. The thesis of this book is that a scale of 1 to 10 should be attempted, crude as that scale might be. Until people start talking about degrees of hazards on such a quantitative scale, little progress can be made toward establishing an effective and orderly strategy for hazard elimination. On a 10-point scale, a "10" is characterized as the worst hazard imaginable, while a "1" is the least significant or mildest of hazards.

The 10-point scale is recommended because such a scale has become very popular in everyday speech. Facilitated by the media, especially television, the public has come to understand a statement such as "on a scale of 1 to 10, that item (tennis match, ski slope, kiss, etc.) was at least a 9." The familiarity of this popular jargon can be employed to characterize workplace hazards.

Table 6.1 is a first attempt to describe subjectively each of 10 levels of hazards. The definitions address basically four types of hazards: fatalities, health hazards, industrial noise hazards, and safety (injury) hazards. A clear-cut delineation is obviously difficult, and some readers no doubt will disagree with the wording of the definitions. Criticisms of the scale will reflect both the shortcomings of the definitions and the biases of the critics themselves. Acoustical experts, for instance, may want to place a high degree of emphasis on excessive noise hazards. Other specialists will want to emphasize other areas.

One critical test is met by the proposed scale. Within each hazard type, each successive level of the scale describes a progressively more severe hazard. Individual industries may devise more suitable definitions, but the idea is to start talking and thinking about hazards in terms of a 10-point scale.

TABLE 6.1 Category Descriptions for a 10-Point Scale for Workplace Hazards

1. "Technical violations;" OSHA standards may be violated, but no real occupational health or safety hazard exists.

2. No real fatality hazard

   Health hazards minor or unverified

   Even minor injuries unlikely

3. Fatality hazard not of real concern

   Health hazards have exceeded designated action levels

   or

   Sound exposure action levels exceeded (e.g., continuous exposure in the range 85–90 dBA)

   or

   Minor injury risks exist, but major injury hazard is very unlikely

4. Fatality hazard either remote or nonexistent

   Health hazards characterized by illnesses that are usually temporary; controls or personal protective equipment may not be required

   or

   Temporary hearing damage will result without controls or protection, and a few workers may incur partial permanent damage

   or

   Minor injuries likely, such as cuts and abrasions, but major injury risk is low

5. Fatality hazard either remote or not applicable

   Long-range health *may* be at risk; controls or personal protective equipment *advisable* or *required* by OSHA

   or

   Hearing damage may be permanent without controls or protection (e.g., continuous 8-hour exposure in the range of 95–100 dBA)

   Major injuries such as amputation not very likely

6. Fatality hazard unlikely

   Long-range health definitely at risk; controls or personal protective equipment *required* by OSHA

   or

   Hearing damage likely to be permanent without controls or protection (e.g., continuous 8-hour exposure in the range 100–105 dBA)

   or

   Major injury such as amputation not very likely, but definitely *could* occur

7. Fatality not very likely, but still a consideration

   or

   Serious long-range health hazards are proven; controls or personal protective equipment essential to prevent *serious* occupational illness

   or

   Hearing damage obviously would be *severe* and permanent without protection (e.g., continuous 8-hour exposure in excess of 105 dBA)

   or

   Major injury such as amputation could easily occur

8. Fatality possible; this operation has never produced a fatality, but a fatality easily could occur at any time

   or

   Severe long-range health hazards are *obvious*; controls or personal protective equipment essential to prevent *fatal* occupational illness

   or

   Major injury is likely; amputations or other major injuries *already* have occurred in this operation in the past

TABLE 6.1   *(Continued)*

9. Fatality likely; similar conditions have produced fatalities in the past; conditions too risky for normal operation; rescue operations are undertaken for injured workers with rescuers using personal protective equipment
10. Fatality imminent; risks are grave; some employees earlier in the day have died or are dying; conditions are too risky even for daring rescue operations except perhaps with exotic rescue protection

One criterion omitted from the scale definitions is cost of compliance, or cost of correcting a given hazard. Cost is a completely different criterion and is almost independent of level of hazard. That is, it can easily cost just as much or more to correct a Category 2 hazard as it does to correct a Category 9 hazard. Cost is an important criterion in the decision-making algorithm, but is omitted from the scale definitions to permit a clear ranking of hazard priority first. Once the hazards have been sorted out, costs of hazard correction can be estimated and capital allocated for such correction according to a rational capital investment policy.

Another missing criterion, perhaps conspicuously so, is any mention of OSHA legal definitions of *imminent danger, serious violation*, and so on. To place these legal designations into fixed positions in the hazard scale would undermine the objectivity of the classification. Many persons have a preconceived notion of what legal penalty should or should not be imposed for a given hazardous situation. This bias is found in OSHA officers as well as their industrial counterparts. For instance, if a plant safety and health manager happens to believe that a given situation is not serious enough to warrant a plant shutdown, he or she would tend to prohibit selection of any designation that would bear the legal OSHA designation "imminent danger." This is despite the fact that reason would place the Category 10 definition into the imminent danger category.

Three credible profiles of the OSHA legal classification superimposed on the proposed 10-point scale are displayed in Figure 6.8. Profile A has an industry flavor and represents the viewpoints of some business executives. Profile A cannot be considered an extreme position because thousands of American businesses are headed by persons who believe that no government official should have the right to step in and close their businesses with or without a court order, regardless of hazards. Therefore, some business executives do not recognize the legal category "imminent danger." Profile A does at least recognize the imminent danger category, although the profile is

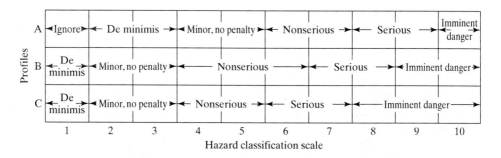

FIGURE 6.8

Three profiles of legal designations for hazards superimposed on the 10-point hazard classification scale.

skewed to the right. Profile C shows a contrasting position, being skewed to the left. Some OSHA officers have demonstrated that their positions are very close to Profile C. Profile C likewise is not the ultimate in the left extreme because some people believe that any fatality or amputation hazard should be classified as serious regardless of the remoteness of the hazard. Profile B represents a middle-of-the-road position.

A final consideration in the classification of hazards would be the industry environment in which the hazard is portrayed. What seems hazardous to a structural steel-worker working 100 feet above the ground on a narrow beam is in an entirely different category from what seems hazardous to an accountant. A similar comparison could be drawn between a coal miner and a computer analyst. It is only hoped that as a first step at least, coal miners should know what other coal miners mean when they talk about Category 4 hazards. Similarly, accountants should be uniform in their conception of Category 9 hazards, for example.

Except for some very broad categories, such as "serious" and "nonserious," federal law has little to say about degree of hazard. No consistent criterion is available to safety and health managers, who must decide which problems must be tackled first. The 10-point scale recommended by this book for ranking safety and health hazards offers an opportunity to bring some order to this perplexing problem. The scale is a vehicle for encouraging all parties to focus on the degree of each hazard so that rational decisions can be made to correct those problems that are indeed significant.

It is more useful to rank hazards if some weight is placed on the likelihood of occurrence of the accident or loss incident. A fatality hazard is of course severe in terms of results, but if the likelihood of occurrence is extremely remote—as in air transport, for example—one cannot say that the hazard itself is severe. Risk analysis is the study that deals with this problem, and the U.S. Air Force has devised a "Risk-Assessment Code (RAC)" (ref. AFI 91-202). The RAC system considers four levels of "severity" and four levels of "mishap probability," as shown in Table 6.2.

TABLE 6.2   Risk-Assessment Codes

Severity		Mishap Probability			
		A	B	C	D
	I	1	1	2	3
	II	1	2	3	4
	III	2	3	4	5
	IV	3	4	5	5

Mishap severity:

1. Death or permanent total disability, resource loss or fire damage more than $1,000,000.
2. Permanent partial disability, temporary total disability in excess of three months, resource loss or fire damage $200,000 or more, but less than $1,000,000.
3. Lost workday mishap, resource loss or fire damage $10,000 or more, but less than $200,000.
4. First aid or minor medical treatment, resource loss or fire damage less than $10,000, or a violation of a requirement in a standard.

TABLE 6.2   (*Continued*)

Mishap probability

(a) Likely to occur immediately or within a short period of time

(b) Probably will occur in time

(c) Possibly will occur in time

(d) Unlikely to occur

RAC Designations

1. "Imminent danger"
2. "Serious"
3. "Moderate"
4. "Minor"
5. "Negligible"

From Table 6.2, it can be seen that the Air Force RAC system results in a scale of 1 to 5 after considering both severity and mishap probability. The scale may be rather arbitrary, but it does make sense. Also, the RAC codes do create some order out of both severity and risk of occurrence in a single code. Case Study 6.10 will demonstrate the generation of a risk-assessment code for a given case of severity and mishap probability.

CASE STUDY 6.10

RISK-ASSESSMENT CODE

A defective condition has been noted in the instrument panel of a military aircraft. The panel often falsely indicates a fault in the oxygen system when in fact no fault exists. Pilots have sometimes ignored this fault indication because they have believed it to be a fault in the instrument itself, not a genuine fault in the oxygen system. The result, although highly unlikely, could be that a real oxygen hazard could go undetected, resulting in possible loss of the aircraft in flight and loss of life. The resulting assessment of the severity of this hazard is Category I and the assessment of mishap probability is Category D. From Table 6.2, the appropriate RAC to assign to this risk is Code 3.

A British standard titled "Standard Code of Practise for Safety of Machinery" (BS5304:1988) sets up a classification system that assigns points for three hazard criteria—severity, potential for injury, and frequency of access—as follows:

Severity

Fatal/LTD	Loss of life, or long-term disability requiring hospitalization or treatment	6 points
Major	Permanent disability, loss of limb or sight, etc.	4 points

| Serious | Loss of consciousness, burns, laceration, broken bones; anything requiring hospital treatment | 3 points |
| Minor | Bruise, small cuts, light abrasion; anything which may require no more than local medical assistance | 1 point |

Potential for injury

Certain	6 points
Probable	4 points
Possible	2 points
Unlikely	1 point

Frequency of access

Frequent	Many times per day	4 points
Occasional	Once or twice a day	2 points
Seldom	Weekly or less	1 point

The procedure is to add the total point score of the three categories to arrive at an overall hazard level or score to be used in decision making to alleviate the hazard (ref. standard) The procedure is demonstrated in Case Study 6.11.

CASE STUDY 6.11

BRITISH STANDARD HAZARD CLASSIFICATION

A punch press is manually operated in a high-production operation at a standard production rate of 720 cycles per hour. In this setup, the operator feeds the press every cycle. If ever the die closes with the operator's hand in the danger zone, an amputation is virtually a certainty. Obviously, every time the operator feeds the press, the hazard is present, but effective engineering controls using two-hand actuating devices makes the possibility of injury each cycle very remote. The problem is to examine severity, potential for injury, and frequency of access to obtain an overall assessment of the hazard level. By referring to the category definitions for each, the following assessment is made: The severity is "Major" (Code 4), because the hazard is an amputation; the potential for injury is very low because of the effective engineering control, "Unlikely" (Code 1); the frequency of access is thousands of cycles every day, so it is assigned a Code 4, "Frequent." The overall assessment is obtained by adding the three codes together to result in an overall assessment of $4 + 1 + 4 = 9$.

The concept of hazard classification can be carried a step further and applied to national decisions to invest billions in risk abatement. There is growing concern for the need for a risk-assessment system that recognizes some level of risk associated with various national priorities for risk abatement. John C. Nemeth (ref. Nemeth) writes, "I am convinced that well-founded, consistent risk assessment is the only way to proceed rationally. We need to get down to business and standardize." Jeremy Main (ref. Main) raises the question of whether our nation is allocating our hazardous cleanup expenditures in a rational way. Main compares $8 billion spent per year dealing with asbestos hazards, which are thought to cause from zero to eight cancer deaths per year, while $0.1 billion spent per year in dealing with radon hazards, which are believed to cause as many as 20,000 cancer deaths per year. Perhaps the nation's policymakers should use some sort of hazard classification scale to determine where the most money should be spent, rather than yielding to whatever thrust is politically popular at the time.

SUMMARY

The sophisticated safety and health manager is not content with one approach to dealing with workplace hazards. There is too much uncertainty to solve the enormous problems neatly with a simple approach, such as "awards for no lost-time accidents" or "fines for anyone who breaks the rules." These two approaches, together with all the others, have their place, but an integrated program using the strengths of all approaches has the greatest potential for success.

While becoming more sophisticated, safety and health managers may fall into the trap of becoming more enamored with their impressive-looking analyses, scientific formulas, and statistics. Some of the best analyses may be subjective, not quantitative. The 10-point hazard classification scale suggested in this chapter represents an opportunity for safety and health managers to talk and think about workplace hazards in terms of *degree*. Corporate top management has been looking for years for this breed of safety and health manager to emerge, who can discern between the really significant problems, the ordinary problems, and the trivial ones.

EXERCISES AND STUDY QUESTIONS

6.1 Name the four categories of seriousness of hazards as recognized by OSHA.

6.2 What is the OSHA designation for minor standards violations that bear little or no relationship to safety and health?

6.3 Consider the list of hazards that follows, and rank each on a scale of 1 to 10 (10 being the worst). Also, classify each into the four OSHA categories according to your opinion.

  (a) Ground plug (third prong) is cut off on a power cord for an office computer.

  (b) Ground plug is cut off on a power cord for a shop wet-vac vacuum cleaner.

  (c) An electric drill with faulty wiring causes an employee to receive a severe shock, after which he refuses to use it. Another employee scoffs at the hazard, claims that he is "too tough for 110 volts," and picks up the tool to continue the job.

6.4 A well-known safety rule is not to pull an electrical plug out of a wall socket by means of the cord. Have you broken this rule? Do you regularly do so? What is the reason for this rule? Do you think the rule is an effective one?

6.5 Do you believe that safety or health rules are "made to be broken"? Why or why not?

6.6 Name four basic approaches to hazard avoidance.

6.7 Recall your first supervisor in your first full-time job. Did he or she even mention safety or health on the job? Was your supervisor's influence on your safety habits positive, negative, or neutral?

6.8 What is the Heinrich ratio?

6.9 What are the three lines of defense against health hazards?

6.10 What is the standard safety factor for crane hoists? for scaffolds?

6.11 Name three general fail-safe principles. Can you think of a real-world example of any such principles?

6.12 What does Murphy's law have to do with occupational safety and health?

6.13 What is the purpose of FMEA?

6.14 Construct a fault-tree diagram describing potential causes of fire in paint spray areas. Compare your analysis with others in the class.

6.15 Construct a fault-tree diagram that describes the ways in which a pair of dice can be thrown to "roll seven." Calculate the "risk" or chances of rolling seven.

6.16 Explain the difference between toxicology and epidemiology.

6.17 Alter the fault-tree diagram of Figure 6.2 to consider the possibility that the portable electric drill might be double insulated (i.e., sheathed in an approved plastic case to prevent electrical contact with the metal tool case).

6.18 In the universal loss incident causation model, what is the difference between proximal factors and distal factors? To which category does management policy belong?

6.19 Explain the concept of point of irreversibility. Does this point guarantee that a personal injury will occur? What are the roles of aggravating and mitigating factors?

6.20 Accident Causes A, B, and C each has a probability of occurrence of about 1 in 1000, but the causes are mutually exclusive. Suppose that Cause B does in fact occur in a given situation. What are the chances that Cause A will occur in this situation?

6.21 Using a pair of dice for a simulation device, suppose that an outcome of 11 represents an industrial accident.

    (a) Draw a fault-tree diagram to illustrate the ways in which this accident could happen.

    (b) Calculate the probability that this accident will happen in a given throw of the dice.

    (c) Are the causes of this accident mutually exclusive?

6.22 The following are some causes of slips and falls:

    (a) oil leaks from forklift trucks

    (b) water or wax on floor during cleaning operations

    (c) ice on walkways or loading docks during winter weather

    (d) slippery heels on footwear

From the perspective of a total plant safety program, are these causes mutually exclusive? Why or why not? For a given single accident, are these causes mutually exclusive? Why or why not?

6.23 The following are three among many causes of injury to an operator of a punch press:

    (a) barrier guard of adequate size but placed too high—worker can reach under the guard.

    (b) barrier guard of adequate size but placed too low—worker can reach over the guard.

    (c) openings in the barrier guard are too large—worker can reach through the guard.

Which of these causes are mutually exclusive?

6.24 A certain type of injury has tangible costs of $15,000 per occurrence and intangible costs estimated to be $250,000 per occurrence. Injury frequency is 0.01 per year, but would be reduced by half with the installation of a new engineering control system. What annual benefit would the new system provide?

6.25 A certain ventilation system would cost a firm approximately $60,000, which can be amortized over its useful life at a cost of $15,000 per year. Annual maintenance costs are expected to be $600 per year and monthly operating costs (utilities) $150 per month. The system is expected to facilitate production by reducing the amount of machine cleaning for an expected annual savings of $1200 per year. The primary benefit of the proposed ventilation system is expected to be the elimination of the need for respirators, which cost the company $4000 per year in equipment, maintenance, employee training, and respiratory system management. The ventilation system is expected to reduce short-term-illness complaints by an average of 6 per year and long-term illnesses by an average of 0.2 per year. Short-term illnesses result in a total cost of $600 per occurrence, including intangibles. Long-term illnesses are expected to result in a total cost of $30,000 per occurrence, including intangibles. Use a cost–benefit analysis to determine whether the ventilation system should be installed. What is the primary benefit of the ventilation system?

6.26 On a scale of 1 to 10 (10 being the worst), how would you rate each of the following hazards?

(a) A 10-foot balcony does not have a guardrail. Workers regularly work close to the edge every day without fall protection.

(b) Same as part (a), except that the working surface is outdoors and is very slippery in rainy weather.

(c) No guardrail on a 10-foot balcony accessed only twice per year by a maintenance worker to service an air conditioner.

(d) An unguarded flat rooftop accessed only by air conditioner maintenance personnel. The closest necessary approach to the edge of the roof is 25 feet.

(e) Broken ladder rung (middle rung of a 12-foot ladder).

(f) Overfilled waste receptacles in lunchroom.

(g) Two-ton hoist rope with dangerously frayed and broken wires in several strands.

(h) Mushroomed head on a cold chisel.

6.27 What limits the region of sphere of control, and what factors belong to this region?

6.28 Under what circumstances is it incorrect to use the simple sum of causal event probabilities to calculate the probability of an event that results from either of two sufficient causal events?

6.29 Event A has probability of occurrence p_a, Event B has probability of occurrence p_b, and A and B are independent. Either A or B is sufficient cause for loss incident Event C to occur. Write a formula to calculate the probability of occurrence of loss incident Event C.

6.30 Event A has probability of occurrence 0.3, Event B has probability of occurrence 0.2, and A and B are independent. Either A or B is sufficient cause for loss incident Event C to occur. Calculate the probability of occurrence of loss incident Event C.

6.31 Study the OSHA standards to find examples of the application of each of the three fail-safe principles.

6.32 What engineering concept appears to have been misapplied in the Kansas City hotel skywalk disaster?

6.33 What is a "deadman control?" Describe an example not given in this book.

6.34 Describe an example of the use of "redundancy" in engineering design not given in this book.

6.35 Defensive driving is an example application of which of the three fail-safe principles?

6.36 Describe how FMEA can be a benefit to a preventive maintenance program.

6.37 It can be said that almost any substance is poison to humans. Explain how this can be true by citing an example of a seemingly harmless substance.

6.38 Explain the term "pharmacokinetics" and how it applies to occupational safety and health.

6.39 In what way is the field of epidemiology useful to occupational safety and health?

6.40 What persons or institutions perform toxicology and epidemiology studies and why? Would safety and health managers usually be expected to perform such studies?

6.41 Which do you think is a more serious hazard, radon or asbestos? Why?

RESEARCH EXERCISES

6.42 From your own experience, from library research, or from interviews with others, construct an actual case history of a fatal accident that was blamed on carelessness, but could have been prevented by a better engineering design.

6.43 Select a real hazard and gather information on the possible causes that could lead to an accident relevant to this hazard. Construct a fault-tree diagram to relate the causes to the loss event.

6.44 Search the Internet for details on the Kansas City hotel skywalk disaster.

6.45 Consider the following accident case history:

On July 4, 1980, three workers, ages 14, 16, and 17, were installing a sign at a bait shop along a state highway. They were using a truck-mounted extensible metal ladder to unload and position an upright steel support for the sign. Two of the workers were holding and guiding the steel support while the third stood on the flatbed truck operating the extensible-ladder controls. The metal ladder came into contact with a 13,200-volt overhead power line. The two workers guiding the steel support were standing on the ground and were subjected to immediate electrocution. The third worker attempted to break contact with the power line by operating the controls, but the controls had become useless, probably because the control wiring had become burned by the high-voltage contact. The worker then leaped from the truck and ran around to the front to try to drive the truck away to break contact. As he grasped for the door handle to the truck cab, he was still standing on the ground, which provided a path for the current through his body. The utility company had equipped the line with a "recloser" that normally would have broken the circuit under these conditions, but for a variety of reasons it failed to do so in this case. Therefore, the power remained on for a rather lengthy period. The high voltage and burning current finally broke down the dielectric strength of the rubber tires and they blew out. This shifted the truck's position, and contact with the power line was broken, but not before one worker had been burned in half and another's legs were burned off; all three workers died. How could future accidents of this type be prevented? Compare the four basic approaches to hazard avoidance in preventing accidents of this type.

STANDARDS RESEARCH QUESTIONS

6.46 Use the OSHA website or the NCM database to search for OSHA General Industry standards that relate to training. Determine the percentage of citations that are classified as "serious."

6.47 Search the OSHA standards for the use of the word *engineering* in any of the General Industry standards.

6.48 From what you have learned in this chapter, compose a list of five words that you associate with the engineering approach to safety and health hazards. Do a search of the OSHA standards to determine whether any of these words appear in the General Industry standards.

CHAPTER 7

Hazards and Their Control

By the time they are given machinery to operate, workers can do little to change the adverse features that designers have imposed on them. However, this chapter may get workers to recognize hazards, to determine whether improvements can and should be made, and to decide whether there has been compliance with OSHA or state standards.

Most of the types of hazards that might be present have been touched on in general terms. Later in this book they will be described in more detail, together with causes and effects of accidents and the precautionary measures that might be taken for their prevention or avoidance. This chapter will be oriented toward hazard and accident control. To clarify some of the terms often used, and their relationships, Fig. 7-1 has been included.[1]

Determining exactly which hazard might be responsible for an accident is not as simple as it sometimes seems. Often, exactly what happened is a complex series of events. Consider the violent rupture of a high-pressure tank made of ordinary, unprotected carbon steel. Moisture can cause corrosion, which reduces the strength of the metal, which ruptures and fragments under pressure (see Fig. 7-2). The fragments hit and injure personnel and damage nearby equipment. Which hazard—moisture, corrosion, reduced strength, or pressure—caused the failure?

Figure 7-2 also illustrates how safeguards can be provided to prevent the mishap and to contain any possible injury or other damage. In this series of events, the moisture started the degradation process. If the tank had been made of stainless steel, there would have been no corrosion; moisture would not have been a problem; and there would have been no damage.

Rupture of the tank, which caused the injury and damage, can be considered the primary hazard. The moisture started the series of events and can be called the cause or the initiating hazard; the corrosion, the loss of strength, and the pressure are contributory hazards. The primary hazard is often indicated by other names: catastrophe, catastrophic event, critical event, or single failure. It can be seen that a primary hazard is one that can directly and immediately cause (1) injury or death; (2) damage to equipment, vehicles, structures, or facilities; (3) degradation of functional capabilities (disruption of plant operations); (4) loss of material (accidental release of large amounts of oil or chemicals).

EXPLANATION OF TERMS*

The following explanations are the authors' attempt to define more precisely terms that are widely used but often in diverse ways.

Hazard: condition with the potential of causing injury to personnel, damage to equipment or structures, loss of material, or lessening of the ability to perform a prescribed function. When a hazard is present, the possibility exists of these adverse effects occurring.

Danger: expresses a relative exposure to a hazard. A hazard may be present, but there may be little danger because of the precautions taken. A high-voltage transformer bank, such as those in power transmission systems, has an inherent hazard of electrocuting someone as long as it is energized. A high degree of danger exists if the bank is unprotected in the middle of a busy, inhabited area. The same hazard is present even when the transformers are completely enclosed in a locked underground vault. However, there is almost no danger to personnel. An above ground installation with a high fence and locked gate has a danger level between these two.
   Numerous other examples can be cited showing how danger levels differ even though the hazard is the same. A person working on a very high structure is subject to the hazard that he could fall to his death. When he wears an anchored safety harness, the danger is reduced but is still present, since the harness might break.

Damage: severity of injury or the physical, functional, or monetary loss that could result if control of a hazard is lost. An unprotected man falling from a steel beam 10 feet above a concrete pavement might suffer a sprained ankle or broken leg. He would be killed in a similar fall from 300 feet. The hazard (possibility) and danger (exposure) of falling are the same. The difference is in the severity of damage that would result if a fall occurred.

Safety: frequently defined as "freedom from hazards". However, it is practically impossible to completely eliminate all hazards. Safety is therefore a matter of relative protection from exposure to hazards: the antonym of danger.

Risk: expression of possible loss over a specific period of time or number of operational cycles. It maybe indicated by the probability of an accident times the damage in dollars, lives, or operating units.

*W. Hammer, *Handbook of System and Product Safety,* Prentice-Hall, Inc., (Englewood Cliffs, N.J.) 1972.

FIGURE 7–1   Explanation of Terms

DETERMINING EXISTENCE OF HAZARDS

Each product or operation may have certain inherent hazards, although the probability of accidents with some may be remote. Each will have only a limited number of primary hazards and a large number of initiating and contributory hazards. A list of primary, initiating, and contributory hazards can be developed in two ways. Experience is the principal one, but it may not include all possibilities of what might occur. The database of experience can be extended with theoretical possibilities. Or the reverse process may be used: the theoretical aspects can be examined and then confirmed by actual experience. The hazards and safeguards for existing equipment and operations, or similar ones, may already be known. Proposed products and operations can be used

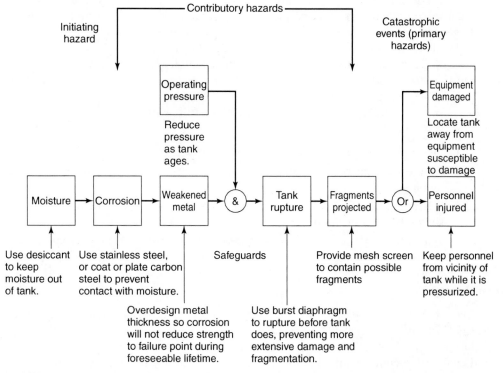

Sequences of events that could cause injury and damage from a rupture of a pressurized steel tank, and possible safeguards.*

*W. Hammer, *Handbook of System and Product Safety,* Prentice-Hall, Inc., (Englewood Cliffs, N.J. 1972).

FIGURE 7–2   Pressure Rupture Accident

to synthesize a new machine tool or piece of electrical equipment. Potential hazards can be determined from experience and theory and evaluated by analyses.

ELIMINATING AND CONTROLLING HAZARDS

It has already been pointed out that hazards can be eliminated or controlled by good design or procedures for accident avoidance. Because of designer or managerial aims and capabilities, the optimum solution for any hazard may depend on the circumstances involved. For example, as pointed out in Fig. 7-3, drills can have different uses, power sources, advantages, and adverse features. All types of hazards can be categorized according to safety. The methods are presented in a rough order of priority of means to eliminate or reduce conditions that could cause accidents, injury, or damage. In general, safety of the system will be improved more, the higher the method is in the order. These indicated preferences may be precluded because of desirable operating aims or the practicability of certain modes of accomplishment. A less safe method may then have to be adopted. Each situation must be evaluated for affecting factors so that a desirable and satisfactory solution can be achieved.

In determining an order of preference, the following general features should be observed:

1. Designs to eliminate hazards are most preferred over any other method.
2. Where safeguards by design are not feasible, protective safety devices should be employed.
3. Where neither design nor safety devices are practical, automatic warning devices should be incorporated.
4. Where none of the above is feasible, adequate procedures and personnel training should be used.

Intrinsic Safety

The most effective method of avoiding accidents is with designs that are "intrinsically safe." Intrinsic safety can be achieved by either of two methods: (1) eliminating the hazard entirely, or (2) limiting the hazard to a level below which it can do no harm. Under either condition no possible accident can result from the hazard in question.

Elimination

A very common example of hazard elimination and accident avoidance is by good housekeeping. Tripping over misplaced objects, slipping on wet or oily surfaces, and spontaneous ignition of trash or oily rags can be eliminated simply by keeping facilities clean and orderly. Numerous examples can be cited, such as:

- Using noncombustible instead of combustible materials. This method has been observed with paints, fabrics, hydraulic fluids, solvents, and electrical insulation.
- Using pneumatic or hydraulic, instead of electric, systems where there is a possibility of fire or excessive heating. Fluid control systems are often applied for this reason.

	ACCIDENT PREVENTION	MINIMIZING AND CONTROLLING DAMAGE
Intrinsically safe {	1. Eliminating hazards 2. Limiting hazard levels 3. Isolation, barriers, and interlocks 4. Fail-safe designs 5. Minimizing failures 6. Safe procedures 7. Backout and recovery	1. Isolation and barriers 2. Minor loss acceptance 3. Personal protective equipment 4. Escape and survival equipment and procedures 5. Rescue equipment and procedures

Although using the lowest numbered option for accident prevention is highly desirable, other considerations may make another option more practical. For example, personnel have been killed when using metal-cased electric drills. Tool manufacturers contend that this was due to improper repairs which resulted in a live conductor touching the metal case when the drill was used. Other potentially fatal conditions could exist when metal-cased tool drilled into a live conductor, or when an energized tool using 110-volt power was dropped into a container of water or other conductive liquid and someone tried to retrieve it while still energized. The following table indicates why and how trade-offs must sometimes be made.

TYPE OF DRILL		ACCIDENT PREVENTION PRIORITY NUMBER AND DESCRIPTION OF SAFETY FEATURES	OTHER ADVANTAGES	ADVERSE FEATURES
MECHANICAL HAND DRILL		1. Elimination of use of electricity eliminates possibility of shock hazard.	Cost of drill is low.	Low mission effectiveness. Tiring to use. Must ensure gears are guarded.
CORDLESS BATTERY DRILL		2. Uses electricity but power level is too low to cause injurious shock.	Can be used safety when operator is in water. Highly portable an convenient. No cord to be caught on projections. Can readily be taken into places with doors or others closed-off places.	Limited power which limits size drill which can be used and type of material which can be drilled. Needs periodic recharging.
THREE-WIRE METAL-CASED DRILL		4. Fail-safe. Third wire provides path to ground for current if there is a short.	Cheap for manufacturers to change from 2-wire tool; only connection on interior of metal case needed for third wire. No need to redesign and provide plastic case.	Path to ground may not be complete so will not be fail-safe. Trying to retrieve a live tool which has been dropped in water may result in fatal shock.
TWO-WIRE METAL-CASED DRILL		5. Increase reliability so there will be fewer failures that users will attempt to fix themselves.	Redesign not needed.	Manufacturers contention that problem due to incorrect repairs may not be valid. Higher reliability means higher cost. Failures may still occur but at reduced rate. Cord flexing where it enters drill may expose live conductor. Dangerous in water.
TWO-WIRE DOUBLE-INSULATED DRILL		4. Plastic protects user against shock if an internal short causes live conductor to contact case.	Two-wire cord slightly cheaper than three-wire. Plastic case may be cheaper than metal.	Plastic not as abuse-resistant as metal. Cord flexing where it enters the case may expose live conductor. Dangerous in water.
COMPRESSED-AIR DRILL		1. Use of compressed air eliminates electricity and possibility of injurious shock.	More power and higher reliability than electric drills.	Very few homes and not all shops have compressed air. Hazards of compressed air system. More expensive. Hose may make use inconvenient.

FIGURE 7–3   Drills—Accident Precautions

- Rounding edges and corners on equipment so that personnel will not injure themselves.
- Eliminating leaks by using continuous lines with as few connectors as possible.
- Eliminating vibration, shock, rail separation, and derailment by using welded and ground joints on railroad lines.
- Avoiding automobile accidents at highway intersections and railroad crossings through use of grade separations and limited-access highways.
- Eliminating protuberances, such as handles, ornaments, and similar devices in vehicles, which could cause injury after a sudden stop.

Hazard-Level Limitation

In certain instances the type of hazard cannot itself be eliminated. However, the level of the hazard might be limited so that no injury or damage will result. Although electricity under some circumstances can prove fatal, it may be possible to eliminate any adverse effects by using low-voltage, low-amperage power, such as 24-volt or battery power. Restriction could be used to keep pressurized systems below dangerous levels. The energy available under any condition, even if there is a failure of any kind, should not permit the hazard to be so great as to cause injury.

Examples of methods by which hazard levels may be limited include:

1. Providing overflow arrangements that will prevent liquid levels from getting too high.
2. Using solid state electronic devices where flammable or explosive gases may be present, so any power requirement will be far less than that required for ignition of a flammable mixture.
3. Ensuring that the concentration of a flammable or toxic gas is far below a dangerous limit. If the limit is exceeded, a blower could be started automatically or an inert gas introduced.
4. Adding dilutents to air where flammable dusts are present to minimize the possibility of an explosion.
5. Incorporating automatic relief provisions to keep pressure within a safe limit.
6. Using grounds on capacitor or capacitive circuits to reduce charge accumulations to acceptable levels after the power is shut off. This will lessen the tendency for a jolting shock.
7. Using sprays or other conductive coatings on materials to limit the level of static electricity that can accumulate.

ISOLATION, LOCKOUTS, LOCKINS, AND INTERLOCKS

These are some of the most commonly used safety measures. Interlock is effective principally because it requires positive actions by operators for procedures to continue, giving personnel opportunities to ensure they are correct. They are predicated on three basic principles, or combinations of the first two: (1) isolating a hazard once it has been recognized; (2) preventing incompatible events from occurring, from occurring at the wrong time, or from occurring in the wrong sequence; and (3) providing a release after suitable and correct action has been taken. Some examples of the major means of providing safeguards follow.

Isolation

Isolation as discussed here employs separation as an accident prevention measure. Later descriptions indicate isolation as a means of preventing injury or damage after an accident has taken place. In each case, there is a variety of means by which isolation can provide safety benefits.

Isolation is used to separate incompatible conditions or materials that together would constitute a hazard. Fire requires the presence of a fuel, oxidizer, and ignition source. Isolating any one of these from the other two will eliminate any possibility of fire. Some grades of bituminous coal are often stored under water, isolating the coal from the oxygen and ignition source needed for fires to start spontaneously. Other common examples of isolation as protective measures include:

1. Isolating workers inside protective garments or equipment to prevent environmental injuries.
2. Using thermal insulation to prevent persons from contacting hot surfaces which can burn them.
3. Using isolators to keep noise inside closed spaces.
4. Potting electrical connectors and other equipment to prevent entrance of moisture or other deleterious materials that could degrade the system.
5. Using "explosion-proof" or encapsulated electrical equipment in flammable atmospheres.
6. Keeping corrosive gases and liquids from incompatible metals or other materials that might be affected adversely.
7. Using lead, water, or carbon to isolate nuclear radiation.

Isolation is also used to limit the effects of controlled energy release where it is not due to an accident. A small amount of explosive to be tested can be placed in a suitable box or vault to absorb or contain the energy. Effects of the explosion can be measured. Or an explosion in the open air can be measured to determine the energy required to activate it, the distance and type of effect that might result, and the safety zones to be used provide isolation in the event of an accident.

Certain materials and processes are harmful unless isolated by suitable protection. Examples of protection include shielding persons from radiation from welding arcs to nuclear emissions, having workers in paint spray booths or sandblasting rooms wear protective equipment, and using gas masks, air packs, or oxygen generators in toxic atmospheres.

An operational activity that generates a problem can be isolated from personnel who can be injured or equipment that can be damaged, or vice versa. An engine producing a great amount of vibration, noise, and heat can be isolated by putting it in a separate room. Or it can be isolated through the use of suitable vibration mounts, noise suppressors, and thermal shields and sinks. Such isolation in a small area should be used only when the hazard, such as an adverse environment, cannot be eliminated by design.

Machine guards are widely used to isolate hazards in industrial plants. These guards are fixed over rotating parts, sharp edges, hot surfaces, and electrical devices to prevent personnel from coming in contact with the dangerous object. Security fences around electrical substations are similar. In such instances, the isolator is fixed. In other cases, such as railroad-crossing guard barriers, the isolator devices are removable when conditions are safe.

Lockouts, Lockins, and Interlocks

Lockouts, lockins, and interlocks include some of the most common means of providing isolation of personnel, equipment, and operations. Lockouts and lockins range from extremely simple devices such as bars on doors to those that are more complicated. Interlocks may be far more complex, since they generally involve stop and release mechanisms.

Lockouts and Lockins

Figure 7-4 lists a few of the measures that can be employed as lockouts and lockins. The difference between the two is relative. A lockout prevents an event from occurring or prevents a person, object, force, or other factor from entering an undesired zone.

A small sampling of the devices that can be used. They may be used in conjunction with each or any others and with variations that might be desirable.

1.   Guards to protect personnel from moving machinery, parts, or cutting devices.
2.   Fenced enclosures or vaults for high-voltage transformers to keep out and protect personnel from electrocution.
3.   Shielding on reactors to keep personnel from nuclear radioactivity.
4.   Storing subbituminous and similar grade coal, which is subject to spontaneous ignition, under water.
5.   Storing oily rags away from air in covered metal containers until they can be disposed of.
6.   Lockouts to keep personnel from open elevator shafts.
7.   Lockouts to prevent opening doors while a hazard exists inside.
8.   Locks on automobile engine systems and steering columns to prevent ignition or turning of wheels.
9.   Safe-and-arm devices in explosive equipment to lock out movement that might lead to an explosion.
10. Safety wiring and other locking devices on nuts and bolts against part movement.
11. Locks securing switch levers to prevent activation of electrical circuits on which work is being done.
12. Lockouts to prevent pumping of highly flammable liquids into or from a tank or tank car unless the system is grounded adequately.
13. Park positions in vehicle transmissions to lock out vehicle movement.
14. Interlocks to deactivate hazardous electrical equipment when panels or drawers are opened.
15. Interlocks on equipment that must be operated in specific sequences.

FIGURE 7–4   Isolation, Lockout, Lockin, and Interlock Devices

A lockin, on the other hand, keeps a person, object, force, process, or other factor from leaving a restricted zone. Locking a switch on a circuit to prevent it from being energized is a lockout in this case; a similar arrangement on a live circuit to prevent current from being shut off is a lockin.

People have been killed when equipment they had deenergized was inadvertently activated by other personnel. Workers repairing electrical circuits they had opened were fatally shocked when the system was energized by someone else who did not realize work was being done on the system. A repairman working inside a vat that contained rotary mixers was killed when someone started the equipment. These accidents could have been avoided by using lockouts, if the switches opening the circuits had been secured so that only persons conducting the repairs, or their supervisors, had the locks or combinations to them. Provisions on circuit breakers permit lockouts and lockins to be made in this way.

Interlocks

Figure 7-5 indicates many of the different types of interlocks and their modes of operation. Interlocks are provided to ensure that event A does not occur under the following conditions:

1. *Inadvertently.* For event A to occur in such cases a preliminary, intentional action, B, is needed—for example, lifting the cover that prevents a critical switch from being activated accidentally.

2. *While condition C exists.* An interlock may be placed on an access door or panel to equipment where high voltage exists. If adjustment must be made and the door or panel is opened, the circuit is inactivated so that the unsafe condition no longer exists. Guard gates at railroad crossings are a combination of isolator, lockout, and interlock. They isolate the tracks and passing train, keep other vehicles and pedestrians from the tracks when a train is imminent, and open to permit traffic to pass when the danger has been removed.

3. *Before event D.* Such interlocks are desirable where the sequence of operations is important or necessary and a wrong sequence could cause a mishap. Manufacturers provide numerous pushbutton switching arrangements with many variations of interlocks. Analyses of desired operating procedures, controls, and the consequences of an error or failure will determine the type of interlock that should be used.

Fail-Safe Designs

Equipment failures produce a high percentage of accidents. And since failures will occur, fail-safe arrangements are often made to prevent personal injury, major catastrophes, damage to equipment, or degraded operations. Fail-safe designs ensure that failures will leave the system unaffected or convert them to states in which no injury or damage will result. In most situations, but not all, this safeguard will result in inactivation of the system. Fail-safe designs can be categorized into three types:

1. In the most common and prevalent, a fail-passive arrangement reduces the system to its lowest energy level. The system will not operate again until corrective

INTERLOCKS

Interlocks are one of the most commonly used safety devices, especially with electrically operated equipment. They take many forms. The following list indicates the principles of the types more frequently used. In some cases, two or more of these principles are involved in the design of one interlocking device. Some interlocks themselves prevent action or motion; other send signals to other devices which prevent initiating the source of the action or motion.

TYPE	MODE OF OPERATION
Limit switches, including: • Snap-acting switches • Positive-drive switches • Proximity switches	A wide variety of limit switches can be used for interlock purposes. They are generally operated by moving an external part of the switch in, out, or sideways to open or close the switch, depending on circuit design. In some cases the limit switch itself will open or close the circuit of which it forms a part; in others, a signal or lack of one from the limit switch will open or close a relay which, in turn, will open or close a power circuit.
Tripping devices	Action releases a mechanical block or triggering device which either permits or stops motion.
Key interlock	Inserting and turning a key in a mechanical lock permits action.
Signal coding	Specifically coded sequences of pulses emitted by a transmitter must match the sequence in a suitable receiver. When the sequences match, the receiver initiates or permits action.
Motion interlock	Motion of the mechanism being guarded against prevents a guard or other access from being opened.
Parameter sensing	Presence, absence, excess, or inadequacy of pressure, temperature, flow or other parameters permits or stops action.
Position interlock	Nonalignment of two or more parts prevents further action.
Two-hand controls	Two simultaneous physical actions by a person are required, sometimes within a specific length of time.
Sequential controls	Actions must be performed in the proper sequence or operation is inhibited.
Timers and time delays	Operation of the equipment can take place only after a specific length of time has passed.
Path separation	Removal of a piece of the circuit or of the mechanical path physically prevents operation.
Photoelectric devices	Interruption or presence of light on a photoelectrical cell generates a signal which can stop or initiate action.
Magnetic or electromagnetic sensing	Presence of a magnetic material stops or initiates operation of the equipment.
Radio-frequency inductive	Sensing of any conductive material, especially steel or aluminum, causes it to operate.
Ultrasonics	Senses the presence of nonporous materials.
Mercury switches	Mercury provides the path between two metal contacts through which current passes. The path can be broken by tilting the switch in which the mercury and contacts are sealed so that mercury flows away from one contact and breaks the path for the current.

FIGURE 7–5   Interlocks

action is taken, but no further damage will result because of the hazard causing the activation. Circuit breakers and fuses for protection of electrical devices are fail-safe devices. Each will open when the system is overloaded or a short-circuit occurs, deenergizing and making the system safe. For renewed operation, the circuit breaker must be reclosed or the fuse replaced.

2. Fail-active design maintains an energized condition that keeps the system in a safe operating mode until corrective and overriding action occurs or that activates an alternative system to eliminate the possibility of an accident. A fail-active design might include a monitor system that activates a visual indicator if a failure or adverse condition occurs in a critical operation. Or it might be a feature by which a malfunction in the warning system itself is indicated by a continuously blinking, differently colored, or auxiliary light or a loud noise. This should provide a very high degree of certainty that the fail-active system is still operative. A battery-operated smoke detector provides one example of a fail-active design. A fail-active design might also be incorporated in a street-crossing signal light that continues to blink when there is a failure.

3. A fail-operational arrangement allows system functions to continue safely until corrective action is possible. This type of design is most preferable, since there is no loss of function. The American Society of Mechanical Engineers requires a fail-safe operational orientation of feedwater valves for boilers. Incoming water must first flow under, rather than over, the valve disk. Detachment of the valve's disk from its stem permits the pressure of the water to continue to raise the disk and for the boiler to flow and keep operating normally. If initial flow had been over the disk, its detachment would have closed the valve, causing stoppage of flow and depletion of the water in the boiler. Before such arrangements were required, such occurrences resulted in lacks of water, increased steam pressures, and violent boiler ruptures.

Much railway equipment is based on fail-safe principles, predicated on the idea that gravity is the only force that can be depended on. As a result, semaphores, signal switches, and the lights to which they are connected are weighted devices. In event of a failure, a heavy arm drops, causing the fail-safe warning signal to be activated.

Other examples of fail-safe devices include:

- Air brakes on railroad trains and large trucks.
- Deadman throttles on locomotives.
- Automatic blocks on railroads.
- Control rods on nuclear reactors, which automatically drop into place to reduce the reaction rate if it exceeds a preset limit.
- Self-sealing breakaway fuel-line connections.
- Automobile headlight covers that open and expose the lights in event of a malfunction.

The term "fail-safe" is sometimes incorrectly employed for redundant arrangements. A redundant arrangement reduces the likelihood of a complete operational failure. With a proper fail-safe system, when any operation fault or failure does take place, no accident will follow except in extreme cases.

It should also be recognized that for any fail-safe device to be a safeguard it must be of proper design. A deficient arrangement may fail or not operate rapidly enough. A fuse in an electrical circuit may not blow fast enough to prevent damage to the system. Or snow or ice could jam the weighted devices used by railroads so that the fail-safe system might not work.

FAILURE MINIMIZATION

Hazards sometimes are such that fail-safe design arrangements cannot be provided. On the other hand, the process may be so critical that even a fail-safe arrangement is less preferable than a system that will fail only rarely. Nevertheless, to ensure that possibilities of failures which could cause accidents are minimized, four principal methods are employed:

1. *Safety factors and margins:* this is probably the most ancient means to minimize accidents by design. Under this concept, components and structures are designed with strengths far greater than those normally required. This is to allow for calculation errors, variations in material strengths and stresses, unforeseen transient loads, material degradation, and other random factors.

2. *Failure-rate reduction:* this is the principle on which reliability engineering is predicated. It endeavors to use components and design arrangements to produce expected lifetimes far beyond the proposed periods of use, thereby reducing probabilities of failure during operation.

3. *Parameter monitoring:* a specific parameter, such as temperature, noise, toxic gas concentration, vibration, pressure, or radiation is kept under surveillance to ensure it is within specified limits and to determine when or if it exhibits an abnormal characteristic. If it does, preventive or corrective action can then be taken.

SAFETY FACTORS AND MARGINS

Theoretically, if an item is to withstand a prescribed stress, making it strong enough to withstand three, four, or five times that stress would reduce the number of failures and accidents; that is, a structure or container that had a safety factor of 4 would fail half as frequently as one that had a safety factor of 2. In practice, the inadequacies and uncertainties in use of safety factors previously pointed out have led to a refinement known as margin of safety. The difference between the two should be understood.

A *safety factor* is expressed as the ratio of strength to stress. Initially, strength (S) was nominal ultimate strength of the part: the average or prescribed value at which it would fail completely. (A similar ratio has also been employed based on yield strength to give a yield factor of safety. A material stretched passed its yield point would never return completely to its original length.) However, it was found that the strength of a specific material was not constant. For example, a lot of steel rods might be required in which each would withstand a stress (L) of 10,000 pounds per square inch (psi). However, differences will occur in the composition of the material involved, manufacturing and assembly, handling, environment, or in usage. As a result, some of the rods will fail at less than 10,000 psi; others at more; the remainder at the stipulated value. Failure will occur when stress becomes greater than strength. Using nominal or prescribed strengths and stresses, normally S/L was made so large that there was no failure. Now, S_{min}/L_{max}, or minimum strength/maximum stress, may be stipulated. By this means, which is not unusual in aerospace systems, it is possible to have a safety factor of 1.0 or 1.25. Such a safety factor as low as 1.25 would indicate a *safety margin* of 0.25 or S_{min}/L_{max}.

Failure-Rate Reduction

Operating components will not last forever. Actions therefore should be taken to limit failures while the system is operating, the rates of failures, and shutdowns of the system, especially any failures that can result in accidents. Methods by which these can be accomplished include:

- Increasing life expectancies of components to longer durations, especially to times longer than is normally required (derating).
- Screening.
- Timed replacements.
- Redundant arrangements.

Derating

Manufacturers are constantly working to produce components with longer lives. They rate their parts under specific conditions and stresses. Reducing the stresses under which components will operate will reduce their failure rates and increase their reliability. One of the stresses most affecting electronic equipment is heat. Failures increase with temperature; reducing temperature increases their lives. In one form of derating, therefore, cooling is provided even when the components operate at their normal capacities.

The principal cause of operating failures is the load factor: the ratio of actual load to rated load. This can be measured by voltage, current, or other indications of internal stress. Closely packed components, such as in some electronic equipment, generate heat, which causes mutual damage to the different parts. Formerly, cooling was necessary or component lives were shortened quickly. With the development of transistorized and embedded circuitry, little heat was required, generated, or transmitted. As the load factor decreases, so does the failure rate, and the longer it is before components will fail.

Derating can also be accomplished through the use of components whose capacity is greater than actually required. (This is the electronic equivalent of using a safety factor.) If components of greater capacity are unavailable, too costly, or too bulky, it may be possible to achieve the same functional result through load-sharing redundant arrangements.

Screening

One means of reducing failures is through close control of component quality. Quality control in the United States has improved greatly because of better quality of foreign manufacturers. Quality control at one time was meant to eliminate those components which failed to meet operational test requirements. Screening for reliability purposes also means eliminating those components that pass the operating tests for specific parameters but indicate they will fail within unacceptable times. Reduction in failure rates of all types, such as for electronics, automobiles, and plant equipment, has also lessened the occurrence of accidents.

Screening can be accomplished in a number of ways. The simplest is by visual inspection and measurement. Other types of tests include: application of normal pressure or voltage tests for short periods of time; accelerated tests during which a much greater stress is imposed over a short time; burn-in tests and tests for the entire periods during which they should operate or at least a warranted time; or step or progressive testing (which will not be explained here). It should be remembered that screening requirements will be less if quality is initially higher and errors fewer.

Timed Replacements

To maintain constant failure rates before wearout failures begin, it is necessary that components be replaced in a timely fashion. Some failures may be so critical because of the accidents they might lead to that they cannot be permitted. Others must be kept to a minimum, while still others merely generate inconvenience. In any event, to maintain operational capability it is necessary that components be replaced before they fail.

Replacements must be timed, because to do so too early is wasteful. It imposes an unnecessary maintenance and supply workload by excessive use of new units. This in turn can increase failures during burn-ins.

There are two means by which timed replacements can be made effectively and efficiently. One is by using data obtained by controlled laboratory testing of similar components or assemblies. The tests indicate the times after which wear out failures can be expected to take place. Replacement times can then be programmed at intervals shorter than these.

The second means is by noting component degradation or drift in operational systems. The output of components in circuits is measured, such as voltage or pressure. Once the output drops off past a stipulated point, which may be long past the prediction of failure, it is replaced. In many cases of large and critical equipment, tests are plotted to show the rate of degradation so that replacements can be predetermined and made at optimal times.

The SOAP (Spectrometric Oil Analysis Program) was developed with this concept in mind to determine when aircraft engines should be overhauled. (The parameter used was determining minute amounts of aluminum, iron, copper, and other metals in engine oil by which wear abrasion can be determined.) Some automobile brake linings now have indicators which indicate wear. In each of these, it is possible to estimate the remaining useful life and when replacement should be made.

Redundancy

Failure rates of complex equipment can often be greatly reduced through redundant arrangements. In addition to parallel and series redundancy, others can be pointed out, all having the aim of lessening the probability of operational failures:

1. *Decision redundancy.* There are a number of types all based on three or five (odd-numbered) circuits having individual outputs and a monitoring unit which decides the action to be taken. With one type (Majority Vote) at least two of the three inputs will decide the action; in another (Median Select), the middle value is chosen. Other, more complex ones have been designed.
2. *Standby redundancy.* An operative unit operates until a failure is indicated; after that another unit is turned on, either automatically, semiautomatically, or manually.

MONITORING

Monitoring devices can also be used to keep any selected parameter, such as temperature or pressure, under surveillance to ensure it remains at proper levels, does not reach dangerous levels, and no contingency or emergency is imminent. Greater benefits can be derived if contingencies are prevented or corrected immediately, rather than in response to an emergency.

Monitors can be employed to indicate whether:

- A specific condition does or does not exist.
- The system is ready for operation and is operating satisfactorily as programmed.
- The measured parameter is normal or abnormal.
- A required input has been provided.
- A desired or undesired output is being created.
- A specified limit is being met or exceeded.

In addition, a monitoring system must lead to suitable corrective action when necessary. This may consist simply of conveying information to an operator, considered to constitute part of the system, who then accomplishes any required tasks. The actions in the overall process involve four principal steps, whether the system consists wholly of hardware, wholly of personnel, or of a mix of hardware and personnel.

Detection

A monitor must be capable of sensing the specific parameter which has been selected in spite of all other stresses that could be expected to exist during an operation or in an environment. A detector may be capable of measuring extremely small concentrations of toxicants in a laboratory. But in an operating environment, vibrations, temperature variations, moisture, electrical interference, or other stress may degrade performance or cause complete failure. The sensing function may be accomplished continuously, continually but intermittently, or intermittently at the desire of an operator. It must be able to sense and provide readings for only those parameters for which it has been selected, without being affected by extraneous undesirable conditions. It must be capable of detecting a hazard at a level low enough to permit awareness of its presence, generally soon enough to permit corrective action long before an emergency arises. The input element of the monitoring device should be located where it can sense the hazard for the selected parameter. Frequently, the value of a monitor is negated because input to sensing device is in a poor location for proper sampling. Fire detectors in homes are sometimes placed in living rooms, but fires generally originate in kitchens or closets where furnaces or hot water heaters are located.

Measurement

The parameter a monitoring device senses may be one in which only one or two bistable conditions can exist; that is, a device is either on or off. The monitor may also be able to determine additional information, such as the existing level of a parameter being monitored continuously or the exceeding of a predetermined level. The second type of monitor permits comparison of existing and predetermined levels. Methods of measurement vary from the very simple to the highly complex. A simple method is to mark a display, such as a dial, with predetermined limits; an indicator then points out the existing level. An operator observes and compares the existing level and the limit to determine whether there is an abnormality. One style of automobile gauge to monitor radiator water temperature is of this type. In the second type of automobile gauge, a light goes on to warn the operator only when the water temperature exceeds a preset level.

Interpretation

An operator must understand clearly the meanings of any readings provided by the monitoring devices. The operator must know whether a normal situation exists, an unusual condition is impending, or corrective action must be taken. Displays and signals should employ means by which personnel are provided information that is easily read and understandable, having the least ambiguity, the minimum possibility of misinterpretation, and the minimal necessity for additional information. Monitors should provide timely and easily recognizable displays and signals. Indicators and signals within a specific system are frequently standardized for this reason. Personnel must be trained and be knowledgeable of the exact meanings of any output of a monitor or warning device. The combination of information from the monitor plus previous training is required to produce a decision on a subsequent course of action. If either one is lacking or inadequate, a suitable course of action may not be possible within the time available, or there may be a delay until the deficiency is eliminated. The most notable case of deficiency in monitoring, interpretation, and response, one that almost resulted in a major accident, was that at the nuclear power plant at Three Mile Island in 1979.

Response

When a monitor indicates a normal situation, no response other than continuation of the action or program is necessary. When corrective action is required, the more information and time available to interpret and analyze it, reach a decision, and respond, the more likely will be the proper and effective decision and response. For this reason, whenever possible, data from the monitor should indicate as early as possible the approach of an adverse condition. In some instances, the level at which the monitor will indicate the existence of a problem should be set far below the actual danger level. For example, air contains approximately 21 percent oxygen; the danger level for respiration is 16 percent. A monitor could indicate when the level of oxygen in an enclosed space drops below 20 percent. The air is still breathable at that point, but the deficiency indicates the existence of a situation that should be investigated for a suitable response. Situations are numerous where early warning could permit proper responses. Threshold limit values (TLVs) are examples; carbon monoxide or flammable gas detectors are others.

When the system is such that the response must be made by a person, analysis of the procedure should have been made to ensure time would be adequate to take corrective action under the circumstances. Occasionally, the attention of a person who should be aware of an unusual situation is focused elsewhere than on a visual indicator. In those instances in which a failure to take timely action could prove disastrous, auxiliary aural alerting or warning devices may be used. Where a serious, critical, or catastrophic condition would result if corrective action were not taken very rapidly, a monitor could be interlocked to automatically activate hazard-suppression or damage-containment devices.

Applications of Monitors

A few of the many applications of monitors are:

- Gas monitors to determine the presence of toxic or flammable substances.
- Infrared detectors to indicate the presence of hot spots or of flames.
- Detectors to determine emissions of pollutants from stacks.
- Liquid level indicators to warn when the fluid reaches a preset high or low limit.
- Governors that activate warning signals or lights or take corrective action automatically when a predetermined speed is exceeded.
- Odorants to indicate leakage of gases or high temperatures of metals, insulations, or other materials.

To ensure they perform properly, monitors (and warning devices) should:

1. Be accurate, quick acting, and easy to maintain, calibrate, and check. Procedures to test and calibrate must be available and used as prescribed.
2. Be selected for performance at a high level of reliability. In extremely critical applications, it may be desirable to permit testing by the operators to determine or indicate any failure of monitor circuitry.
3. Have independent and reliable sources of power and circuitry for monitoring and warning about critical functions.
4. Require an energy level lower than that which would constitute, contribute to, or activate a hazard in the event of a failure.
5. Not provide a path that could cause degradation of the entire system, change of a safe condition, inadvertent action, or other adverse effect because of a failure.

Buddy System

The buddy system may also be employed as a means of monitoring and safeguarding persons who undertake hazardous operations. The buddy system has been employed for many years by Boy Scouts, Girl Scouts, and similar organizations for hazardous activities like swimming or in industrial plants.

Two methods have been employed. In the first, two persons, who constitute a buddy pair, are subjected to the same hazard at the same time and under the same conditions. Each must ensure the well-being of the other, monitoring the other's activities, or providing assistance when required. Power company personnel who must work on live high-voltage electrical systems use this type of mutual aid and surveillance.

In the second type of buddy system, only one person of the pair is exposed to the hazard. The other acts as a lifeguard whose sole duty is to protect and assist the person in danger, should the need arise. A common example in industrial work is the task during which a worker must enter a tank to accomplish cleaning or repair. A buddy is stationed outside to monitor the well-being of the person inside. The buddy may provide warnings on any adverse condition that he or she may note, assist the worker if aid is needed, or call for outside assistance when it is required.

The outside buddy in this system should have no duty except that of monitoring the worker in danger. He or she might be authorized to perform such minor activities as passing tools when required. However, under no circumstance should the buddy have to leave the assigned station to obtain those tools. This prohibition against leaving includes performing any errand for the worker being monitored, even at the worker's own request. A means for communicating with the other personnel for other supplies or assistance should formerly have been devised and instituted.

Procedures for operations involving the buddy system must indicate what each person is responsible for and must do, and the hazards that must be monitored. The procedure should include a list of tools, supplies, and devices that might be needed to avoid any omission or call for them. Monitoring by devices should also be done often by the worker in danger. Supervisors must ensure that participating persons are aware of their duties and know the procedure, that required equipment, materials, and safety devices are available, and that means of communication have been arranged. Everyone should know what action to take in the event of a contingency, how to use emergency equipment, and how to ensure it is available and adequate.

Although they may not be designated as parts of the buddy system, other personnel may be employed to monitor hazardous conditions A worker can monitor road conditions and use red flags to tell vehicle drivers and equipment operators whether passage is safe. Pilot cars can be monitors for wide or dangerous loads on highways. They precede the dangerous load and monitor the route for obstructions and other hazards. When there appears to be inadequate clearance, danger to other personnel, or possibility of collision with another vehicle, the pilot car warns the vehicle that follows.

WARNING MEANS AND DEVICES

Warning means and devices are means of avoiding accidents by attracting or focusing attention of the operator or other person on an item that constitutes a hazard. Warnings are required by law to inform workers, users, and the public about any dangers that might not be obvious. Failure to warn, is in itself, considered a defect by the courts. Thus, engineers are legally responsible when, having failed to eliminate a hazard, they instead use warnings. In this case they use a procedural instead of a design means. Unless automatic equipment is used to control the results of monitoring, any alerts to potentially unsafe conditions or situations are by means of human senses.

Every method of identifying and notifying personnel that a hazard exists requires communication. All human senses have been and are used for this purpose. Figure 7-6 lists how the senses can be used as monitoring and warning devices. They are presented in a rough order of frequency in which these senses are used. With them are cited examples of their uses.

Vision is the principal sense, and signs and labels are the prime means, by which information of the existence of hazards is transmitted. Figure 7-7 points out some of the most important aspects and requirements doing this properly.

It has been reported 27 million Americans are functionally illiterate, so that they cannot read a label on a bottle. A stockyard worker destroyed a head of cattle because he couldn't read the word "POISON" on the bag he thought was feed. A Navy recruit caused $250,000 damage to equipment trying to follow the pictures in the text of a repair manual to hide his illiteracy. Compounding the problem is the fact that many personnel are literate only in foreign languages. It is estimated that damages in billions of dollars occur annually because workers can't read instructions.

The American National Standards Institute recently issued ANSI Z535.2-1998 Standard for Environmental and Facility Safety Signs. This revision attempts to establish specifications for signs to alert persons to: (1) the type of the hazard, (2) the degree of the seriousness of the hazard, (3) the consequences that can result from that hazard, and (4) what to do to avoid the hazard. It specifies the placement of text and symbols in relation to the headers. Text is flush left with mixed case. It recommends the use of multiple pictographs on a single sign to help overcome language and educational barriers.

SAFE PROCEDURES

The need to follow prescribed procedures has been mentioned before. Safe procedures should include any warnings established by the analysis. Unfortunately, since many people do not read operating procedures until they have run into difficulty ("when all else fails, read the instructions"), and ignore warnings, this method has a lower priority rating in means of preventing accidents.

BACKOUT AND RECOVERY

A failure, error, or other adverse condition may eventually develop into a mishap. By this time a contingency or emergency may exist. By suitable action an accident can be avoided from this abnormal situation, which may be an extremely dangerous one. Failure to act correctly or adequately can permit the situation to deteriorate into a mishap. This interim period extends from the time the abnormality appears until normality is recovered or accident develops. If recovery takes place, the incident can be considered a near miss.

THE SENSES AS WARNING DEVICES

Sense	Means	Description	Example
1. Visual	a. Illumination	a. A hazardous area is more brightly illuminated than nonhazardous surrounding areas.	a. Having well-lit highway intersections, obstacles, stairs, and transformer substations.
	b. Discrimination	b. Paint a physical hazard in a bright color or in alternating light and dark colors.	b. A structure (such as a pole), piece of equipment, or fixed object which could be hit by a moving vehicle is painted yellow or orange. OSHA standards require that the inside of the door to an electrical switch box be painted orange so that the fact that it is open can be recognized easily.
	c. Notes in instructions	c. Warning and caution notes are inserted in operations and maintenance instructions and manuals to alert personnel to hazards.	c. A warning in a car owner's manual to block the wheels before jacking the car to change a tire.
	d. Labeling	d. Warnings are painted on or attached to equipment.	d. "NO STEP" markings on hydraulic or pneumatic lines; high voltage; jacking points.
	e. Signs	e. Placards warn of hazards.	e. Road signs indicating hazards; "NO SMOKING" signs; EXPLOSIVE, FLAMMABLE, or CORROSIVE signs on trucks carrying such material.
	f. Signal lights	f. Colored or flashing lights (or reflectors) attract attention to a hazard or indicate urgency.	f. Red flashers on construction barricades at night; swinging red lights at railroad crossings; yellow caution lights at intersections; traffic lights.
	g. Flags and streamers	g. Tags or pieces of cloth are used to warn of danger.	g. A tag on a switch to indicate circuit is being worked on; a red streamer at the end of a long load protruding over the rear of the vehicle; colored strips of cloth on wires, ropes, and cables to make them more easily visible; flags used by flagmen at road construction sites to warn motorists when it is safe to proceed.
	h. Hand signals	h. A set of hand motions is used to pass instructions, warnings, and other information from one person to another.	h. Signals to the crane operator from a man guiding a load being lifted into place.

FIGURE 7–6   The Senses as Warning Devices

2. Auditory	a. Alarms	a. A siren, whistle, or similar sound device provides warning of existing or impending danger.	a. A siren indicates that there is a fire in a plant; a siren or whistle warns personnel to clear an area where blasting is to take place.
	b. Buzzer	b. Alerts a person that a specified time has passed or that time has arrived to take the next step in a sequence of actions.	b. Some compressed-air packs contain buzzers that sound when the pressure in the tank has decreased to a predetermined level, or after a preset time has passed.
	c. Shout	c. Voice action to warn of a danger.	c. One person warns another of an obstruction.
3. Smell	a. Odor detection	a. Presence of an odorous gas can indicate the presence of a hazard.	a. An odorant is added to refined natural gas (which has no odor) so that leaks can be readily detected.
		b. Burning materials give off characteristic odors	b. The presence of an unseen fire can sometimes be detected by characteristic odors of products of combustion.
		c. Overheating equipment can be recognized by the odor generated.	c. Vaporization of oil can permit detection of a hot bearing; odor of hot, steaming water can warn a car driver of a broken radiator hose.
4. Feel	a. Vibration	a. Rough running of equipment can indicate the presence of a problem and impending failure.	a. Vibration of a rotating shaft can signal a loss of lubrication, wear, and damage.
		b. Corrugations or vibration inducers in a road can warn a driver of a hazard.	b. Lane and shoulder markers in a road can warn a sleepy driver when he is going off the road or out of his lane.
	c. Temperature	c. Excessively high temperature can warn of a problem.	c. A maintenance man may be able to detect by its temperature a bearing that is acting abnormally; a temperature increase in an air-conditioned space may warn of equipment problems; excessively high temperature of a cooling fluid may indicate a possible problem in the equipment being cooled.
5. Taste	a. Ingestion	a. May indicate that material taken into the mouth is dangerous.	a. Acid, bitter, or excessively salty taste may indicate that material is not proper for consumption.

FIGURE 7–6 Continued

All employers and manufacturers have a duty to warn workers of hazards in the workplace. A failure to do so which results in an injury has long been considered a negligent act which may also be considered a design deficiency.

Labels are a visual type of warning device, a means of alerting personnel to the existence of a hazard. They are probably the commonest means now used to warn of hazards. In spite of this, they often neither are adequate as a tool of accident prevention nor satisfy the legal duty to warn of hazards. As a result there is much litigation because of accidents in which there were improper failures to warn. Below are some of the principal aspects that should be known regarding label warnings.

A warning label, to be considered adequate, must contain at least certain items of information, Others are advisable and recommended. There must be

1. A key word (see below) to attract the attention of the worker, user, or other person who potentially might be in danger, such as WARNING, POISON, FLAMMABLE, or EXPLOSIVE. Warning labels should be of legible size and located where they are easily apparent.
2. Information on the nature of the hazard to be guarded against. Labels should be simple, easy to understand, and not open to misinterpretation. Statements should be directed toward the educational level of persons to be warned.
3. Action to be taken to avoid injury or damage. The word WILL should be used instead of MAY if there is a reasonable possibility the hazard might produce injury.
4. A brief statement of the consequences that might result if the indicated action is not taken.
5. A brief instruction on appropriate emergency action to minimize harm if the hazard happens.
6. Accessible wording. The labeling must be in a language knowledgeable to the worker or user. Where workers or users may be from different countries, the labels should be multilingual in the languages expected.
7. Preferably, a logo of an exclamation mark within an equilateral triangle or other symbol to alert personnel to the hazard. Logos and symbols should be as universal as possible. Words, signs, logos, or symbols should be consistent.

Key word: ANSI Z535.2-1998 defines three choices for signal words to be used in headers on signs or labels:
1. CAUTION indicates a potentially hazardous situation which, if not avoided, may result in minor or moderate injury. It may also be used to alert against unsafe practices.
2. WARNING indicates a potentially hazardous situation which, if not avoided, could result in serious injury or death.
3. DANGER indicates an immediately hazardous situation which, if not avoided, will result in death or serious injury.
Header background colors should be yellow with "caution," orange with "warning," and red with "danger." Lettering for DANGER should be white.[56]

Further: Use of a warning label or sign is an indication of awareness a hazard exists. Manufacturers or designers should do their reasonable best to eliminate or properly control any hazards if accidents or litigation are to be avoided.

FIGURE 7–7   Label Warnings

Actions that can be taken include:

1. Normal sequence restoration, which may be possible, during which the situation can be corrected without damage. A change may simply eliminate an error, being made directly to the correct step in a sequence, or action can revert to a desired point. Another means is by stopping the entire procedure, such as by hitting a stop button. After that the procedure can be restarted as desired.

2. Inactivating only malfunctioning equipment that (a) is nonessential to the entire operation, (b) can be spared because of redundancy, (c) has already fulfilled its function, and (d) may be replaced by a temporary substitute.

3. Suppressing the hazard by immediately reducing it to a level where immediate danger no longer exists. After spillage of a small amount of gasoline, the possibility of an accident might be eliminated by flushing it away with water and creating a normal atmosphere.

If the emergency is not suitably countered, the result will be an accident. Following are means of lessening any adverse effects by damage minimization and containment.

DAMAGE MINIMIZATION AND CONTAINMENT

As long as a hazard exists, there is the possibility, however remote, that an accident will result, without our knowing when it will occur. Functional requirements and cost considerations make it impossible to eliminate all hazards or to incorporate safeguards for complete protection. Some hazards must be accepted, and accidents will happen. Some of the protective means of minimizing and containing effects of accidents include physical isolation, personal protective equipment, energy-absorbing mechanisms, "weak links," and escape and rescue.

PHYSICAL ISOLATION

Isolation has already been indicated as a means of accident prevention. It is also frequently used to minimize the results of violent release of energy, such as by use of:

1. Distance, by citing possible points of accidents far from persons, equipment, or vulnerable structures. Quantity-distance criteria for explosive safety are predicated on this principle. Standards are set for the amounts of explosives that can be located and at what distances from other critical areas or items so they will not be harmed by an accidental explosion.

2. Deflectors to lessen damage by deflecting or absorbing energy. The remainder should then constitute less than the amount that would be damaging. Energy may be deflected by such means as heat reflectors from fires, noise shields, or sloped barricades between explosive storage buildings.

3. Containment to prevent the spread of fire, such as sprinkler systems or water sprays.

4. Barriers of metal, concrete blocks, or other impenetrable or nonconductive material.

Personal Protective Equipment

This connotes the equipment persons might wear for protection against an accident. Although some types might be used for protection against both adverse environments and accidents, their potential use in accidents is pointed out here. Needs for such equipment vary from protection against environments that are hazardous, against questionable conditions where an adverse condition may or may not have taken place, or against accidents. The need for personal protective equipment can be divided into three categories:

1. For scheduled hazardous operation. Spray painting would require protective clothing even during scheduled operations, but also if it took place inadvertently.

2. For investigative and corrective purposes. It may be necessary to determine whether the environment is dangerous because of a leak, contamination, or other condition. The type of material might be toxic, or corrosive, or unknown. The leak might be simply suspected or its concentration uncertain. The protective equipment must be capable of providing protection against a wide range of hazards, which might be unknown.

3. Against accidents. This may constitute the severest requirement, because the first few minutes after an accident takes place may be the most critical. Reaction time to suppress or control any injury or damage is extremely important. Because of this, protective equipment must be simple and easy to don and operate, especially because it is often required at a time of stress.

The equipment must not degrade performance unduly, and it must be reliable and suitable for the hazard that might be involved. It must work as intended, or the worker might be exposed to an unsuspected and fatal hazard. Therefore it should have been more stringently designed and tested than equipment for normal purposes.

Many employees resist the use of personal protection equipment. Therefore, management must be have a proactive program and must shoulder responsibility to encourage and enforce this hazard control.

WEAK LINKS

A "weak link" is one designed to fail at a level of stress that will minimize and control any possibility of a more serious failure or accident. "Weak links" may be such simple items as perforations that permit tearing of paper products along desired lines. For safety purposes, weak links have been used in electrical, mechanical, and structural systems.

The most common use of a weak link has been with electrical fuses, which have been designed to fail before more valuable parts are damaged. The heat generated by passage of current through a low-melting-point metal causes the circuit to open before the current load becomes dangerous during a short-circuit. Other means of limiting extensive damage include: boilers with mechanical fuses that melt when water levels drop excessively, so that steam can escape and there is no rupture; sprinkler systems that open to release water for fire extinguishing; shear pins that fail at designed stresses to prevent damage to equipment being driven; or panels that will fail along designed fault lines to provide openings so personnel can escape.

Weak links all have an inherent problem. Although the damage that might result is minor, there will be damage, namely failure of the weak link. Thus, a circuit breaker limits damage, but it can be closed without adverse effects, which is not the situation with a fuse. A fuse or other weak link makes the system inoperable and must be replaced before it can be used again. Because of these, in some extremely critical designs, weak links are used as secondary equipment. A safeguard, such as a pressure relief valve, might fail to operate properly. At a higher, but still safe, pressure, the weak link would open, reducing the excess of an explosion.

ESCAPE, SURVIVAL, AND RESCUE

An emergency may continue to deteriorate until it is necessary to abandon or sacrifice structures, vehicles, or equipment to avoid injury to personnel. Following unsuccessful efforts to recover from an emergency, it may be necessary to leave the danger area, abandon ship, or bail out. This is the point of no return. And for such situations, escape, survival, and rescue procedures and equipment are vital: lives depend on them.

Escape and survival refer to efforts by personnel to save themselves using their own resources; rescue refers to efforts by other personnel to save those endangered. Although such actions might never be necessary, what is needed are adequate designs, procedures, suitable equipment, and knowledge of their use. The failure of equipment may be worse than if no equipment had been provided at all, putting the victim in an even worse situation. In addition, there is the stress or traumatic shock of the accident. Some actions might be possible up to a specific time, after which they are not. A pilot who is flying in an aircraft may have the option of either parachuting or attempting a forced landing. If the pilot jumps to escape, he or she is committed to use the parachute and must survive in the air. If the parachute fails, the probability of survival is low.

Escape and Survival

In some cases, escape and survival in the event of an accident may be a fairly easy process; under slightly different conditions it might be extremely difficult or impossible. After a fire in a single-storied plant, workers might escape by simply walking out a door and survive in the open air. Fire in a high-rise building might permit no escape.

A suitable analysis should have determined the hazards and accidents that could occur and how to combat their effects. Escape routes should be prescribed adequate for the number of personnel who would use them. Routes and exits should be marked conspicuously (OSHA standards require them) so they can be followed easily. Emergency lighting may be necessary. Safety zones should be established to which workers could withdraw.

Rescue Procedures and Equipment

There is the possibility that persons involved in an accident might not be able to escape under their own resources, so rescues may be attempted by other persons. The abilities of rescuers vary. Such persons might be: (1) fellow workers familiar with the plant, hazards, and equipment, and who may have been advised of what to do in any emergency, (2) untrained persons unfamiliar with the equipment, (3) personnel familiar with the hazards in general but not with specific equipment or materials involved, or (4) persons knowledgeable and capable of handling the need. Thus, a rescuer may be anyone from a passerby or a plant helper to a trained firefighter, chemical explosives expert, or mine cave-in expert.

For anyone to be able to provide assistance, especially for volunteers, certain facilities should have been provided. Prominently marked latches on the outside of aircraft are advised that inform rescuers how to open hatches so injured crewmen can be removed in rescue attempts.

BIBLIOGRAPHY

[1]. Willie Hammer, *Product Safety Engineering and Management* (Englewood Cliffs, NJ: Prentice-Hall, Inc., 1980), p. 113.

[2]. American National Standards Institute, *ANSI Z535.2-1998 Standard for Environmental and Facility Safety Signs,* New York.

EXERCISES

7.1. Discuss the different categories of hazards.

7.2. What is the best means of accident prevention? List five examples.

7.3. How can the magnitudes of hazards be limited? Describe how a design can be intrinsically safe.

7.4. How can isolation be used to keep personnel from accidents?

7.5. What is meant by making equipment fail-safe? How can it be done?

7.6. What are lockouts, lockins, and interlocks? Give examples of each. Describe some types of interlock devices and how they work.

7.7. How are monitors used to prevent accidents? Give five applications. List the characteristics a good monitor should have.

7.8. What is the buddy system and how is it used? What are the differences between the buddy system and the two-man concept?

7.9. Tell how the human senses can be used as monitoring and warning devices and give some examples of each.

7.10. List some features that are required or incorporated in any proper warning label or sign according to the common law.

7.11. What are back-out and recovery as they apply to accident prevention? How are they related to contingencies and emergencies?

7.12. List some means by which injury or damage can be minimized in the event of an accident.

7.13. What is a "weak link"? Describe some common types.

7.14. Describe the relationship between escape, survival, and rescue. Tell how equipment designs and procedures can be developed for them.

CHAPTER 8

Job Hazard Analysis

OSHA 3071
2002 (Revised)

⊚SHA **Occupational
Safety and Health
Administration**

U.S. Department of Labor

Job Hazard Analysis

U.S. Department of Labor
Elaine L. Chao, Secretary

Occupational Safety and Health Administration
John L. Henshaw, Assistant Secretary

OSHA 3071
2002 (Revised)

Contents

Who needs to read this booklet?

This booklet is for employers, foremen, and supervisors, but we encourage employees to use the information as well to analyze their own jobs and recognize workplace hazards so they can report them to you. It explains what a job hazard analysis is and offers guidelines to help you conduct your own step-by-step analysis.

What is a hazard?

A hazard is the potential for harm. In practical terms, a hazard often is associated with a condition or activity that, if left uncontrolled, can result in an injury or illness. See Appendix 2 for a list of common hazards and descriptions. Identifying hazards and eliminating or controlling them as early as possible will help prevent injuries and illnesses.

What is a job hazard analysis?

A job hazard analysis is a technique that focuses on job tasks as a way to identify hazards before they occur. It focuses on the relationship between the worker, the task, the tools, and the work environment. Ideally, after you identify uncontrolled hazards, you will take steps to eliminate or reduce them to an acceptable risk level.

Why is job hazard analysis important?

Many workers are injured and killed at the workplace every day in the United States. Safety and health can add value to your business, your job, and your life. You can help prevent workplace injuries and illnesses by looking at your workplace operations, establishing proper job procedures, and ensuring that all employees are trained properly.

One of the best ways to determine and establish proper work procedures is to conduct a job hazard analysis. A job hazard analysis is one component of the larger commitment of a safety and health management system.

What is the value of a job hazard analysis?

Supervisors can use the findings of a job hazard analysis to eliminate and prevent hazards in their workplaces. This is likely to result in fewer worker injuries and illnesses; safer, more effective work methods; reduced workers' compensation costs; and increased worker productivity. The analysis also can be a valuable tool for training new employees in the steps required to perform their jobs safely.

For a job hazard analysis to be effective, management must demonstrate its commitment to safety and health and follow through to correct any uncontrolled hazards identified. Otherwise, management will lose credibility and employees may hesitate to go to management when dangerous conditions threaten them.

What jobs are appropriate for a job hazard analysis?

A job hazard analysis can be conducted on many jobs in your workplace. Priority should go to the following types of jobs:

- Jobs with the highest injury or illness rates;

- Jobs with the potential to cause severe or disabling injuries or illness, even if there is no history of previous accidents;

- Jobs in which one simple human error could lead to a severe accident or injury;

- Jobs that are new to your operation or have undergone changes in processes and procedures; and

- Jobs complex enough to require written instructions.

Where do I begin?

1. **Involve your employees**. It is very important to involve your employees in the hazard analysis process. They have a unique understanding of the job, and this knowledge is invaluable for finding hazards. Involving employees will help minimize oversights, ensure a quality analysis, and get workers to "buy in" to the solutions because they will share ownership in their safety and health program.

2. **Review your accident history**. Review with your employees your worksite's history of accidents and occupational illnesses that needed treatment, losses that required repair or replacement, and any "near misses" — events in which an accident or loss did not occur, but could have. These events are indicators that the existing hazard controls (if any) may not be adequate and deserve more scrutiny.

3. **Conduct a preliminary job review**. Discuss with your employees the hazards they know exist in their current work and surroundings. Brainstorm with them for ideas to eliminate or control those hazards.

   If any hazards exist that pose an immediate danger to an employee's life or health, take immediate action to protect the worker. Any problems that can be corrected easily should be corrected as soon as possible. Do not wait to complete your job hazard analysis. This will demonstrate your commitment to safety and health and enable you to focus on the hazards and jobs that need more study because of their complexity. For those hazards determined to present unacceptable risks, evaluate types of hazard controls. More information about hazard controls is found in Appendix 1.

4. **List, rank, and set priorities for hazardous jobs**. List jobs with hazards that present unacceptable risks, based on those most likely to occur and with the most severe consequences. These jobs should be your first . priority for analysis.

5. **Outline the steps or tasks**. Nearly every job can be broken down into job tasks or steps. When beginning a job hazard analysis, watch the employee perform the job and list each step as the worker takes it. Be sure to record enough information to describe each job action without getting overly detailed. Avoid making the breakdown of steps so detailed that it becomes unnecessarily long or so broad that it does not include basic steps. You may find it valuable to get input from other workers who have performed the same job. Later, review the job steps with the employee to make sure you have not omitted something. Point out that you are evaluating the job itself, not the employee's job performance. Include the employee in all phases of the analysis—from reviewing the job steps and procedures to discussing uncontrolled hazards and recommended solutions.

Sometimes, in conducting a job hazard analysis, it may be helpful to photograph or videotape the worker performing the job. These visual records can be handy references when doing a more detailed analysis of the work.

How do I identify workplace hazards?

A job hazard analysis is an exercise in detective work. Your goal is to discover the following:

- What can go wrong?

- What are the consequences?

- How could it arise?

- What are other contributing factors?

- How likely is it that the hazard will occur?

To make your job hazard analysis useful, document the answers to these questions in a consistent manner. Describing a hazard in this way helps to ensure that your efforts to eliminate the hazard and implement hazard controls help target the most important contributors to the hazard.

Good hazard scenarios describe:

- Where it is happening (environment),

- Who or what it is happening to (exposure),

- What precipitates the hazard (trigger),

- The outcome that would occur should it happen (consequence), and

- Any other contributing factors.

A sample form found in Appendix 3 helps you organize your information to provide these details.

Rarely is a hazard a simple case of one singular cause resulting in one singular effect. More frequently, many contributing factors tend to line up in a certain way to create the hazard. Here is an example of a hazard scenario:

In the metal shop (environment), while clearing a snag (trigger), a worker's hand (exposure) comes into contact with a rotating pulley. It pulls his hand into the machine and severs his fingers (consequences) quickly.

To perform a job hazard analysis, you would ask:

- **What can go wrong?** The worker's hand could come into contact with a rotating object that "catches" it and pulls it into the machine.

- **What are the consequences?** The worker could receive a severe injury and lose fingers and hands.

- **How could it happen?** The accident could happen as a result of the worker trying to clear a snag during operations or as part of a maintenance activity while the pulley is operating. Obviously, this hazard scenario could not occur if the pulley is not rotating.

- **What are other contributing factors?** This hazard occurs very quickly. It does not give the worker much opportunity to recover or prevent it once his hand comes into contact with the pulley. This is an important factor, because it helps you determine the severity and likelihood of an accident when selecting appropriate hazard controls. Unfortunately, experience has shown that training is not very effective in hazard control when triggering events happen quickly because humans can react only so quickly.

- **How likely is it that the hazard will occur?** This determination requires some judgment. If there have been "near-misses" or actual cases, then the likelihood of a recurrence would be considered high. If the pulley is exposed and easily accessible, that also is a consideration. In the example, the likelihood that the hazard will occur is high because there is no guard preventing contact, and the operation is performed while the machine is running. By following the steps in this example, you can organize your hazard analysis activities.

The examples that follow show how a job hazard analysis can be used to identify the existing or potential hazards for each basic step involved in grinding iron castings.

Grinding Iron Castings: Job Steps

Step 1. Reach into metal box to right of machine, grasp casting, and carry to wheel.

Step 2. Push casting against wheel to grind off burr.

Step 3. Place finished casting in box to left of machine.

Example Job Hazard Analysis Form

Job Location: Metal Shop	*Analyst:* Joe Safety	*Date:*

Task Description: Worker reaches into metal box to the right of the machine, grasps a 15-pound casting and carries it to grinding wheel. Worker grinds 20 to 30 castings per hour.

Hazard Description: Picking up a casting, the employee could drop it onto his foot. The casting's weight and height could seriously injure the worker's foot or toes.

Hazard Controls:

1. Remove castings from the box and place them on a table next to the grinder.

2. Wear steel-toe shoes with arch protection.

3. Change protective gloves that allow a better grip.

4. Use a device to pick up castings.

Job Location: Metal Shop	**Analyst:** Joe Safety	**Date:**

Task Description: Worker reaches into metal box to the right of the machine, grasps a 15-pound casting and carries it to grinding wheel. Worker grinds 20 to 30 castings per hour.

Hazard Description: Castings have sharp burrs and edges that can cause severe lacerations.

Hazard Controls:

1. Use a device such as a clamp to pick up castings.

2. Wear cut-resistant gloves that allow a good grip and fit tightly to minimize the chance that they will get caught in grinding wheel.

Job Location: Metal Shop	*Analyst:* Joe Safety	*Date:*

Task Description: Worker reaches into metal box to the right of the machine, grasps a 15-pound casting and carries it to grinding wheel. Worker grinds 20 to 30 castings per hour.

Hazard Description: Reaching, twisting, and lifting 15-pound castings from the floor could result in a muscle strain to the lower back.

Hazard Controls:

1. Move castings from the ground and place them closer to the work zone to minimize lifting. Ideally, place them at waist height or on an adjustable platform or pallet.

2. Train workers not to twist while lifting and reconfigure work stations to minimize twisting during lifts.

Repeat similar forms
for each job step.

How do I correct or prevent hazards?

After reviewing your list of hazards with the employee, consider what control methods will eliminate or reduce them. For more information on hazard control measures, see Appendix 1. The most effective controls are engineering controls that physically change a machine or work environment to prevent employee exposure to the hazard. The more reliable or less likely a hazard control can be circumvented, the better. If this is not feasible, administrative controls may be appropriate. This may involve changing how employees do their jobs.

Discuss your recommendations with all employees who perform the job and consider their responses carefully. If you plan to introduce new or modified job procedures, be sure they understand what they are required to do and the reasons for the changes.

What else do I need to know before starting a job hazard analysis?

The job procedures discussed in this booklet are for illustration only and do not necessarily include all the steps, hazards, and protections that apply to your industry. When conducting your own job safety analysis, be sure to consult the Occupational Safety and Health Administration standards for your industry. Compliance with these standards is mandatory, and by incorporating their requirements in your job hazard analysis, you can be sure that your health and safety program meets federal standards. OSHA standards, regulations, and technical information are available online at www.osha.gov.

Twenty-four states and two territories operate their own OSHA-approved safety and health programs and may have standards that differ slightly from federal requirements. Employers in those states should check with the appropriate state agency for more information.

Why should I review my job hazard analysis?

Periodically reviewing your job hazard analysis ensures that it remains current and continues to help reduce workplace accidents and injuries. Even if the job has not changed, it is possible that during the review process you will identify hazards that were not identified in the initial analysis.

It is particularly important to review your job hazard analysis if an illness or injury occurs on a specific job. Based on the circumstances, you may determine that you need to change the job procedure to prevent similar incidents in the future. If an employee's failure to follow proper job procedures results in a "close call," discuss the situation with all employees who perform the job and remind them of proper procedures. Any time you revise a job hazard analysis, it is important to train all employees affected by the changes in the new job methods, procedures, or protective measures adopted.

When is it appropriate to hire a professional to conduct a job hazard analysis?

If your employees are involved in many different or complex processes, you need professional help conducting your job hazard analyses. Sources of help include your insurance company, the local fire department, and private consultants with safety and health expertise. In addition, OSHA offers assistance through its regional and area offices and consultation services. Contact numbers are listed at the back of this publication.

Even when you receive outside help, it is important that you and your employees remain involved in the process of identifying and correcting hazards because you are on the worksite every day and most likely to encounter these hazards. New circumstances and a recombination of existing circumstances may cause old hazards to reappear and new hazards to appear. In addition, you and your employees must be ready and able to implement whatever hazard elimination or control measures a professional consultant recommends.

Appendix 1
Hazard Control Measures

Information obtained from a job hazard analysis is useless unless hazard control measures recommended in the analysis are incorporated into the tasks. Managers should recognize that not all hazard controls are equal. Some are more effective than others at reducing the risk.

The order of precedence and effectiveness of hazard control is the following:

1. Engineering controls.

2. Administrative controls.

3. Personal protective equipment.

Engineering controls include the following:

- Elimination/minimization of the hazard—Designing the facility, equipment, or process to remove the hazard, or substituting processes, equipment, materials, or other factors to lessen the hazard;

- Enclosure of the hazard using enclosed cabs, enclosures for noisy equipment, or other means;

- Isolation of the hazard with interlocks, machine guards, blast shields, welding curtains, or other means; and

- Removal or redirection of the hazard such as with local and exhaust ventilation.

Administrative controls include the following:

- Written operating procedures, work permits, and safe work practices;

- Exposure time limitations (used most commonly to control temperature extremes and ergonomic hazards);

- Monitoring the use of highly hazardous materials;

- Alarms, signs, and warnings;

- Buddy system; and

- Training.

Personal Protective Equipment—such as respirators, hearing protection, protective clothing, safety glasses, and hardhats—is acceptable as a control method in the following circumstances:

- When engineering controls are not feasible or do not totally eliminate the hazard;

- While engineering controls are being developed;

- When safe work practices do not provide sufficient additional protection; and

- During emergencies when engineering controls may not be feasible.

Use of one hazard control method over another higher in the control precedence may be appropriate for providing interim protection until the hazard is abated permanently. In reality, if the hazard cannot be eliminated entirely, the adopted control measures will likely be a combination of all three items instituted simultaneously.

Appendix 2
Common Hazards and Descriptions

Hazards	Hazard Descriptions
Chemical (Toxic)	A chemical that exposes a person by absorption through the skin, inhalation, or through the blood stream that causes illness, disease, or death. The amount of chemical exposure is critical in determining hazardous effects. Check Material Safety Data Sheets (MSDS), and/or OSHA 1910.1000 for chemical hazard information.
Chemical (Flammable)	A chemical that, when exposed to a heat ignition source, results in combustion. Typically, the lower a chemical's flash point and boiling point, the more flammable the chemical. Check MSDS for flammability information.
Chemical (Corrosive)	A chemical that, when it comes into contact with skin, metal, or other materials, damages the materials. Acids and bases are examples of corrosives.
Explosion (Chemical Reaction)	Self explanatory.
Explosion (Over Pressurization)	Sudden and violent release of a large amount of gas/energy due to a significant pressure difference such as rupture in a boiler or compressed gas cylinder.
Electrical (Shock/ Short Circuit)	Contact with exposed conductors or a device that is incorrectly or inadvertently grounded, such as when a metal ladder comes into contact with power lines. 60Hz alternating current (common house current) is very dangerous because it can stop the heart.

Hazards	Hazard Descriptions
Electrical (Fire)	Use of electrical power that results in electrical overheating or arcing to the point of combustion or ignition of flammables, or electrical component damage.
Electrical (Static/ESD)	The moving or rubbing of wool, nylon, other synthetic fibers, and even flowing liquids can generate static electricity. This creates an excess or deficiency of electrons on the surface of material that discharges (spark) to the ground resulting in the ignition of flammables or damage to electronics or the body's nervous system.
Electrical (Loss of Power)	Safety-critical equipment failure as a result of loss of power.
Ergonomics (Strain)	Damage of tissue due to overexertion (strains and sprains) or repetitive motion.
Ergonomics (Human Error)	A system design, procedure, or equipment that is error-provocative. (A switch goes up to turn something off).
Excavation (Collapse)	Soil collapse in a trench or excavation as a result of improper or inadequate shoring. Soil type is critical in determining the hazard likelihood.
Fall (Slip, Trip)	Conditions that result in falls (impacts) from height or traditional walking surfaces (such as slippery floors, poor housekeeping, uneven walking surfaces, exposed ledges, etc.)
Fire/Heat	Temperatures that can cause burns to the skin or damage to other organs. Fires require a heat source, fuel, and oxygen.
Mechanical/ Vibration (Chaffing/ Fatigue)	Vibration that can cause damage to nerve endings, or material fatigue that results in a safety-critical failure. (Examples are abraded slings and ropes, weakened hoses and belts.)

Hazards	Hazard Descriptions
Mechanical Failure	Self explanatory; typically occurs when devices exceed designed capacity or are inadequately maintained.
Mechanical	Skin, muscle, or body part exposed to crushing, caught-between, cutting, tearing, shearing items or equipment.
Noise	Noise levels (>85 dBA 8 hr TWA) that result in hearing damage or inability to communicate safety-critical information.
Radiation (Ionizing)	Alpha, Beta, Gamma, neutral particles, and X-rays that cause injury (tissue damage) by ionization of cellular components.
Radiation (Non-Ionizing)	Ultraviolet, visible light, infrared, and microwaves that cause injury to tissue by thermal or photochemical means.
Struck By (Mass Acceleration)	Accelerated mass that strikes the body causing injury or death. (Examples are falling objects and projectiles.)
Struck Against	Injury to a body part as a result of coming into contact of a surface in which action was initiated by the person. (An example is when a screwdriver slips.)
Temperature Extreme (Heat/Cold)	Temperatures that result in heat stress, exhaustion, or metabolic slow down such as hypothermia.
Visibility	Lack of lighting or obstructed vision that results in an error or other hazard.
Weather Phenomena (Snow/Rain/Wind/Ice)	Self explanatory.

Appendix 3
Sample Job Hazard Analysis Form

Job Title:	Job Location:	Analyst	Date
Task #	Task Description:		
Hazard Type:	Hazard Description:		
Consequence:	Hazard Controls:		
Rational or Comment:			

Safety Analysis

GENERAL

Safety analysis is a necessity in today's litigious society. Companies that do not analyze may not prevent accidents which are preventable and may find their ability to defend themselves in a postaccident lawsuit compromised. The standard to which the courts hold management is prudence, foreseeability, and reasonableness. Prudence requires that: (1) production systems, products, and facilities be analyzed for safety, and (2) proper preventive measures follow the analysis. A prudent manager analyzes. An attempt must be made to foresee the foreseeable. This attempt must be reasonable. The key is reason. Analysis is simply the application of reason. There are two types of reason: inductive and deductive. If a company can demonstrate that they made a reasonable attempt to foresee the foreseeable by applying system safety analysis inductive and deductive techniques and responding to the analyses with proper preventive actions, the company has a strong legal position. They can show they were reasonable and prudent in trying to foresee and avoid accidents, provided that they have carefully documented their efforts.

The philosophy developed by system safety engineers is that accident prevention can and must begin as soon as the idea for a new system or operation is conceived. Methods of analyses have been developed to this end which can be undertaken early. The analyses can indicate tentatively any hazards that might be present in any proposed operation, the types and degrees of accidents that might result from hazards, and the measures which can be taken to avoid or minimize accidents or their consequences. As more and more details become available after the initial analysis on the characteristics of the proposed system or operation, they can be expanded further and further to determine more intimately where there might be potential causes of accidents, their effects, and safeguards needed. Almost 90 techniques have been developed, used, or proposed.[1] This chapter includes a few important ones to indicate some of the methodologies now in wide use. This may make occupational safety engineers aware of some types of detailed analyses they might want to undertake.

Some of these techniques start at the component level and reason upward to find what "undesirable end events" might occur from that components fault or failure. These "bottom-up" techniques are based on inductive reasoning. Some techniques start with the undesired event which is to be avoided and reason down to identify which components of the system could contribute to the undesired event through their fault or failure. In systems where there is a critical potential for catastrophe, the prudent manager must make every effort to foresee and avoid the catastrophe. Everything is not foreseeable, but the manager must make a thorough effort to foresee when there is a potential for a catastrophe. This means the manager will use both inductive and deductive system safety analysis, if feasible. Preferably, the inductive analysis will be conducted blind to the deductive analysis, and vice versa. The results of the two analyses will then be compared. Hopefully, the undesirable end events identified in the inductive analysis will match those the deductive analysis started with; the component faults and failures identified in the deductive analysis will match those components the inductive analysis started with. Where the inductive and deductive techniques do not match, the deficient analysis is corrected. This double-blind cross-check is a strong indicator of a reasonable effort to foresee the foreseeable, and when accompanied by prudent corrective actions, places management in a very defensible position.

PRELIMINARY HAZARDS ANALYSIS

The first method generally used in the systematic process of determining hazard causes, effects, and deterrents is the preliminary hazards analysis. As its name implies, this is an initial study from which analysis efforts can be expanded further. It is fairly broad in scope, investigates what hazards might be present, whether they can be eliminated entirely, or if not, the best way to control them. If the hazard cannot be eliminated, the analyst determines whether there are standards or methods by which the hazard could, should, or must be controlled. A review is made of the functions to be performed and whether the environments in which they must be performed will have any adverse effects on personnel, equipment, facilities, or operations.

According to Greek mythology, Daedalus wanted to escape from Crete where he and his son Icarus were being held captive by the king because of his skill as an artificer. Daedalus made wings of feathers, flax, and beeswax with which he and Icarus could fly to Greece. Before they flew off, Daedalus told Icarus:

> My boy, take care
> To wing your course
>   Along the middle air;
> If low, the surges
>   Wet your flagging plumes;
> If high, the sun
>   The melting wax consumes.

Daedalus's instruction to his son can be taken to be an elementary preliminary hazard analysis. However, Daedalus, not being an experienced safety engineer, did not go far enough in his analysis. His analysis and the preliminary hazards analysis a modern safety analyst might prepare are shown in Fig. 9-1.

[It can easily be seen from this example that system safety engineers are smarter than designers. We safety engineers can figure out potential ways of getting killed which Daedalus didn't even consider, and we can even indicate safety measures by which he could have prevented Icarus's accident (he flew too close to the sun, the wax melted off his wings, and he fell to his death). Modern designers, on the other hand, are not nearly as smart as Daedalus; they have never been able to figure out how to make flyable wings out of feathers, flax, and beeswax.]

Each product or operation will have a limited number of hazards, which can be determined as soon as a few facts are known. For example, the proposed product is to use electrical power. The hazards, which can potentially be present when electrical power is in use, could include any or all of the following: electrical shock; burns from hot equipment; fire due to arcing, sparking, or very hot surfaces; inadvertent starts of equipment; failure of equipment to operate at a critical time so that an accident will occur; radiation effects; and electrical explosions. Numerous conditions can lead to each of these, but these are the basic hazards. If the electrical product uses small batteries, such as for transistorized equipment, most of the hazards mentioned will not present. The analysis can therefore be limited to those which could possibly exist, no matter how improbable. Progress of the design can be monitored thereafter to determine whether the hazard can be eliminated; and if it cannot be, how best it could be controlled; and if it is controlled, whether or not the control appears to be adequate and how the adequacy of the control can be verified. At this point, very rough estimates might be made of the probability of an accident due to that hazard, and of the severity of its probable effects.

A practice has been initiated in which the preliminary hazards analysis list, which is prepared in tabular form, is broken down into individual items. Each item is recorded (Fig. 9-2) and then tracked through development or modification of a system, product, or operation to ensure that adequate consideration is given to its hazard elimination/control. (To assist in the tracking, visualizations, such as in the fault-tree method described later, can be used.) When all necessary actions are completed to eliminate or acceptably control the hazard, the item is signed off, since no further action is required. (An item should never be signed off with a comment that an action will be taken, is scheduled to take place, or a similar entry. Signoff is considered accomplished only after the proposed action has been completed and shown to be adequate.)

As design or planning progresses, studies are made of the hardware and facilities, through reviews of assemblies of their major components, their proposed interrelationships and interfaces with each other and with personnel, environments that could affect them, and the effects they could generate on personnel, other components and assemblies, and the environment.

Some information does not lend itself well to an analysis presented solely in a tabular form. A narrative format can then be added to include addition data. For example, an analysis presented in columnar form might indicate that a hazard was an accidental fire. To have a fire requires a fuel, oxidizer, ignitable mixture, and source of ignition. Detailed information on each item could then be listed separately, with details on the many fuels, oxidizers, and sources of ignition.

PRELIMINARY HAZARD ANALYSIS

IDENTIFICATION_____Mark I Flight System_____

SUBSYSTEM_____Wings_____   DESIGNER_____Daedalus_____

HAZARD	CAUSE	EFFECT	PROBABILITY OF ACCIDENT DUE TO HAZARD	CORRECTIVE OR PREVENTIVE MEASURE
Thermal radiation from sun	Flying too high in presence of strong solar radiation	Heat may melt beeswax holding feathers together. Separation and loss of feathers will cause loss of aerodynamic lift. Aeronaut may then plunge to his death in the sea.	Reasonably probable	Make flight at night or at time of day when sun is not very high and hot. Provide warning against flying too high and too close to sun. Maintain close supervision over aeronauts. Use buddy system. Provide leash of flax between the two aeronauts to prevent young, impetuous one from flying too high. Restrict area of aerodynamic surface to prevent flying too high.
Moisture	Flying too close to water surface or from rain.	Feathers may absorb moisture, causing them to increase in weight and to flag. Limited propulsive power may not be adequate to compensate for increased weight so that the aeronaut will gradually sink into the sea. Result: loss of function and flight system. Possible drowning of aeronaut if survival gear is not provided.	Reasonably probable	Caution aeronaut to fly through middle air where sun will keep wings dry or where accumulation rate of moisture is acceptable for time of mission.
Inflight encounter	a. Collision with bird	Injury to aeronaut	Remote probability	a. Select flight time when bird activity is low. Give birds right-of-way.
	b. Attack by vicious bird	Injury to aeronaut	Remote probability	b. Avoid areas inhabited by vicious birds. Carry weapon for defense.
Hit by lightning bolt	Bolt thrown by Zeus angered by hubris displayed by aeronaut who can fly.	Death of aeronaut	Happens occasionally	Aeronaut should not show excessive pride in being able to perform godlike activity (keep a low profile).

FIGURE 9–1   Preliminary Hazard Analysis

HAZARD REPORT

IDENTIFICATION/TITLE _____

EQUIPMENT/SYSTEM/SYSTEM _____

_____

PERSON INITIATING REPORT: _____

REPORT NO. _____
DATE INITIATED: _____
DATE THIS REPORT: _____
SIGNATURE: _____

CLOSEOUT DATE: _____

DESCRIPTION OF HAZARD AND ACCIDENT WHICH MIGHT RESULT:

EVENTS AND CONDITIONS WHICH MIGHT CONTRIBUTE TO THE HAZARD OR ACCIDENT:

POSSIBLE MEANS TO ELIMINATE OR CONTROL HAZARD OR ACCIDENT EFFECTS:

ESTIMATED PROBABILITY OF ACCIDENT OCCURRENCE:

	CURRENT CONDITION	WITH CONTROL		CURRENT CONDITION	WITH CONTROL
FREQUENT	_____	_____	REMOTE	_____	_____
REASONABLY PROBABLE	_____	_____	EXTREMELY IMPROBABLE	_____	_____
OCCASIONAL	_____	_____		_____	_____

MEANS OF VERIFYING ADEQUACY OF CONTROL/APPLICABLE SAFETY REQUIREMENTS:

ORGANIZATION/PERSON TO TAKEN ACTION:

STATUS OF ACTION TO BE OR HAVE BEEN TAKEN:

FIGURE 9–2   Hazard Report

FAILURE MODES AND EFFECTS ANALYSIS

One of the methods used to accomplish safety analyses has been derived from reliability engineering: Failure Modes and Effects Analysis (FMEA). FMEA is an inductive technique. It is used to determine how long a piece of complex equipment will operate satisfactorily and what the effects of any failure of individual components might be. The method is intended for analyses of proposed equipment and systems. An occasion might arise in which it would be highly desirable for an occupational safety engineer to determine whether or not the manufacturer of industrial equipment and systems to be purchased and installed had had such an analysis made, and to understand how failures might occur, modes and frequencies of failures, and the necessity for proper and timely maintenance and replacements.

In this method of analysis, the constituent major assemblies of the product to be analyzed are listed. Each assembly is then broken down into subassemblies and their components. Each component is studied to determine how it could malfunction and cause downstream effects. Effects might result on other components, and then on higher-level subassemblies, assemblies, and the entire product or system. Failure rates for each item are determined and listed. The calculations are used to determine how long a piece of hardware is expected to operate between failures, and the overall probability that it will operate for a specific length of time. It is the best and principal means of determining where components and designs must be improved to increase the operational life of a product. It is best used to analyze how often and when parts must be replaced if a failure, possibly affecting safety, must be avoided.

Until the use of Boolean mathematics, described in the next paragraph, FMEA calculations were often erroneous. Also, because many component failures would have no effect on safety, that aspect of an FMEA does not involve accident possibilities. Also, failure modes and effects analysis is limited to determination of all causes and effects, hazardous or not. Further, the FMEA does very little to analyze problems which could arise from operator errors (unless the system analysis includes the human as a component), or hazardous characteristics of equipment created by bad design or adverse environments (unless the scope of the analysis includes these elements). The FMEA is excellent for determining optimum points for improving and controlling product quality. Another method, fault-tree analysis, has been found more effective for safety purposes.

FAULT-TREE ANALYSIS (FTA)

In 1959 the Air Force became concerned with the potentially catastrophic events that could occur with the Minuteman missile then being developed by Boeing. The Air Force contracted with Bell Laboratories to develop a method of analysis by which probabilities of occurrence of events with which they were concerned could be computed. The Air Force wanted to know the possibilities and probabilities that a missile could be launched or a warhead activated inadvertently, and the chance of either of these being done intentionally by an unauthorized person in an act of sabotage.

Two years later Bell Laboratories completed the project. The new method, fault-tree analysis, involved Boolean logic in ways similar to those being used increasingly in electronics industries. It is a deductive technique. Safety engineers of the Boeing

Company adopted the proposed method and became its foremost proponents. They added to the symbols that Bell Laboratories had proposed. They organized the method so it could be computerized to permit calculating the probabilities of the problem with which the analyst was concerned. Although still used to determine probabilities of mishaps in complex systems or operations, fault-tree analysis is being used far more frequently to logically analyze the possibilities of potential accidents due to hazards, and the quantitative safety level.

At first the fact that Boolean logic (and arithmetic), with which few engineers were familiar at the time, was its basis gave many people the impression the method could be used only by mathematicians. (Some of the first Boeing employees involved in making those early safety analyses were mathematicians.) It turned out that Boolean logic was fairly simple to understand. One of the fundamental principles is that any statement, condition, act, situation, or process could be described as being in either one of two states. Something could be true or false, on or off, up or down—but not both; it would go or not go; or it could be fully open or not fully open (closed or partially open). There were no middle or intermediate positions.

FAULT-TREE SYMBOLS

Primary Event Symbols

- Basic Event, such as a component failure—*Circle.*
- Conditioning Event, a condition which must be satisfied before the event above the gate can occur—*Ellipse.*
- Undeveloped Event, an event not fully developed because of a lack of information or significance—*Diamond.*
- Normal Event, expected to occur during system operation—*House-shape.*

Intermediate and Top Event Symbol

- Output Event, those that should be developed or analyzed further to determine how they can occur (the top output event is called the end event; the others are called intermediate events)—*Rectangle.*

Basic Gate Symbols

- AND condition (or gate): All events leading into it from underneath must occur before the event leading out of it and at the top can occur. In a fault-tree Boolean equation, the AND condition is generally expressed by AB, A × B, or (A) (B) = C.
- OR condition (or gate): Any event leading into it from underneath will cause the event leading out of it at the top to occur. In a fault-tree Boolean equation, the OR condition is generally expressed by +, such as A + B = C
- A transfer symbol: the events which will occur where this is shown will be the same as where the inverted triangle with the same identification is shown—*Triangle.*

The either and-or, on-off situation applies to any condition, event, or other occurrence, but there can be any number of conditions, events, or occurrences. For example, a fire requires: (1) a fuel, (2) oxygen, and (3) sufficient heat to ignite. The fuel, oxygen, and ignition heat each either will be present or will not be present. But they must all be present to have a fire; if one is not, there will be no unacceptable risk of fire. The three occurrences are bound together in a so-called "CONDITIONAL AND" gate. The condition is that the ambient fuel and oxygen is within flammable range (see Fig. 9-3, G5). The CONDITIONAL AND is shown in Fig. 9-3 as an AND gate with a triangle inside (below G1).

In contrast to the "AND" gate is the "OR" gate. The OR gate may be simply a restatement of the gate's output, or it may have two or more events as inputs. When two or more events or conditions are possible as alternatives, any one will produce the specific result envisioned. All of the occurrences need not be present at the same time, as they would with an "AND" condition. The use of some of these symbols is shown in Fig. 9-3, a simplified Fault-Tree Analysis (FTA) of a top event of an unacceptable risk of fire with a system consisting of a fuel tank and fuel line. A fuel could be any one of hundreds. Figure 9-3 arbitrarily limits the analysis to fuel from a gasoline fuel tank. Tank leaks and line leaks are shown as primary component faults, indicated by the circle symbol at G6 and G7. Since air is normally present in the ambient for which the example fault tree is drawn, "Oxygen in the air" is shown in a "house" symbol at G3. A source of ignition could be a lit match, an open pilot light, a hot surface, a mechanical spark, an electrical arc, and so on, but it must be a source of heat sufficient to heat the fuel until self-sustained combustion occurs (for example, to greater than 536°F for 60 octane gasoline). Any one ignition source could contribute to a fire, but there must be one. The fault tree in Figure 9-3, for sake of brevity, shows that the analyst did not wish to pursue the identification of sources of ignition; therefore, there is a diamond below "Ignition Source >500 F Present" at G4. Ordinarily the identification of ignition sources would occur and be shown on the tree as inputs to a gate below the G4 event. "Fuel spill during operations" is elected not to be pursued further and is shown with a diamond at G8. Gates are numbered in this figure, and the tree is drawn using CAFTA for Windows.[2]

A fault-tree analysis works like this: the end effect (called the top event), such as a specific type of injury, accident, damage, or occurrence whose possibility is to be analyzed, is selected. The top event may be chosen from a known potentially hazardous condition, determined by a previous analysis (for example by a preliminary hazards analysis), an undesirable occurrence, or a specification requirement. (A few examples are shown in Fig. 9-4.) A specification requirement might state: "Reactor temperature will not exceed 600°C." (The designer prepared the specification on the basis that temperatures exceeding this level are undesirable and may lead to a potentially hazardous condition.) The top event for the fault tree might then be: "Reactor Temperature Exceeds 600°C." The analysis effort is then oriented to establishing those possible conditions, failures, errors, and other events which could contribute to or permit a temperature greater than 600°C to occur.

The analyst determines whether or not these contributory conditions and events must all occur (AND condition) to cause the top event or whether or not any of them alone can do it (OR condition). Then each contributory condition or event is analyzed further in the same way.

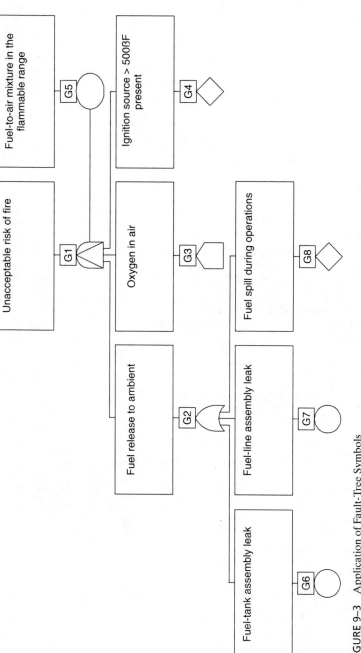

FIGURE 9–3   Application of Fault-Tree Symbols

SAMPLE TOP EVENTS FOR FAULT TREES

Injury to .
Radiation injury .
Inadvertent start of .
(Equipment to be named) activated inadvertently.
Accidental explosion of .
Loss of control of .
Rupture of .
Damage to .
Damage to   from .
Thermal damage to .
Failure of   to operate (stop) (close) (open).
Radiation damage to .
Loss of pressure in .
Overpressurization of .
Unscheduled release of .
Premature (delayed) release of .
Collapse of .
Overheating of .
Uncontrolled venting of   (toxic, flammable, or high-pressure gas).
(Operation to be named) inhibited by damage

FIGURE 9–4   Sample Top Events for Fault Trees

If this procedure is continued and laid out in a diagrammatic form, it will develop into a "tree" (which looks more like tree roots). As the tree proceeds down from the top event, "branches" are created. Proceeding down the tree and branches, an analyst can see what the contributing causes might be. Conversely, going up a branch indicates the effects resulting from any notation or combination below.

The symbols used by some fault-tree analysts are more extensive than shown or discussed in this chapter. For example, there are several gates in addition to the AND gate and the OR gate, and gates and events are numerically coded. In another usage, each box is numbered; a separate table is prepared in which the numbers listed contain more detailed information on that event, action, or condition. The safeguard action recommended can be described.

Fault-Tree Construction Rules.   There are several ground rules and procedural rules for fault-tree construction. One basic ground rule is to write a fault as a fault. This is a fault tree, and the events within the tree, except those normal events shown as a house, are fault events and should be written as faults. Procedural rules are: (1) no miracles, (2) complete the gate, and (3) no gate-to-gate lash-ups. "No miracles" simply means that what normally happens will happen and the analyst cannot invent some way out. "Complete the gate" means that the analyst completes all inputs to a gate before proceeding to develop the tree elsewhere. "No gate-to-gate lash-ups" means that there is always an intermediate event (placed in a rectangle) between gates.

Figure 9-5 shows the top levels of a fault-tree analysis of a powder-actuated fastener tool (similar to a nail gun) for the top undesired event, "PERSONNEL INJURY UPON FIRING OF TOOL." Three personal injury events are foreseen in the use of the tool on a prescribed underwater construction task of interest.[3] Personnel could be struck by the fastener, by fragment(s) of the workpiece, or by the tool itself. Each is developed using the FTA construction rules mentioned above. The first event, "PERSONNEL STRUCK BY FASTENER . . . ," has a path below it, through an AND gate and below it an OR gate. The OR gate output is FASTENER IN FREE FLIGHT; it has three inputs—INADVERTENT FIRING, FASTENER PASSES THROUGH WORKPIECE, FASTENER RICOCHET. These inputs are developed further elsewhere, as indicated by the transfer symbol. For example, the top event of a tree for INADVERTENT FIRING would transfer in to the same event shown at the triangle marked "1". Space does not permit showing the rest of the tree referred to by the transfer symbols. These transfers have trees at least as extensive as the top part of the tree shown in the figure. Thus, the reader can imagine why these are called "trees," because the logic causes the formation to spread wider at the base, giving the appearance of a Christmas tree triangular shape.

When all the branches and their interrelationships are considered, the analyst can arrive at all the possibilities of the top event occurring. Sometimes it may be desirable to analyze only one branch or sequence at a time. For example, in Fig. 9-5, the sequence on the tree beginning: "PERSONNEL IMPACTED BY TOOL UPON FIRING" has an OR gate with one input that is a restatement of the output. Below the restatement is an AND gate with two events as its input, "OPERATOR IN RECOIL PATH" and "SEVERE TOOL RECOIL." If both occur together, there is some probability of injury. That path leads directly to the top undesired event. Such a combination

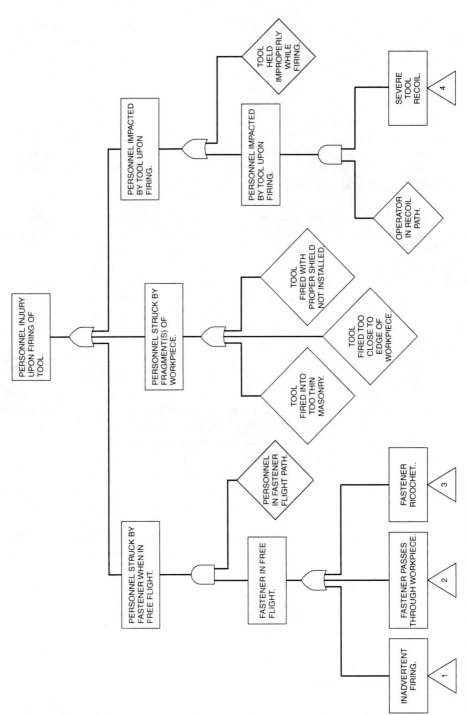

FIGURE 9–5 Powder-Actuated Tool—Partial FTA

of events that lead to the top is called a *cut set*. A minimal cut set is made up of the fewest events in a path to the top event.

Some times only one thing has to happen to reach the top undesired event. This is called a "single-point failure" and is a very undesirable system feature. There are four single-point failures in Fig. 9-5. Can you find them? (*Hint:* A single-point failure will have only OR gates between it and the top event). A tree can be evaluated qualitatively by finding all cut sets and ordering them by single, double, triple, . . . , *n*-point failures. In general, safer systems will have few, if any, low *n*-point failures. Single-point failure events must be examined most critically. Corrective action by a design change is often advisable, optimally by interposing an AND condition (such as a simultaneous action to be taken by an operator).

All of the possible sequences which could result in a top event, such as injury upon firing the tool, can be found. If a probability of each of the initiating bottom events is applied, it becomes possible to calculate the top events. Which sequence is most likely to occur can be determined. Or if there are two or more cut sets (sequences), their probabilities can be compared. If a probability of any calculated event is high or excessive, corrective steps could be taken to lessen it.

Quantitative Fault Trees

With a quantitative analysis, it is not correct to add the probabilities of the cut sets to obtain the overall probability of the top event. Too many duplications (redundancies) would distort the result. Therefore it is necessary to eliminate the redundancies by using Boolean mathematics (see Fig. 9-6). Sometimes the probability of an accident might be lessened adequately for acceptance by increasing the reliability of the parts and equipment involved. The probability of occurrence must be assessed and a determination made whether the risk probability of the event occurring is acceptable.

A redundancy exists when the same event is shown more than once (which may happen in two or more branches), or one event may be the subevent of another. Boolean mathematics permits elimination of redundancies. If it is not done, the ultimate probability value will be in error (Fig. 9-6).

When a quantitative analysis is to be made, each entry on a tree must be expressed in language or a symbol which permits a probability to be applied. Boolean mathematics is then used in writing and simplifying equations by which the probability of the top event can be expressed in terms of probability of the initiating events and their relationships.

FTA methodology can be applied to almost any system or operation. Very detailed analyses of very complex systems can extend down to the level of the individual component, human action, environmental effect, or hazardous characteristic to show their cause-and-effect relationships as they contribute to the potential problem which has been selected as the top event.

Fault Tree for Investigations

A fault-tree analysis can be used in accident investigation by selecting as the top event the accident which occurred. A tree could be prepared listing all possible contributing factors. These factors are then examined one by one to determine whether or not they

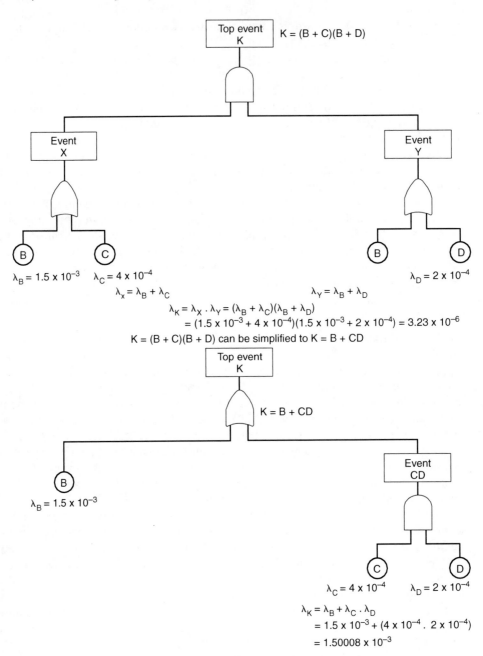

FIGURE 9–6 Correctly Calculating Quantitative Fault Trees

could possibly have occurred. If they had not been possible in the accident situation being analyzed, they are eliminated. The remaining events of the tree indicate what the initiating cause might have been. Probabilities assigned to each possibility would permit preparation of a list of priorities by which investigations for previously undetermined facts should be made. A generic, "universal" logic tree for accident investigations and safety program evaluations is Management Oversight Risk Tree (MORT). MORT is based on fault-tree analysis concepts.[4]

Limitations of Fault-Tree Analyses

One of the very few limitations of fault-tree analysis is that the tree indicates only the events included which will contribute to the occurrence of the top event. Should the analyst fail to include any possible event, the analysis is inadequate.

SAFETY ANALYSIS METHODS MANDATED FOR PROCESS SAFETY MANAGEMENT

Safety analysis techniques are now mandated by regulations for some industries. This program requirement is examined below, and the techniques it suggests that are not already covered in this chapter are described and explained.

In the mid-1990s, industries with processes that involved "highly hazardous chemicals" (HHCs) were placed under requirements by OSHA (29 CFR 1910.119) to conduct process hazard analysis and have a process safety management program.[5] The program is triggered by above-threshold quantities of any of 136 different, listed chemicals. The purpose of this standard is to prevent or minimize the consequences of a catastrophic release of toxic, reactive, flammable, or explosive highly hazardous chemicals from their use, storage, manufacturing, handling or on-site movement by industry.

The elements of a Process Safety Management Program (PSM) are shown in Table 9-1.

The importance of this standard is that it requires safety analysis and names certain analytic techniques to use or their equivalent. "The employer shall use one or more of the following methodologies that are appropriate to determine and evaluate the hazards of the process being analyzed. . . . What-if, Checklist, What-if/Checklist, Hazard and Operability Study (HAZOP), Failure Mode and Effects Analysis (FMEA), Fault Tree Analysis, or an appropriate equivalent methodology" [29 CFR 1925.64(e)(2)].

What-if.   In "What-if?" analysis, an analysis team reviews the covered process from beginning to end. At each step in the process they think of questions that begin with "What-if. . . ." They address procedural, hardware and software errors and produce a tabular listing of these questions and their answers. This constitutes a set of potential accident scenarios, their consequences, and remedial recommendations. Report form can be narrative, but use of a matrix table often provides clarity.

Checklist.   The "Checklist" method applies a list of specific items, usually taken from industry standards, consensus codes, industry guidelines, etc. The list is prepared by an experienced safety engineer, familiar with the covered process and the

TABLE 9–1 Elements of a Process Safety Management Program

Elements	Description
Process Safety Information	Requires compilation of written process safety information, including hazard information on HHCs, and information on technology and equipment of the covered process.
Employee Involvement	Requires a written plan of action for involving employees inthe conduct and development of process hazard analyses and process safety management, and for providing employees access to the information required by the standard.
Process Hazard Analysis	Specifies that process hazard analysis be conducted and updated and revalidated at least every five years. Must be retained for the life of the process.
Operating Procedures	Requires these be in writing and include clear instructions for safely conducting activities of the covered process. Steps for each operating phase, operating limits, safety and health considerations, and safety systems and their functions must be readily accessible to involved workers. They must reflect current operating practice, and must implement safe work practices for special circumstances such as lockout/tagout and confined-space entry.
Training	Operators of the covered process must be trained in the overview of the process and in the operating procedures. Training must emphasize specific safety and health hazards, emergency operations, and safe work practices. Refresher training is required at least every three years.
Contractors	Contract employers are required to train their employees to safely perform their jobs at the process site. Must document that employees received and understood training and assure that contract employees know about the potential process hazards and the worksite employer's emergency action plan. Must assure that contract employees follow safety rules of the facility. Must advise the worksite employer of hazards that contract work itself poses or hazards identified by contract employees.
Prestartup Safety Review	A safety review is required for new facilities and significantly modified work sites to confirm that the construction and equipment of a process are to design specs. Must assure that adequate safety, operating, maintenance, and emergency procedures are in place and that process operator training has been completed. For new facilities process hazard analysis must be performed and its outstanding action items resolved and safety implemented before startup. Modified facilities must meet management-of-change requirements.
Mechanical Integrity	Written procedures must be established and maintained for the ongoing integrity of process equipment, particularly those components which are part of a covered process.
Hot Work	Hot work permits must be issued for hot work operations conducted on or near a covered process.
Management of Change	Written procedures must be established and implemented to manage changes to facilities that affect a covered process. Employees must be informed of changes.
Incident Investigation	Requires employers to investigate as soon as possible, but no later than 48 hours, after incidents which did result or could reasonably have resulted in catastrophic releases of covered chemicals. An investigation team which includes at least one person knowledgeable in the process involved and others with knowledge and experience in incident investigation and analysis must develop a written report on the incident. Reports must be retained for five years.
Emergency Planning and Response	An emergency action plan must be developed and implemented. It must include procedures for handling small releases.
Compliance Audits	Employers must certify that they have evaluated compliance with process safety requirements at least every three years. Prompt response to audit findings and documentation that deficiencies are corrected are required. The two most recent audit reports must be retained.
Trade Secrets	Requires that certain information be available to employees. Employers may enter into confidentiality agreement with employees to prevent disclosure of trade secrets.

company's policies and procedures. The items are usually in form of a questionnaire to be applied to the covered process or system. Those parts of the design which are not adequate should be revealed when the checklist is applied. Then corrective measures are identified.

What-if/Checklist.   The What-if/Checklist Analysis uses the list of What-if questions and supplements it with a checklist. Therefore, it is a combination of the above two methods, as its name suggests.

Hazard and Operability Study (HAZOP).   HAZOP addresses each element in a process.[6] The elements must first be identified. The expected way each element operates is determined. Deviations from the intended or expected operations and parameters are identified using guide words. The consequences from the deviating element are estimated. Causes of the deviations, currently planned (or used) hazard controls, and inadequate controls are identified. The study is conducted by a team made up of five or six persons usually including a team leader familiar with HAZOP, a safety and health expert, a manager/supervisor, a technical person, a senior process operator, a maintenance person, a chemist, etc. The quality of the results will depend upon the quality of the team selected.

The team will start by collecting process information from piping and instrumentation diagrams (P&ID), written operating instructions, material safety data sheets, plant models, Safety Analysis Reports (SARs), etc. They then review each element step by step through each line or process. At each element they apply key words or guide words to tease out the potential deviations from normal expectations of a design parameter. The guidewords are shown in Table 9-2.

The hazard and operability consequences, if any, for each deviation are determined and documented. The actions or changes in plant methods which will prevent the deviation or reduce the consequences are identified. If the cost of the changes can

TABLE 9–2   HAZOP Guide Words

Key Word	Meaning	Comment
No/Not	Complete negation of design intention	No part of the design intention happens, e.g., "No flow," "No pressure," etc.
More, less	Quantitative increase or decrease	Refers to quantities, properties, and duration of design parameters, such as flow rate, temperature, etc.
As well as	Something else occurs in addition to design intention	Design intentions are achieved, plus additional things occur.
Part of	Only part of design is achieved	Partial addition or removal of material occurs. Activities are incomplete.
Reverse	The opposite of the design intention	Reverse flow of material, electrical current, voltage polarity. Backward installation (e.g., check valve), opposite chemical reaction (e.g., decomposition).
Other than	Complete substitution	Original design intention is not accomplished; a different activity occurs—e.g., leak, rupture.

be justified, the team then must agree on the change and who will be responsible for the action. The team then must follow up to make sure that the action has been taken. If the cost is not considered to be justifiable, the team must agree to accept the risk. One or more reports of the evaluation are made, usually including tabular representations of the results. Team decision making is at the heart of this methodology.

This technique as well as the others in this chapter are supported by software. The reader is advised to "surf the net" for the latest. Arthur D. Little Company is one source.[7]

Job Safety Analysis (JSA).   The purpose of this technique is to uncover and correct hazards which are intrinsic to or inherent in the workplace. It should be done with a team that includes the worker, supervisor, safety engineer, and management. Its success depends upon the rigor this team exercises during five steps: (1) Select a job, (2) Break the job down into steps, (3) Identify the hazards and determine the necessary controls of the hazards, (4) Apply the controls to the hazards, and (5) Evaluate the controls.

Eliminating, controlling, and minimizing hazards are becoming more and more necessary for work plants to comply with the standards of regulatory agencies. Formerly, chemical plants were built in which hazardous environments existed and where operators were safeguarded, theoretically, by use of protective equipment, such as gas masks, whose need was established after operations had begun. Some government agencies, such as OSHA, have adopted policies of "deterrence" and will not countenance the existence of hazardous conditions. Intrinsically safe environments are being required in which operators can work without the need for protective equipment, which is often inadequate, and which workers find burdensome and inconvenient and will not wear. To ensure that regulatory agencies do not require extensive and expensive retrofits of corrective equipment, it is highly advisable that analyses be made early to recognize potential problems and their solutions. The billions required to revise and correct designs and procedures at Three Mile Island and other nuclear power plants are a prime example of need for proper and adequate analysis and planning for safety purposes.

BIBLIOGRAPHY

[1] System Safety Society, *System Safety Analysis Handbook,* July 1993.

[2] Electric Power Research Institute and Science Applicatons International Corporation, *CAFTA for Windows Fault Tree Analysis System User's Manual,* July 1995.

[3] W. H. Muto, B. A. Caines, and D. L. Price, *System Safety Analysis of an Underwater Marine Tool,* VPISPO/NAVSWC-78-1, 91 pp., 1978

[4] D. Conger and K. Elsea, *MORT User's Manual,* 1998, Conger & Elsea, Inc., 9870 Highway 92, Ste. 300, Woodstock, GA 30188.

[5] "29 Code of Federal Regulations 1910.119, Process Safety Management of Highly Hazardous Chemicals," *Federal Register,* vol. 57, no. 36, Feb. 24, 1991.

[6] C. Bullock, F. Mitchell, and B. Skelton, "Developments in the Use of the Hazard and Operability Study Technique," *Professional Safety,* Aug.1991, pp. 33–40.

[7] Arthur D. Little, "HAZOPtimizer: Documentation and Reporting Software," 1991.

EXERCISES

9.1. For what purpose is a preliminary hazards analysis used? When should it be prepared? Describe the information that might be included.

9.2. For analysis of what type of problems is failure modes and effects analysis beneficial? What aspects does such an analysis not include?

9.3. Describe the steps in preparing a fault-tree analysis.

9.4. Give an example of a situation involving an AND condition for an event to occur. An OR condition.

9.5. How can the top events for fault trees be selected?

9.6. Following are hypothetical specification requirements for equipment. Indicate what the top event might be if a fault tree were prepared for each:

NO WORKER INJURY BECAUSE CRANE FAILS.

ELEVATOR IS NOT TO MOVE WHILE DOOR IS OPEN.

EMERGENCY BUTTON TO STOP OPERATION OF MACHINE.

9.7. What is a single-point failure? Give an example.

9.8. What is a cut set? What would be the relationship between a cut set and a single-point failure?

9.9. How can a fault-tree analysis be used for accident investigations?

9.10. What are the advantages of performing safety analyses before equipment is designed or purchased or an operation begun?

9.11. What are the elements of a Process Safety Management program? (*Note:* This program mandates that system safety analysis techniques be used.)

9.12. What is HAZOP? How is it performed?

CHAPTER 10

Pressure Hazards

On April 27, 1865, the side-wheeler steamer *Sultana* carried more than 2,000 Union soldiers, far more than her normal capacity, up the Mississippi. Many of the soldiers were eagerly hurrying home after being released from Southern prison camps. Quick repairs had been made to the vessel's leaky boilers at Vicksburg and again at Memphis. A few miles north of Memphis the boilers blew up, with an explosion heard miles away. It tore the *Sultana* apart, hurling men and parts of the vessels hundreds of feet. It was estimated that 1,600 to 1,700 died either from the explosion or from drowning. (No accurate determination of the number of men killed was possible because no passenger count had been made.) The pressures at which the Sultana's boiler normally operated, and even the pressure at which it ruptured so violently, would be considered low compared with pressures in common use today.

It is not necessary to have much pressure to have conditions where serious injuries and damage can occur. It is commonly and mistakenly believed that injury and damage will result only from high pressures. Actually, there is no agreement on the term "high pressure," beyond the fact that it is greater than normal atmospheric pressure.

A hurricane wind can drive a straw endwise into a tree or wooden telephone pole. Yet a 70-mile-per-hour wind exerts a pressure of only one-tenth of a pound per square inch (0.1 psi) (see Fig. 10-1); a wind of 120 miles per hour has a dynamic pressure of only 0.25 psi.

The American Gas Association indicates that a high-pressure gas distribution line is one which operates at a pressure of more than 2 psi. The American Society of Mechanical Engineers (ASME) rates only those boilers which operate at more than 15 psi as high-pressure boilers. OSHA standards state: "High-pressure cylinders mean those with a marked service pressure of 900 psi or greater." The military services and related industries have categorized above-atmosphere pressures as

Low pressure—1 atmosphere to 500 psia.
Medium pressure—500 to 3,000 psia.
High pressure—2,000 to 10,000 psia.
Ultrahigh pressure—above 10,000 psia.

Pressure: A physical force against a fluid. The unit force magnitude equals the unit pressure times the unit area the force covers. In the United States, the most common indication of pressure is in pounds per square inch (psi). Other units of pressure: pressures are often indicated in metric terminology, feet or inches of water, inches of mercury, atmospheres, and millibars of atmospheric pressure.

Standard water pressure: in the United States, one cubic foot of water weighs 62.4 pounds, which works out to be 4.33 pounds per square inch.

Standard atmospheric pressure: is 14.7 pounds per square inch.

Absolute pressure (psia): is pressure measured from the point at which no particles of any fluid exist to create a pressure. Absolute pressure is that of atmospheric pressure plus that indicated on a gage.

Gage pressure (psig): is that shown on a meter.

Static pressure: is pressure when the fluid is quiescent and the force it exerts is only that due to the gravitational weight of the liquid. Dynamic pressure is pressure exerted due to the kinetic-force movement of a fluid.

Water pressure: is often designated in heights of water above atmospheric. Such usages are generally expressed in feet or inches of water. Vacuum is the measure of pressure less than that of the standard atmosphere.

Stored pressure energy: the expansive energy contained in a fluid.

Pump: a device to increase the pressure of a liquid. A blower does the same for a gas.

Pressure regulator: a device to maintain a constant pressure or flow rate from a source whose pressure must be limited and which might change.

Accumulator: a device used to dampen pulsations in a fluid system.

Pressure relief valve: a device which permits discharge of fluid from a system if it exceeds a set value.

Rupture disk: a thin membrane which prevents flow in a fluid system until the membrane breaks because its designed rating is exceeded, permitting discharge of the fluid.

Ullage: the amount by which a cylinder falls short of being full, usually the amount of gas left to prevent any excessive increase because of a temperature rise.

FIGURE 10–1   Pressure Definitions

The term "high pressure" can therefore be almost any level prescribed for the equipment or system in use. For accident prevention purposes, any pressure system must be regarded as hazardous. Hazards lie both in the pressure level and in the total energy involved. Here, again, the hurricane can be used as an example: its relatively low pressure can exert a force against a building that can devastate the structure.

The term "high pressure" will therefore be used in this chapter in a comparative sense of any pressure greater than that of a standard atmosphere, but without any set quantitative value. Some fundamental precautionary measures to be used with pressure systems are given later in Fig. 10-4.

Pressure-Vessel Rupture

When the expansive force of a fluid inside a container exceeds the container's strength, it will fail by rupture. A slow rupture may also occur by popping of rivets or by the opening of a crack which provides passage for leakage of fluid. When bursting is rapid and violent, the result will be destruction of the container—frequently with fragmentation, and sometimes with generation of a shock wave. If personnel are in the vicinity, injuries could result from impacts from fragments. A shock wave produced by a rupture can produce blast effects similar to and as damaging as those generated by detonations. The rupture of a pressure vessel occurs when the total expansive force acting to cause the rupture exceeds the vessel's strength.

The process by which a boiler rupture occurs can be described as follows. When heat is applied to water in the boiler, its temperature increases to the boiling point, causing it to evaporate, and the steam to exert pressure. Generally the steam leaves the boiler and is replaced by new supplies of water. When the input of heat from the boiler equals that removed by steam flow, equilibrium is reached and pressure remains constant. If steam flow output is prevented or restricted so it is inadequate to remove all the excess heat supplied, the temperature and pressure in the boiler will increase. If inadequate supplies of fresh water are not provided, any water vapor can turn to dry gas and then increase in pressure. If a safety device is not provided or is inadequate to limit gas pressure to a safe value, the strength of the boiler might be exceeded, causing it to fail. (A boiler can also fail at normal pressures if its strength has been degraded in any way.)

Boilers are therefore equipped with safety valves, which permit pressures to be relieved if they exceed set values (Fig. 10-2). Low points in boilers are provided with fusible plugs. During normal operations the plugs are covered with water, which keeps them relatively cool. If the water level drops too far, the plugs become uncovered, are no longer protected by the water, get hot, and melt. This opens another path for relief of steam pressure.

UNFIRED PRESSURE VESSELS

On January 15, 1919, in Boston, Massachusetts, pressure destroyed a 50-foot-high, 90-foot-diameter tank full of molasses that was used for the fermentation of alcohol. The rupture loosed 2.3 million gallons of molasses into the streets, immediately killing a milkman in a horse-drawn wagon. The flood then knocked down track supports of an elevated railway, so that several persons riding there fell to their deaths. It took months to clean up the molasses. The plant owners were ordered to pay $1 million in damage claims.

Pressure vessels do not have to be fired to be hazardous. Inputs of heat can occur in other ways. The heat of the sun on outdoor pressure vessels is a common example. Portable cylinders, some of which at room temperature contain gases at pressures up to 2,000 psi when filled, should be stored only in shaded areas. (The vapor pressure of carbon dioxide is 835 psi at 70°F and 2,530 psi at 140°F; nitrous oxide is 745 psi at 70°F and 2,450 at 140°F.) Pressure vessels inside buildings should not be located near sources of

PRESSURE-RELIEVING DEVICES

Type	Use	Method of Operation
Safety valves	Gas or vapor	Safety valves are frequently called "pop" valves because they pop full open when a preset pressure is exceeded.
Spring-loaded		Opens when the total force, due to static pressure upstream of the valve, exceeds the preset force of a spring acting on the opposite side of a valve plug.
Weight-lever		The force on the plug closure is exerted by a lever on which weights are mounted. Combinations of lever-arm distances and weights provide a simple and reliable means of setting these devices. Their use is generally restricted to stream boilers operating at less than 100 psig.
Solenoid		Transducers sense pressure in the vessel being protected. If the established limit is exceeded, a signal is sent to energize a solenoid which opens the valve. Electrical power is required; if power fails, the device becomes inoperative. For this reason, use of solenoid-actuated safety valves is confined to noncritical service.
Pilot		This is a two-stage valve which overcomes the disadvantages of a large, single-stage direct-acting valve. A small pilot piston controls the area above the poppet of the valve. When the pilot opens, the pressure above the main poppet is reduced so that it rises off its seat. The valve has better control and its stability is better than a single-stage valve of similar capacity.
Relief valves	Liquids	Relief valves do not pop full open when a preset valve is exceeded, but open slightly and then open further as the pressure increases.
Spring-loaded		Similar to the spring-loaded safety valve, except that it is for liquid use and does not open fully when first activated.
Power-actuated		Movements to open or close are modulated and controlled entirely by an auxiliary source: electric, air, steam, or hydraulic power activated by a pressure sensor upstream of the valve.
Safety-relief valves	Liquid, gas, vapor	Can be used as either a safety valve or a relief valve, depending on the application.
Vacuum breaker	Air	Action is similar to that of a spring-loaded safety or relief valve, except that the atmospheric pressure outside the vessel, being higher than that inside, forces it open.

FIGURE 10–2   Pressure-Relieving Devices   Continued on page next page

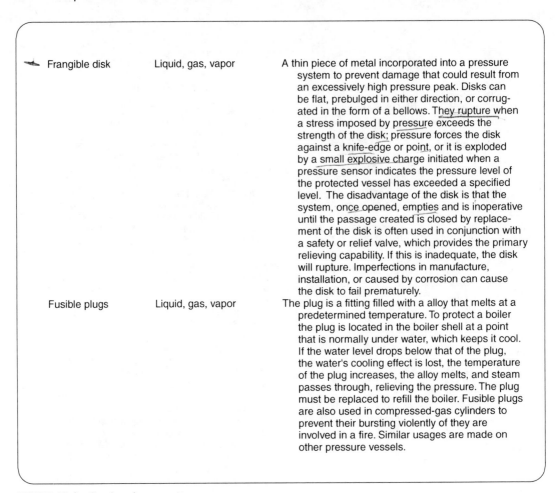

| Frangible disk | Liquid, gas, vapor | A thin piece of metal incorporated into a pressure system to prevent damage that could result from an excessively high pressure peak. Disks can be flat, prebulged in either direction, or corrugated in the form of a bellows. They rupture when a stress imposed by pressure exceeds the strength of the disk; pressure forces the disk against a knife-edge or point, or it is exploded by a small explosive charge initiated when a pressure sensor indicates the pressure level of the protected vessel has exceeded a specified level. The disadvantage of the disk is that the system, once opened, empties and is inoperative until the passage created is closed by replacement of the disk is often used in conjunction with a safety or relief valve, which provides the primary relieving capability. If this is inadequate, the disk will rupture. Imperfections in manufacture, installation, or caused by corrosion can cause the disk to fail prematurely. |
| Fusible plugs | Liquid, gas, vapor | The plug is a fitting filled with a alloy that melts at a predetermined temperature. To protect a boiler the plug is located in the boiler shell at a point that is normally under water, which keeps it cool. If the water level drops below that of the plug, the water's cooling effect is lost, the temperature of the plug increases, the alloy melts, and steam passes through, relieving the pressure. The plug must be replaced to refill the boiler. Fusible plugs are also used in compressed-gas cylinders to prevent their bursting violently of they are involved in a fire. Similar usages are made on other pressure vessels. |

FIGURE 10–2   Continued

heat, such as radiators, boilers, or furnaces. Vessels containing cryogenic liquids can absorb heat from normal environments that could cause boiling of liquids and very high pressures. Gas compression can cause an increase in temperature and very high pressures.

Aerosol cans and other pressurized containers might be thrown into a fire. Warnings on cans caution against disposing of cans in this way. Formerly, these cans would explode violently, but aerosol cans are now made with a low-melting-point alloy which acts as a fusible plug (see Fig. 10-2).

Excessive Pressures from Nonthermal Sources

A vessel or container can be overpressurized so that it fails. The simplest example is the bursting of a child's balloon. An automobile tire may normally be filled to a pressure of 30 psi. However, if it is filled from a tank which holds compressed air at 100 psi, there is the possibility the tire could be pressurized to a point at which it fails.

The *Safety Journal* (Vol. 29, No. 3) reported 11 cases where beer kegs became pressurized with carbon dioxide gas and exploded, causing eight deaths and much property damage. Although the system was a low-pressure one, many of the explosions were due to the lack of pressure-release devices, dirt in the regulator, or improper use of the regulating valve. Practically all pressure-vessel failures occur at flaws in the material where stresses are concentrated. If the flaw is serious enough, failure may occur at or below the normal operating pressure. If the vessel is overpressurized, it will fail at a weak point, where a flaw exists.

In September 1969 a high-pressure natural gas line near Houston, Texas, became blocked internally. The compressors kept packing gas into the line, raising the pressure until the line failed.

Another common source of injury is through pressure-gauge failure. In such instances, the thin-walled bourdon tube or bellows inside the case fails under pressure, generally because of metal fatigue or corrosion. Unless the case is equipped with a blowout back, the face of the gauge will rupture, propelling fragments toward the normal location of a person reading the gauge. A blowout back does not prevent failures but it ensures that no fragments will be propelled toward viewers. Boiler furnaces have blowout panels in case there is an explosion due to delayed ignition of unburned fuel gases.

DISCHARGES FROM SAFETY VALVES

To lessen the possibility of a rupture because of overpressurization, safety valves are often provided. Possible discharges from such valves should be conducted to locations where they constitute no danger, especially if the fluid discharged is very hot, flammable, toxic, or corrosive. On September 25, 1916, a tank car filled with gasoline was left in the freight yard at Ardmore, Oklahoma, where it remained for two days. The second day was sunny and hot. The gasoline vaporized, creating pressure in the tank so that the safety valve opened. Gasoline vapor escaped for several hours, blanketing the neighborhood and filling buildings with a combustible mixture. Ignition occurred, followed by an explosion. The flame was described as "fire bounding along the ground in streaks," with reports of clothing being ignited as far away as 350 feet from the tank car. All buildings within 400 feet were completely wrecked. Gasoline vapors spread through the streets so that buildings 1,200 feet away were damaged.

In 1973, a safety valve on a pressurized vessel at the El Segundo, California, plant of the Standard Oil Company opened, releasing oil over the surrounding neighborhood. Houses, cars, structures, vehicles, and the landscape far from the plant were contaminated by the windborne oil.

DYNAMIC PRESSURE HAZARDS

The pressures in cylinders of compressed air, oxygen, or carbon dioxide are over 2,000 psig when the cylinders are full. A large cylinder, such as that used for oxygen for oxyacetylene welding, will weigh slightly more than 200 pounds. The force or thrust generated by gas flowing through the opening left when a valve breaks off a cylinder can be 50 to 20 times greater than the cylinder weight. This can be compared to the propulsion system of a rocket or guided missile, which generally produces a thrust only 2 to 3 times the weight of the vehicle being propelled.

Spectacular accidents have occurred when such charged cylinders were dropped or struck so that the valve broke off. The cylinder took off, in some cases smashing through buildings and rows of vehicles, creating the tremendous havoc that a heavy steel projectile traveling at high speeds can generate. Computations indicate that if a valve is broken off, a cylinder filled to 2,500 psig can reach a velocity of 50 feet per second in 1/10 of a second. Safeguards to prevent accidents with pressure cylinders are presented in Fig. 10-4.

Whipping of Hoses and Lines

Whipping of flexible hoses can also generate injury and damage. In one instance, the end fitting of a compressed-air line was not tightened adequately when the line was connected. The line separated when it was pressurized. It then began whipping about until it hit and killed a worker by crushing his skull. Such types of accidents are not restricted to pressurized gas lines but may occur with water hoses as well. A whipping line of any kind can tear through and break bones, metal, or anything else with which it comes in contact. All high-pressure lines and hoses should be restrained from possible whipping by being weighted with sand bags at short intervals, chained, clamped, or restricted by all of these means. Rigid lines should be preferred to flexible hoses, but if the latter must be used, they should be kept as short as possible. Rigid lines should also be secured, especially at bends and fittings, since an accidental disconnection could cause even these lines to whip. Workers should be instructed never to attempt to grab and restrain a whipping line. The valve that controls flow to the line should be shut.

Other Effects

Failure to realize the consequences of flow from a compressed gas system can generate many injuries. No pressurized systems should be worked on. Each pressurized vessel or line should be considered hazardous until all pressure has been released. This can be done by checking a gauge directly connected to the container or line (after making sure that the gauge works and the valve to the gauge is open), by opening a test cock (without standing in front of it), or by noting the equipment or line is already open to the atmosphere.

An airman in a launch facility for a ballistic missile system was working on a nitrogen gas line that was pressurized to almost 6,000 psi. He failed to determine whether the line had been depressurized. He loosened the bolts of a flange, which separated slightly. A very thin sheet of compressed gas shot out, cutting into his leg like a knife.

Personnel have been warned that such effects could occur. If a pressurized line is suspected, no attempt should be made to use fingers to probe for a leak. They might be cut by the gas. A bit of cloth on a stick, a soap-and-water solution, or sprays specifically made for the purpose can be used with safety.

It has already been pointed out that a hurricane wind, with a pressure of only 0.25 psi, can drive a straw endwise into a wooden pole. Dirt, debris, fillings, and other particles can be blown by compressed gas, which would probably have a far higher pressure, into an eye or through the skin. OSHA standards permit compressed air to be used for cleaning purposes if its pressure is less than 30 psi (some states permit even less), if there is effective guarding against chips, and if personal protective equipment is used. The harm which can be done by indiscriminate use of compressed air at these pressures can be considerable. It should be general practice that compressed air never be used for cleaning clothes or anything near a person's body. The safeguards on compressed-air guns supposedly prevent chips, dirt, and other small particles from blowing back to the user. However, these particles can ricochet off equipment or walls back to the user, be driven by the jet into the skin, hit other nearby persons, or contaminate the environment.

Cases have been cited in which compressed air entered the circulatory system through cuts in the skin. A case cited by the Navy illustrates this:

> After washing some machine parts in a cleaning solvent, a mechanic held them in his hand and blew compressed air over them to dry them. He had a small cut on one finger. A little bit later, the man complained that he felt he was going to explode. Somebody took him to a hospital, where his trouble was diagnosed as air bubbles in his bloodstream. The cause was the compressed air striking the cut and entering his circulatory system. He recovered, but other people have died from this kind of injury.

A similar case was described in the TWA Safety Bulletin:

> In a Massachusetts plant, a woodworker, covered with sawdust, held the compressed air nozzle 12 inches away from the palm of his left hand and opened the valve. Before realizing what was happening, his hand swelled up to the size of a grapefruit. Severe shooting pains started from his finger tips to his shoulder. The most excruciating pain was in his head, as though the top of his head were coming off. When found, he was actually holding down the top of his head with one hand .... (Apparently the man recovered.)

It should also be a firm company rule that no person will direct a compressed air at any other persons, especially in horseplay. Even the restricted pressures permitted by OSHA can cause fatal injuries when applied to any body opening.

WATER HAMMER

Water hammer is caused by a sudden stoppage of liquid flow so that a shock effect occurs, which can cause the rupture of a line. The mass of liquid had momentum. If the flow is terminated abruptly by closing a valve at the downstream end of a line, the momentum of the liquid is transformed into a shock wave (water hammer) which is transmitted back upstream.

The shock is transmitted back through the liquid because liquids are practically incompressible. The energy shock involved may be adequate to break fittings and lines, especially if they are made of brittle materials which do not stand shock well. To avoid damage to liquid lines, the use of quick-closing valves should be avoided. If they must be used, the shock can be alleviated by a suitable air chamber or accumulator connected to the lines slightly upstream of the valve. The air in the chamber provides a cushion which can be compressed to absorb the energy of the water hammer.

A water-hammer problem can be recognized by its noise. It provides a warning that the problem exists. Failure to take remedial action may result in the violent rupture of a line, often with fragmentation that could cause injury to nearby personnel and equipment, or leaks at joints and fittings.

Ruptures during startups of steam lines are not uncommon. When a piece of steam equipment has been shut down, residual steam will condense. If it is not drained properly, the condensate remains as a liquid. When the steam is turned back on again, it may propel a slug of condensate ahead until it violently hits a bend, causing noise and possibly damage. Compressed-gas systems may accelerate dirt or debris inside a line to high speeds when the line is pressurized. Here again, the solid matter can cause rupture of a line and possible damage to downstream equipment.

NEGATIVE PRESSURE (VACUUMS)

The negative difference between atmospheric and below-atmospheric pressure or vacuum can be as damaging as a positive one, even when both are positive pressures in the absolute sense. Unintended vacuums or negative pressures can be extremely damaging, because structures involved may not be built to withstand reversed stresses.

In one instance, a large intercontinental ballistic missile was shipped in an aircraft from the high-altitude Denver location where it had been manufactured to the sea-level base where it was to be launched. The propellant tanks were sealed to prevent entrance of moisture or contaminants. There the internal pressure of the sealed-in air was that of the atmosphere at Denver. When the plant landed at the sea-level field, the ambient pressure was much higher. The difference in the two pressures caused the tanks to collapse, because they had not been built to sustain external loads.

Much of the damage done by high winds during hurricanes and tornadoes is due to negative pressures. Most building are designed to take positive loads but not to resist negative pressures. Such negative pressures might be generated on the lee side when winds pass over. Although the actual difference is very small, the area over which the total negative pressure will act is very large, so a considerable force is involved. For example, a roof on a small house may be 1,500 square feet. If the difference in pressure is only 0.05 psi, the force tending to tear off the roof equals $1500 \times 144 \times 0.05$, or 10,800 pounds (equivalent to 5 tons of weight).

Condensation of vapors is another source of vacuum pressure which could cause collapse of closed containers. A liquid occupies far less space than does the same weight of its vapor. A vapor which cools, such as steam, will liquefy, leaving water in the space which it occupied, and the partial pressure will decrease greatly. Unless the vessel is designed to sustain the load imposed by the difference between the outside and inside pressures, or unless a vacuum breaker is provided, collapse may occur.

TESTING OF PRESSURE SYSTEMS

Each pressure system should be tested prior to use, and pressure vessels should be tested periodically after that to determine their adequacy for continued service. Wherever possible, hydrostatic testing, using water and not a gas such as steam or compressed air, should be used. If the vessel being tested fails suddenly, the rapid expansion of gas might cause the rupture to be violent, possibly generating a blast wave with injury or damage. Hydrostatic testing, using water as a fluid, has two major advantages. Leaks created by pressurization of a vessel can be detected easily. The test can then be interrupted or continued with increased care. Because fluids expand little, in case of a vessel's rupture, no shock wave will be generated. Although the potential energy of the compressed water may be converted to kinetic energy, any fragments will be propelled for only small distances (far less than in a gas rupture).

Tests are usually conducted to proof pressures. A proof pressure test will generate stresses which should not exceed the yield strength of the container or its metal. Proof pressures are usually 1.5 or 5/3 times the maximum expected operating pressure (under nonshock conditions) of the vessel. Strain measurements indicate whether any permanent deformation remains after the pressure is released. Proof pressure tests may call for pressure to be increased to the required value, held for a specific time while it is being inspected, and then released and reinspected. Sometimes this cycle may have to be repeated.

Less common is the burst pressure test. When such a test is conducted, the vessel may leak because it will be stressed beyond its yield point and be permanently deforment, but it will not rupture. A vessel subjected to a burst pressure test cannot be reused for the function for which it was made. Burst pressure tests are therefore used only to test prototypes or a sampling of a large number being produced, to verify the adequacy of calculations and manufacture.

Nondestructive testing methods are also used to inspect pressure vessels. Dye penetrant, magnetic particle, radiography, and ultrasonics are some methods used. Many of these tests are used in conjunction with pressure testing, sometimes being made before and again after being subjected to the proof pressure.

If a flaw is located, it often becomes necessary to determine what corrective action should be taken. So many factors are involved in such a determination that only one recommendation can be made: Follow the recommendation of the inspector who made the tests.

LEAKS

Leaks are another possible hazard source. Possible causes of leakage can be categorized as follows:

- *Poorly designed systems or connections:* the possibility of leakage exists wherever there is a connection in a system containing a fluid. It is therefore advisable to keep the number of connections to a minimum. Elimination of short pipe segments and the use of welded lines are beneficial in this respect.
- *Separable connection:* where necessary, these should be selected with care, since certain types have greater tendencies to leak than others. The numerous designs of flanged, screwed, and mated fittings offer a broad variety suitable for any type of fluid, hazard involved, proposed system use, speed of separation, and cost.
- *Fluid contained:* the type of fluid in the system may influence the leakage hazard. Gases have a greater tendency to leak from or into a pressurized container than do liquids, but a liquid will be a greater problem where weight alone causes a leakage. Leakage will be less with higher-velocity fluids than with a fluid of low viscosity.

- *Inadequately fitted or tightened parts:* cross-threading and lack of adequate engagement of screwed parts are in this category. Bolts on flanged fittings or nuts on mated connections which are not tightened may permit separation of surfaces when pressure is applied. Lack of compression seals, gaskets, and packings will permit liquids and gas to leak. Failure to close valves adequately will allow fluids to flow through.

- *Fittings loosened by vibration:* this situation is especially likely where connections are in lines not secured against movement. Vibrations transmitted will not only loosen screwed connections but also lessen tension on nuts and bolts holding together flanges and other types of connections, open valves, and cause damage to seals, packings, and gaskets.

- *Cracks and holes:* these are caused by structural failure. Overpressurization can cause stresses in container walls, which can crack and open under tension caused by the pressure. Cracks may be generated where a sharp object scratches a metal surface. A hole can be caused by an impact by a sharp object on a container wall. A hole may be produced where the side of a hose or pipe vibrates against a hard surface.

- *Porosity:* metals may be porous or contain defective matter in which they were cast or welded, permitting the slow passage of fluid. Seals, packing, or gaskets may be materials that allow passage of fluid. Nonmetallic sheet materials used for diaphragms or containers may be permeable. Materials suitable as sealants for pressurized systems may be unsuitable for vacuum systems.

- *Corrosion:* corrosion can create holes which can extend entirely through the metal of a container. Corrosion can roughen surfaces so that passages exist where mating metal surfaces should create barriers to flow of fluid. Corrosion can weaken metals so that cracking and failures create openings. It can permit the failure of nuts, bolts, and other devices which hold connectors together.

- *Worn parts:* parts can wear out or be damaged during use. Disassembly and reassembly of parts can cause stripping of threads, cuts in gaskets, and damage to mating surfaces. Flexing of rubber and plastic hoses by changes in pressure, kinking and unkinking, or dragging them on rough surfaces will wear them out and cause them to leak. Continued exposure of nonmetallic materials to solar radiation can cause their deterioration and failure.

- *Interference:* dirt, contamination, or other solid materials can prevent close contact between faces of flanges, threads, gaskets, or other mating surfaces of connectors. Valves may not be able to seat properly in the closed position, allowing continued flow of fluid.

- *Overpressurization:* excessive pressures can cause overstressing of the container, possibly causing distortion, cracking, or separation, leading to leakage. It can increase the rate to flow through a hole so that formerly permissible leakage becomes unbearable.

- *Temperature:* higher temperatures may cause the loosening of connections where dissimilar metals are joined because of the difference in expansion. Increases in temperature will reduce viscosity so that systems may begin to leak. Organic sealants may begin to ooze out. Cold can cause organic materials to crack to permit flow of pressurized gases to areas where they may have adverse effects (as happened to one of the solid propellant boosters for the space vehicle *Challenger*).

- *Operator errors:* valves, drains, or other closure devices may not have been closed adequately to stop flow, or they may have been opened in error. Containers may have been overfilled so that a liquid reached a level where leakage or overflow occurs.

EFFECTS OF LEAKAGE

One of the chief effects of leakage is the release of fluids which are flammable, toxic, radioactive, corrosive, injurious, or damaging in other ways. The degree of hazard involved with each of these would be one factor in the determination of the amount of leakage permissible.

- *Materials contamination:* fluid leakage from a tank, hose, or other container can cause damage of materials with which the fluid comes in contact, even without creating other hazards. Leaks of oil or colored fluid may make fabrics or foodstuffs unusable. Contaminants in a container may degrade the purity of its contents so that it cannot be used—for example, oil leaking into a tank of gasoline.
- *Loss of stores:* leakage of containers can result in loss of material required for other operations or for economic purposes. Lubricants leaking from a bulk storage tank might create a fire hazard. Loss of oil by leakage from an engine may cause a lack of lubrication and consequent engine failure due to increased friction, wear, and heat.
- *Loss of system fluids:* certain items of equipment, such as hydraulic actuating devices, are dependent on the presence of an adequate supply of fluid. Depletion or loss of the fluid can make the system less effective by decreasing the response or by causing it to fail entirely.
- *Loss of system pressure:* some pressurized systems may not be able to maintain the level of pressure necessary for their operation. Pneumatic and vacuum systems fail or are less effective if leaks are present.
- *Electrical hazard:* water or other conductive fluids leaking into electrical connectors or onto live electrical equipment can cause short circuits. Water leaking onto floors near electrical equipment can increase the shock hazard to a person standing there. Rain leaking into a car's engine can prevent it from operating.
- *Temperature:* leakage of cold liquid on a hot surface can cause it to contract and crack; hot glass is especially susceptible. The presence of fluids leaked onto hot operating equipment can reduce its effectiveness by increasing heat loss. Leakage of warm air into refrigerated equipment may ruin food and increase operating costs. On cold equipment, the fluid may freeze and cause blockage of parts' movement or of heat flow.
- *Moisture:* leakage of moisture into an enclosed space may increase humidity to a point at which it becomes harmful to personnel, material, and equipment. Insulation wet from leakage will be degraded and lose its effectiveness.

LEAK DETECTION

Detection of massive leaks is generally comparatively easy, actual flow or its effects often being readily detectable. Jets of leaking liquids can be seen, splashes or pools of liquid can be noted, and losses can be measured. Containers can be equipped with liquid-level indicators or pressure devices to measure conditions inside the container, which will indicate losses and of leakage taking place. A container and its contents can be weighed to determine the extent of any leakage.

Discharges of gases can sometimes be noted by the whistling noises produced. Care should be taken to avoid probing with fingers for very high-velocity leaks from very high-pressure systems. Such thin, knifelike jets can be powerful enough to cut through skin and bone. A simple method for searching for invisible gas leaks is to use cloth streamers on a stick as indicators. The streamers are passed over a suspected area; any gas leak will cause the ribbons to flutter.

Very small leaks are more difficult to locate, but detectors are available for the purpose. Some are used for any type of gas or liquid; others have specific uses only. Soap solutions and bubbles are simple, cheap, and generally effective for small gas leaks. Initially, the unaided ear was used. Now, extremely small leaks can easily be detected by sonics and vibrations through electronically amplified devices.

Another method in common use is the addition of an odorant. Hazardous gases that lack odors are given one which is easily detectable. Other types of equipment usable as leak detectors: oxygen, combustible gas, infrared, ultraviolet, clathrate, and others. Leakage of a radioactive gas can be detected by a suitable detector of radioactivity.

A problem in determining the point of leakage is that pressure can cause temporary enlargement though which leakage occurs; but when the container empties and flow stops, it may be difficult to find where the leak took place. Pressure in a closed container may create stresses in its walls which expand gaps between gaskets or seals and metal surfaces, holes, or cracks. As pressure is reduced in the container by loss of fluid, any gaps, holes, or cracks may decrease in size or even disappear. Under such conditions, where the opening and leakage are small, it may be necessary to keep the system pressurized to determine where the leak is taking place. Only the minimal pressure necessary to determine any leakage should be used, since the small existing fault may lead to a complete rupture or failure of the container.

DYSBARISM AND DECOMPRESSION SICKNESS

Dysbarism is the collective name given to physical disturbances in the body caused by variations in pressure. Many of these disturbances result from, and are particularly damaging because of, rapid pressure changes. Some have been known by other names, although produced by the same two basic causes: (1) release from solution of gas in the blood and (2) expansion of free gas in the body cavities.

The amount of gas that will remain in solution in any liquid at any temperature is dependent on the partial pressure of the gas (Henry's law). This variation with pressure is especially true in the blood, where its temperature is almost constant. Gases in the bloodstream include oxygen, carbon dioxide, nitrogen, and other inerts. Oxygen and carbon dioxide are chemically bound to the red cells, oxygen more so than carbon dioxide. Nitrogen has the highest partial pressure of the gases present, but it is present in solution, not in chemical combination. Nitrogen is the chief contributor to dysbarism.

The partial pressure of nitrogen at sea level is 570 torr (mmHg). At pressures greater than that, an increased amount of nitrogen will enter solution; as pressures decrease, it will leave the blood. The rate at which it leaves the solution governs the severity of any problem that may arise. If the change in pressure takes place slowly, the free nitrogen has an opportunity to leave the body with no damage. As an underwater swimmer proceeds deeper, more and more of the gas breathed goes into solution in the blood. In this case, the increased gas in solution is not only nitrogen but also oxygen, which is in excess to that which goes into chemical combination in the blood cells. Ascent of the swimmer must be slow to permit the gas freed because of the decreasing pressure to be eliminated from the body.

Analyses of pressure effects indicate that obese or older persons are more prone to decompression sickness than are thinner and younger people. This is attributed to the greater amount of fat present in the obese or older person, in which nitrogen can dissolve. Fat will dissolve five times as much nitrogen as would the plasma of the blood. The central nervous system may also be disturbed by rapid and severe pressure changes, which may affect the person's ability to coordinate movements and to maintain equilibrium. The person may suffer from vertigo and disorientation, and sensory perception may be reduced. The person may become dizzy, suffer from headaches, and in extreme cases even suffer partial paralysis. These changes do not often result from changes in altitude, but they may occur in deep underwater swimming or when working under very high pressures. The pressure at a depth of 32 feet of water equals the entire height of the atmosphere, and swimmers have gone as deep as 700 feet. For such swimmers, changes in depth must be made with care if damage to the body is to be avoided.

Bends is an ailment involving pain in the joints, muscles, or bones (which results in the limb affected being held in a bent position from which it is difficult to straighten, hence the name), generally considered to be caused by the formation of gas bubbles. Bubbles will form when the rate of gas release from the blood and tissue is greater than its rate of elimination from the body, generally through the respiratory passages and lungs. Studies of symptoms indicate that the principal locations of bends are the knees, shoulders, elbows, and wrists. The reason for the localization in these areas is not yet clear; it has been theorized it may be due to the positions of the joints, restriction of circulation, deposits of fat, and other restrictions.

Effects similar to those of bends have been given other names: caisson disease and decompression sickness. Caisson disease was the earliest to become a problem, occurring to workers under air pressures much greater than 1 atmosphere. When the pressure was rapidly reduced, such as when workers went too quickly from a pressurized to an unpressurized environment, they suffered pains and symptoms similar to bends. In addition, they might have skin itch or rash, visual defects, difficulty in breathing, or paralysis. The first pressurized caisson was used in England in 1851, but it was in an operation after that the first man died of caisson disease after working under a pressure of 40 psi (88 feet). Of 600 men working on the foundations of the St. Louis Bridge over the Mississippi, 119 suffered from the disease, 14 of whom died.

Decompression sickness is a general term which includes bends (due to a rapid ascent from great depths of water), caisson disease (due to a rapid decrease from high air pressure to 1 atmosphere), and aeroembolism (due to a rapid decrease in pressure from altitude). It differs slightly from dysbarism, which also includes the effects caused by differences in pressures between gases trapped in body cavities and barometric pressure.

Chokes are believed to be due to expansion in the lungs and respiratory passages because of the pressure of gas released. This may cause difficulty in breathing, coughing, and pains in the chest which may vary from a tightness to a burning sensation. Skin disturbances include rashes and discoloration. Rashes occur principally on the abdomen, thighs, and chest, where there are considerable amounts of fatty tissue. Rashes are usually accompanied by pain and itching and a coloration which varies from light red to purple-red. This is believed to be due to dilation of blood vessels in the skin by the gas released from the blood. In especially severe cases, such as may occur from caisson disease or ascents from great depths of water, bleeding into the tissues may result. Rashes and mottling are regarded as signs of danger. Other effects are itching and prickling of the skin, sensations of hot or cold, or release of tissue fluids immediately under the skin.

Aeroembolism concerns the same problem; however, it is induced by rapid changes in pressure where the barometric pressure is one atmosphere or less. It first became apparent with the use of aircraft capable of rapid ascents to high altitudes. Aeroembolism involves one factor which may cause it to be more damaging than that of caisson disease. At higher altitudes, not only will gases physically come out of solution, but oxygen will be released from its combination within the red cells. Ebullism, or boiling of body fluids, occurs at altitudes of 63,000 feet or more, when pressure inside the body is less than 5 torr.

Gas in Body Cavities

Free gas within the body cavities also may cause pain and injury to persons subjected to rapid changes in pressure. One of the commonest symptoms is the "stuffed" feeling or pain in the ears caused by blockage of the Eustachian tube. This tube connects the middle ear with the pharynx at the back of the mouth. Blockage prevents equalization of the air pressure on the opposite sides of the ear drum, causing distention of the ear drum and pain in the ear. If the blockage is partial, movement of the jaws may be adequate to clear the tube and relieve the pain. Temporary but complete blockage may occur when a person has a cold or sinus trouble. Rapid changes in pressure during an illness may be dangerous, and such experiences as flying, underwater swimming, or activities under elevated pressures should be avoided. A decrease in altitude from 8,000 to 3,000 feet causes an increase in barometric pressure of 2.25 psi. Swimming to a depth of a little more than 5 feet will produce the same effect.

Pressure changes can also cause pain in the teeth. It may be a dull ache or a sharp, severe pain. In some cases, fluid in the mouth may enter under fillings as altitude changes, causing the pain. It is also believed that other instances were "referred" pains (pains which seemed to originate in the teeth, but were actually due to sinus troubles).

Expansion of gas in accordance with Boyle's law in abdominal cavities, such as the stomach, colon, and bowel, may cause "gas pains." This is almost always due to an increase in altitude and a decrease in barometric pressure. When bloating and pains do occur, they generally appear during ascent or soon after. The gas is mostly nitrogen from air which was swallowed, and from changes in food in the digestive system, with some diffusion of oxygen and carbon dioxide from the bloodstream. Pains often disappear immediately with passing of wind or belching.

Effects on Bone

Nitrogen released in the arteries may block the flow of blood to the bones. Unless the block is removed, the portions of bone affected may begin to deteriorate from lack of nourishment and oxygen. This effect is known as aseptic necrosis. If the block is not removed, a new blood passage will form to the bone to feed the cells there. However, sudden shocks and pressures before the bones heal can cause pieces to break off. The problem is especially critical when it involves a joint, so that permanent crippling results. Aseptic necrosis itself is not painful, so symptoms may appear only after six months to a year after repeated attacks of bends.

Decompression Injury Prevention

Decompression sickness (or one of the variants mentioned) is normally not a problem with atmospheres of less than 18 psig. OSHA Regulations for Construction require that preventive measures be undertaken for persons who have been subjected to pressures of 12 psig or more. The time required for decompression from this and higher pressures depends on the pressure and the duration of the exposure. The OSHA regulations include tables and other information which must be followed for decompression without adverse effects.

Soon after the reasons for decompression sickness were postulated, it was found that the only remedy was to resubject the victim to high air pressure. Each construction site involving operation in compressed air at pressures greater than 12 psig must have completely equipped locks for compression and decompression through which crews can enter and leave the work area, and also a medical chamber for emergencies. If any worker appears to have symptoms of decompression sickness, the worker is put into the medical chamber and subjected once again to the pressure at which he or she had been working. Decompression is then carried out very slowly, since bubbles once formed are difficult to dispose of. The recompression will, however, reduce the bubbles' size so the effects are mitigated.

Each compressed-air worker must be provided with an identification badge which the worker is to wear at all times. The badge must have the employee's name, address of the medical chamber, telephone number of the physician in charge, and instructions that in case of an emergency of unknown or doubtful cause or illness, the worker can be rushed to the medical chamber.

COMPRESSED-GAS CYLINDERS

The widespread use of compressed gases in portable cylinders makes it advisable that safety engineers be familiar with their characteristics, hazards, safety features, and precautionary measures which should be observed in their use. The properties of most of the gases generally transported and handled in portable cylinders are listed in Fig. 10-3.

The gases drawn from cylinders are stored therein in one of three ways: permanent gases, liquified gases, and dissolved gases.

Permanent Gases

Permanent gases have boiling points of −150°F or lower. At room temperatures they cannot be liquefied, no matter how high the pressure. Oxygen, nitrogen, and helium are examples of permanent gases.

Liquefied Gases

Liquefied gases liquefy at temperatures of −130°F or higher at 1 atmosphere, but can be liquefied and maintained as liquids at higher pressures. Such gases include propane, chlorine, and butane. Carbon dioxide is also in this category but becomes a solid rather than a liquid. Opening the valve of a cylinder in which a liquefied gas is stored permits gas to vaporize and flow out and additional liquid to evaporate. The pressure of a gas in the cylinder will depend on the vapor pressure of the liquid, which, in turn, depends on the liquid's temperature.

Dissolved Gases

Only one common gas, acetylene, is used as a dissolved gas in cylinders. Acetylene will decompose and explode violently at pressures between 15 and 16 psig. Acetylene cylinders are therefore filled with calcium silicate, an inert porous material, which is then saturated with acetone. Acetylene is then pumped into the cylinder, where it goes into solution in the acetone. Acetone will hold 35 times its own volume of acetylene. The maximum pressure for such cylinders is 250 psig at 70°F. The acetylene should not be drawn from the cylinder at a pressure greater than 15 psig.

Sizes and Volumes

Compressed-gas cylinders vary in size, the smallest being 2 inches O.D. by 15 inches long. The size most commonly seen in industrial plants is 51 inches high with an outside diameter of $8\frac{1}{2}$ or 9 inches. Cylinders of nitrogen and acetylene have larger diameters.

The volume, weight, and pressure of gas loaded into a cylinder varies with its characteristics. The pressure at which a permanent-gas cylinder may be filled is marked on the shoulder of the cylinder. A marking of D.O.T. 3A-2000 indicates that the cylinder, produced in accordance with D.O.T. Specification 3A, is designed for a filling pressure of 2,000 psig at 70°F. Cylinders with nonflammable gases such as nitrogen and helium may be overfilled to a pressure of 10 percent greater. The pressure in a permanent-gas cylinder will decrease in proportion to the amount of gas used. The

PRESSURIZED-GAS CHARACTERISTICS

Gas	Formula	Boiling Point (°F)	Cylinder Pressure (psig)	Physical State in Cylinder	Specific Volume (ft³/lb)	Flammability L.F.L–U.F.L (%)	Toxicity	Odor	D.O.T. Label	Other Hazards
Acetylene	C_2H_2	Sublimes	250	In Solution	14.7	2.5–81	Slightly narcotic	Garlic like	Red gas	
Air		–312.7	2,640 max.	Gas	13.3		Nontoxic	None	Green	High pressure
Allene	C_3H_4	–30.1	102	Liquid	9.6	2.1	Probably anesthetic	Sweet	Red gas	
Ammonia	NH_3	–28.0	114	Liquid	22.6	15–28	TLV, 50 ppm; dangerous through inhalation and body contact	Pungent, irritating	Green	
Argon	Ar	–302.6	1,875 max.	Gas	9.7	—	Suffocation only	None	Green	High pressure
Arsine	AsH_3		90	Gas	5.0	Limits unknown	Highly toxic; TLV, 0.05 ppm	Garlic like	Poison and red gas	
1,3-Butadiene	C_4H_6	24.06	22	Liquid	6.9	2–11.6	Slightly anesthetic; TLV, 1,000 ppm	Mildly aromatic	Red gas	
Butane	C_4H_{10}	31.1	16.3	Liquid	6.4	1.9–8.5	Slightly anesthetic	Faintly disagreeable	Red gas	
1-Butene	C_4H_8	20.7	24	Liquid	6.7	1.6–9.3	Slightly anesthetic	Slightly aromatic	Red gas	
Carbon dioxide	CO_2	–109.3	830	Liquid	8.8	—	Suffocation; TLV, 5,000 ppm	None	Green	
Carbon Monoxide	CO	–312.7	1,500 max.	Gas	13.8	12.5–75	Chemical asphyxiant; TLV, 50 ppm	None	Red gas	
Carbon sulfide	COS	–58.4	160	Liquid	6.5	11.9–28.5		Rotten eggs	Red gas	
Chlorine	Cl_2	–30.1	85	Liquid	5.4	—	TLV, 1 ppm; by inhalation + contact	Pungent, irritating	Green	Supports combustion

FIGURE 10–3   Pressurized-Gas Characteristics   Continued on next page

PRESSURIZED-GAS CHARACTERISTICS

Gas	Formula	Boiling Point (°F)	Cylinder Pressure (psig)	Physical State in Cylinder	Specific Volume (ft³/lb)	Flammability L.F.L–U.F.L (%)	Toxicity	Odor	D.O.T. Label	Other Hazards
Chlorine trifluoride	ClF_3	53.15	6	Liquid	4.2	–	TLV, 0.1 ppm; by inhalation + contact	Sweet, irritating	White	Highly reactive
Cyanogen	$(CN)_2$		60	Liquid	7.4	6–32	TLV, 10 ppm	Pungent; almond like	Poison gas	
Cyclopropane	C_3H_6	–27.15	75	Liquid	9.2	2.4–10.4	Anesthetic; TLV, 400 ppm	Ethereal	Red gas	
Dimethyl ether	$(CH_3)_2O$	–12.68	60	Liquid	8.4	3.4–18.0	Anesthetic	Slightly ethereal	Red gas	
Ethane	C_2H_6	–127.53	543	Liquid	12.8	3.0–12.5	Suffocation only	None	Red gas	
Ethyl chloride	C_2H_5Cl	54.3	5	Liquid	6.0	3.8–15.4	TLV, 1,000 ppm	Pungent, ether like	Red gas	
Ethylene	C_2H_4	–154.7	1,200	Gas	13.8	2.7–34	Anesthetic	Sweet	Red gas	High pressure
Ethylene oxide	C_2H_4O	51.3	35 max.	Liquid	7.7	3.0–100	TLV, 50 ppm	Irritating	Red	
Fluorine	F_2	–306.6	300	Gas	10.2	–	TLV, 0.1 ppm	Sharp, penetrating	Red gas	Highly oxidizing; no safety relief device
Helium	He	–452.0	2,120 max.	Gas	96.7	–	Suffocation	None	Green	High pressure
Hydrogen	H_2	–423.0	2,400 max.	Gas	192.0	4.0–7.5	Suffocation	None	Red gas	High pressure
Hydrogen Chloride	HCL	–121.0	613	Liquid	10.9	–	TLV, 5 ppm; by inhalation and contact	Pungent, suffocating	Green	
Hydrogen fluoride	HF	67.1	1	Liquid	17	–	TLV, 3 ppm; inhalation and contact	Sharp, penetrating	Corrosive	Highly irritating
Hydrogen sulfide	H_2S	–75.3	252	Liquid	11.2	4.3–45	TLV, 10 ppm	Rotten eggs	Red	

FIGURE 10–3 Continued

PRESSURIZED-GAS CHARACTERISTICS

Gas	Formula	Boiling Point (°F)	Cylinder Pressure (psig)	Physical State in Cylinder	Specific Volume (ft³/lb)	Flammability L.F.L–U.F.L (%)	Toxicity	Odor	D.O.T. Label	Other Hazards
Isobutane	iso-C_4H_{10}	10.9	31	Liquid	6.5	1.8–8.4	Slightly anesthetic	Faintly sweet	Red gas	
Isobutylene	C_4H_8	19.6	24	Liquid	6.7	1.8–9.6	Unknown, probably anesthetic	Faintly Coal gas	Red gas	High pressure
Krypton	Kr	–243.2	590 max.	Gas	4.6	–	Suffocation	None	Green	High pressure
Methane	CH_4	–258.9	602 max.	Gas	23.7	5.0–15.0	Suffocation	None	Red gas	High pressure
Methyl bromide	CH_3Br	38.2	13	Liquid	4.1	10.0–15.0	TLV, 20 ppm; inhalation and contact	Chloroform like	Poison	
Methyl Chloride	CH_3Cl	–11.36	59	Liquid	7.6	7.0–17.4	TLV, 100 ppm	Faintly sweet	Red gas	
Methyl-mercaptan	CH_3SH	42.7	11	Liquid	7.5	3.9–21.8	TLV, 10 ppm	Extremely disagreeable	Red gas	No safety relief device
Monomethyl-amine	CH_3NH_2	20.6	29	Liquid	12.1	4.2–20.8	TLV, 10 ppm	Strong ammoniacal	Red gas	No safety relief device
Natural gas	Mixture		2,400 max.	Gas	24.0	3.8–17	Suffocation	Depends on odorant	Red gas	High pressure
Neon	Ne	–410.6	2,070 max.	Gas	19.2	–	Suffocation	None	Green	High pressure
Nitric oxide	No	–241.1	500	Gas	12.9	–	TLV, 25 ppm	Slightly irritating	Poison gas	Highly reactive
Nitrogen	N_2	–320.46	2,640 max.	Gas	13.8	–	Suffocation	None	Green	High pressure
Nitrogen dioxide	NO_2	70.1	0	Liquid	4.7	–	TLV, 5 ppm	Slightly irritating	Poison gas	Highly reactive
Nitrous oxide	N_2O	–129.1	745	Liquid	8.7	–	Anesthetic	Sweet	Green	High oxidizing
Oxygen	O_2	–297.4	2,640 max.	Gas	12.1	–	–	None	Green	High oxidizing; high pressure

FIGURE 10–3   Continued

PRESSURIZED-GAS CHARACTERISTICS

Gas	Formula	Boiling Point (°F)	Cylinder Pressure (psig)	Physical State in Cylinder	Specific Volume (ft³/lb)	Flammability L.F.L–U.F.L (%)	Toxicity	Odor	D.O.T. Label	Other Hazards
Phosgene	$COCl_2$	45.6	11	Liquid	3.9	–	TLV, 0.1 ppm	Musty hay	Poison gas	
Propane	C_3H_8	–43.8	110	Liquid	8.7	2.2–9.5	TLV, 1,000 ppm	Faintly disagreeable	Red gas	
Propylene	C_3H_6	–53.9	137	Liquid	9.4	2.4–10.3	Suffocation	Faintly sweet	Red gas	
Sulfur dioxide	SO_2	14	34	Liquid	5.9	–	TLV, 5 ppm	Pungent, irritating	Green	
Sulfur hexafluoride	SF_6	–59.4	310	Liquid	2.5	–	Suffocation	None	Green	
Trimehthylamine	$(CH_3)_3N$	37.17	13	Liquid	6.0	2.0–12	TLV, 10 ppm; inhalation and contact	Fishy	Red gas	No safety relief device
Vinyl chloride	C_3H_3Cl	7.0	34	Liquid	6.2	4.0–22	Unknown; probably anesthetic	Pleasant	Red gas	Carcinogen
Vinyl fluoride (inhibited)	C_2H_3F		355	Liquid	8.4	Unknown	Unknown; probably anesthetic	Sweet	Red gas	
Vinylmethyl ether (inhibited)	C_3H_8O	42.8	28	Liquid	6.7	Unknown	Unknown; probably anesthetic	Sweet	Red gas	
Xenon	Xe	–162.4	503 max.	Gas	2.9	–	Suffocation	None	Green	High pressure

*TLV of vinyl chloride was 500 ppm until it was determined vinyl chloride is a carcinogen. The matter is being studied at this time to determine whether a maximum should be set or no exposure permitted

FIGURE 10–3   Continued

PRECAUTIONARY MEASURES FOR USE WITH
COMPRESSED-GAS CYLINDERS

1.   Compressed gas-cylinders should be operated and handled only by personnel who have been instructed in proper procedures for their use and in the hazards involved.

2.   Personnel using the contents of a compressed-gas cylinder should be familiar with the properties of the contents, the hazards involved, and precautionary and emergency measures to be taken for those hazards.

3.   Cylinders should not be banged, dropped, or permitted to strike each other or against other hard surfaces.

4.   Cylinders should be secured by chain to a fixed support to prevent them from being dropped or from falling over. The cylinder valve should never be opened unless the cylinder is secured, since the thrust from the gas might cause the cylinder to fall.

5.   Cylinders should not be dragged, slid, or rolled. Small cylinders may be carried by one man; larger ones by two men or by a suitable truck on which the cylinder can be secured firmly.

6.   Cylinders should be protected from anything that will cut, gouge, or damage the metal and reduce the strength of the cylinder. No one should bang the cylinder with a hard object to determine how full it is.

7.   Protective caps should be kept on the cylinders wherever the cylinders are not in use, or are to be transported from one place to another.

8.   The cylinder valve should be kept closed wherever the cylinder is not in actual immediate use.

9.   Cylinders should be protected against heat, which would increase the gas temperature and pressure. Outdoors they should be stored in shaded locations and not where direct rays of the sun could hit them. They should not be stored near other sources of heat, such as boilers, furnaces, radiators, or hot process equipment.

10. Cylinders should not be stored near sources of ignition or near flammable materials such as oil, gasoline, or wastes. Cylinders containing flammable gases should not be stored near cylinders containing oxygen or other oxidizers. Inside a building, there should be a separation of at least 20 feet between oxygen and fuel-gas cylinders unless there is a fire-resistive partition between the two. Cylinders should not be permitted to come in contact with electrical circuits.

11. No tampering of safety relief devices should be permitted, and no attempt should be made by the user to remove, repair, or modify cylinders, valves, or safety relief devices. In case of any problems, the cylinder should be capped and returned to the supplier.

12. The user should examine the label and markings on the cylinder prior to connection to make certain that it contains the gas he intends to use. Any cylinder whose content is not positively identifiable by markings should be returned to the supplier.

13. The cylinder valve should be opened slowly and the valve and fittings watched closely for signs of leaks. If the valve leaks, it should be closed, and the cylinder stored in a location where leakage will not constitute a hazard, marked as leaking, and returned to the supplier.

FIGURE 10–4   Precautionary Measures for Use with Compressed-Gas Cylinders   Continued on next page

14. If a valve sticks, never hit it with a hard object to loosen it. Return the cylinder to the supplier.

15. Acetylene cylinders should always be kept in an upright position -to avoid loss of the acetone in which the acetylene is dissolved.

16. Acetylene should not be used at pressures exceeding 15 psi.

17. Oil, grease, or other combustible material should never be used to lubricate or clean valves, regulators, gauges, or fittings on cylinders holding oxygen or other oxidizer.

18. Before an attempt is made to remove a regulator from a cylinder, make certain the regulator is depressurized by closing the cylinder valve and releasing all pressure from the regulator.

19. When a toxic or highly reactive gas is to be used, a cylinder holding the smallest amount necessary for the operation should be used.

20. Cylinders should not be kept in unventilated enclosures such as cabinets or lockers.

21. Fuel-gas cylinders with total capacities exceeding 2,000 standard cubic feet or 300 pounds of liquefied petroleum gas should not be kept inside a building except when in use or ready for immediate use.

FIGURE 10–4   Continued

cylinder should be considered empty when it is down to 25 psig. Empty cylinders should be marked with a tag or label or the letters "MT" on the side of the cylinder.

Since acetylene should not be used at a pressure greater than 15 psig, the rule considering a cylinder empty at 25 psig does not hold. Acetylene, especially for welding, is generally used at a pressure of 5 to 8 psig. A cylinder can be considered empty when it no longer provides an adequate supply of gas.

Cylinders loaded with a liquefied gas are not filled completely; a small vapor space is left for expansion (ullage). This is accomplished by prescribing the "filling density" that is permitted. The filling density is the ratio (expressed as a percentage) between the weight of the liquid to be loaded and weight of water which would totally fill the cylinder. A liquefied-gas cylinder should also be considered empty when its pressure reaches 25 psig. Figure 10-4 lists precautions.

Markings

Each cylinder must be marked with its chemical name to indicate its contents. The name must be applied by a means not readily removable; it may be stenciled or stamped or printed on a label. If the cylinder is to be shipped by an interstate carrier, it must also carry a pertinent D.O.T. label. In addition, other labels are frequently added with a warning of the hazard involved and precautionary measures that should be taken.

HIGH-PRESSURE SYSTEMS (PNEUMATIC AND HYDRAULIC)

1. All personnel who maintain, repair, or operate pressure equipment should be familiar with their hazards and the precautionary measures which must be observed.

2. Only qualified and authorized personnel should install, maintain, repair, adjust, or operate pressure system equipment, especially the safety devices involved.

3. Personnel assigned to work on pressure systems should be familiar with the locations and purposes of control valves, and with procedures for emergency depressurization.

4. Pressurized equipment and lines should be depressurized before any repairs are attempted or any effort made to loosen or open any parts. Pressure vessels and lines should be considered hazardous until it has been absolutely determined that all pressure has been released. Personnel should themselves ensure that a system is depressurized either by checking a gauge connected to the immediate line or equipment, by opening a test cock, or by noting that a disconnection in a line already exists. A pressurized line should not be bled by loosening a fitting.

5. All pressure-system components should be marked to indicate their rated pressure and direction of flow.

6. Face shields or goggles should be worn by all persons working on or with pressure systems.

7. Compressed air at pressures greater than 30 psig should not be used to clean filings, shavings, or other solid particles from work areas or from equipment unless protective equipment is worn. Compressed air should not be used to clean clothing or parts of the body.

8. Compressed air should never be directed at another person or used in horseplay.

9. Pressure systems being installed or repaired should be kept clean and free of dirt or debris, which might be accelerated to high speeds in the lines and cause internal damage to piping or equipment.

10. Rigid lines should be used where possible, instead of flexible hose. Lines should be secured on both sides of a bend, at suitable intervals along straight runs, and near connection fittings.

11. Where a flexible hose is necessary, it should be as short as possible. It should be adequately clamped (preferably) or chained to a secure fixture of strength adequate to restrain the hose in case it breaks. A long hose should be weighted down with 100-pound lead weights (preferably) or sandbags, or otherwise secured along its length, at 6-foot intervals. The entire length of the hose should be contained by a structural system separate from the hose, but in no way interfering with its normal flexibility.

12. Hose should not be used at a pressure greater than its manufacturer's rating. The hose should be checked to determine whether it is intended for use at the pressure desired. Hoses and fittings should meet appropriate industry or governmental standards. When not in use, hose should be plugged or capped and stored in a designated location where it will not be subject to deterioration.

13. No pressure line should be used as a step.

14. Pressure vessels, hoses, lines, and other equipment should be tested periodically and at the pressures indicated in prescribing regulations, codes, or standards.

15. No system requiring a pressure regulator, pressure-reducing valve, safety valve, or other relieving device should be activated unless it is in place and in operable condition. Only qualified and authorized personnel should change the settings on these valves and regulators. Where changes are made, the valves should then be tested to be certain that they are operating at the desired settings.

16. Each high-pressure vessel and any line which could be closed off should be equipped with a suitable relieving device. There should be no shutoff valve between the vessel or line and the relieving device. The relieving device must be sized to permit flow which will keep pressure to a safe level.

17. Safety and relief valves should be tested at prescribed intervals. Test levers should be left unsecured so that the valve will operate freely. Leaking valves should be replaced. The discharge from a pressure-relieving device must be sized to permit flow which will keep pressure to a safe level.

18. Valves should be checked periodically to ensure that they will work adequately and safely under the pressures which will exist in the systems in which they are installed. Valves should not be installed in an inverted position, since they might fill with debris and be impossible to close.

FIGURE 10–5   High-Pressure Systems (Pneumatic and Hydraulic)   Continued on next page

19. Valves should be used only in the manner for which they are designed. Gate valves should be used only in the fully opened or fully closed positions.

20. Where possible, valves should be installed in fail-safe configurations so that any valve failure will result in the safest possible condition for the system.

FIGURE 10–5   Continued

Cylinders are often color-coded. Unfortunately, there is no industry standard for the colors of the various gases in the cylinders for industrial usage. Cylinders for medical use are color-coded green. All cylinders used by the Department of Defense are color-coded using a system of basic colors and stripes; the basic colors indicate the type of hazard the gases in the cylinder represent, and the stripes indicate the gas.

Safety Devices

All D.O.T.-approved cylinders must have safety devices except hoses that are (1) 12 inches or less in length, exclusive of the neck, and with an outside diameter of $4\frac{1}{2}$ inches or less unless they are charged to 1,800 psig or more; (2) filled with fluorine, or other poisonous gas or liquid; or (3) charged with nonliquefied gas under 300 psig.

Some types of pressure relieving devices used on compressed-gas cylinders are safety relief valves, rupture (frangible) disks, and fusible metals. Frangible disks are set to burst at pressures far above those of the gases contained in the cylinder but below the pressure at which the cylinders must be hydrostatically tested periodically. Sometimes a combination of frangible disk and fusible metal is also used. The disk will function only after a temperature is reached at which the fusible metal melts. The problem with the frangible disk/melting alloy combination is that a temperature might be reached which is too low to melt the alloy but high enough to cause the cylinder to burst. Any cylinder might also rupture if intense localized heating occurs, weakening the cylinder so that it fails before any pressure relief device is actuated. See Fig. 10-5 for precautionary measures to be used with high-pressure systems. Figures 10-6 and 10-7 are checklists which can be used to alert safety engineers to potential pressure problems.

HAZARDS CHECKLIST–PRESSURE

Possible Effects

High pressure:
  Injury:
    Eye or skin damage due to blown dirt or other solid particles
    Whipping hoses hit personnel
    Lung, ear, and other body damage by overpressurization
    Cutting by thin, high-pressure jets

  Container ruptured (internal pressure) or crushed (external
    pressure):
    Blast effects
    Fragments of ruptured container blown about

Leakage:
  Leaks in lines and equipment designed for lower pressures
  Blowout of seals and gaskets
  Release of toxic, corrosive, flammable, odorous, or high-
    temperature fluids
  Loss of system fluids
  Early fuel exhaustion
  Loss of system pressure
  Loss of lubricants
  Contamination and degradation of materials
  Slippery of surfaces
  Short-circuiting of electrical circuits and equipment]
  Displacement of air or other gas by liquid
  Vibration and noise

Possible Causes

High pressure:
  Overpressurization:
    Connection to system with excessively high pressure
    Regulator failure
    Heated gases in closed containers
    Heating fluids with high vapor pressures
    Water hammer (hydraulic shock)
    Deep submersion
    High acceleration of liquid system
    Warming cryogenic liquid in a closed or inadequately
      ventilated system
    Excessively high combustion rate for boiler, evaporator, or
      other fired vessel
  Pressure relief failure:
    No pressure relief valve or vent
    Faulty pressure relief valve or vent
    Relief inadequately sized
  Failure at normal pressure:
    Deteriorated pressure vessel or lines
    Inadequate connection
    Failure or improper release of connectors
    Inadequate restraining devices

Leakage:
  Reservoir losses:
    Overfilling of container
    Erroneously open drain or connection
    Inadequately fitted or tightened parts
    Worn parts and connections
    Fittings loosened by vibration
    Cracks caused by structural failure
    Porosity or other weld defect
    Contact surfaces inadequately finished or dirty
    Wrong type of gasket or seal
    Cuts in seals, gaskets, or hoses
    Hose holes caused by wear, kinking, or deterioration
    Hole torn by impact

FIGURE 10–6   Hazards Checklist—Pressure   Continued on next page

Blowout of seals and gaskets
Permanent deformation of metal containers
Excessively rapid motion of hydraulically or pneumatically
 activated equipment
Unsecured container propelled about by escaping gas

Low pressure:
 System inoperable
 Implosion of pressure vessel
 Inadequate air for respiration
 Physiological damage (atelectasis)

Pressure changes:
 Compressive heating
 Joule-Thomson cooling
 Physiological disturbances (cramps, the bends)
 Condensation of moisture

Low pressure:
 Compressor or pump failure
 Condensation or cooling of gas in a closed system
 Decrease in gas volume due to combustion in a closed system
 Inadequate design against implosion forces
 Increased altitude

Pressure changes:
 High gas compression
 Rapid expansion of gas
 Rapid change of altitude
 Rapid rise toward surface from underwater
 Explosive decompression

FIGURE 10–6 Continued

CHECKLIST—PRESSURE HAZARDS

1. Has each pressure vessel been designed, manufactured, tested, and installed in accordance with the applicable code?
2. Has each pressure vessel been proof-pressure tested after manufacture and periodically in the plant?
3. Are all the lines, fittings, and hoses rated for the pressures they must withstand? Have they been pressure tested?
4. Where tires must be inflated to high pressures, is the operator protected in case of a rupture?
5. Are flex hoses and their connections secured to prevent whipping if there is a failure?
6. Is any pressure vessel or system located near, or can it be subjected to, an unintended high heat input which will raise the pressure to a dangerous level?
7. Is it possible to accidentally connect a pressure vessel or system to a source of pressure greater than that for which the system, product, or any component was designed?
8. Does each container or line which might be overpressurized have a relief valve, vent, or burst diaphragm to protect it?
9. Will the exhaust from each relieving device be conducted away for disposal? Are toxic or flammable fluids either prevented from being exhausted or disposed of properly?
10. Is there a program for periodically testing each pressure device, relief device, and regulator?
11. Is each container which holds a flammable, toxic, corrosive, or otherwise dangerous fluid suitably identified and marked? Has each such container or line been analyzed to determine the effects of leakage? Could a leak of a flammable fluid, gas or liquid, come in contact with a source of ignition?
12. Are there instructions to ensure that any leaked or spilled fluid should be cleaned up immediately?
13. Should the system, assembly, line, or vessel be marked with a warning that it is to be depressurized before any work is started on it? Have maintenance personnel been instructed regarding this requirement? Is there a means to depressurize each pressure system to permit work on it?
14. Are personnel who work with compressed air or other pressurized fluid required to wear face shields?
15. Has "horseplay" with compressed air been forbidden?
16. Does any line with rapidly moving fluid have a quick-closing valve or other shutoff device which could result in water hammer and a shock wave?
17. Is there a possibility of a closed pressure-vessel collapse because of condensation of steam or other gas, decrease in altitude, or excessive operation of a vacuum pump? Does such a vessel have a vacuum relief valve?
18. Are large vacuum tubes which might implode if damaged adequately protected?
19. Do direct-reading pressure gauges have shatterproof glass or plastic faces, and blowout plugs at the rear?
20. Is flexible hose protected against chafing, twisting, or other damage?
21. If there is an accumulator, does it have a warning indicating the maximum operating pressure and other operating instructions necessary to avoid injury?

FIGURE 10–7   Checklist—Pressure Hazards

EXERCISES

10.1. Give three definitions of high pressure. Why should there be different levels for different applications?

10.2. What could cause a pressure vessel to rupture?

10.3. Explain the difference between proof pressure and burst pressure.

10.4. What is the principal difference between a safety valve and a relief valve?

10.5. What precautions should be taken in the event of discharges from safety valves?

10.6. Why must pressurized gases be secured carefully?

10.7. Why must a pressurized system be deenergized before being worked on? How could this be done?

10.8. What causes water hammer, what are its effects, and how can it be avoided or eliminated?

10.9. List seven causes of leakage.

10.10. List seven possible adverse effects of leakage.

10.11. What are the relationships among dysbarism, decompression sickness, bends, chokes, and gas pains?

10.12. Discuss what must be done to prevent decompression sickness. What should be done if a person shows symptoms of decompression sickness?

10.13. What are the three means by which gases are maintained in gas cylinders?

10.14. What types of relieving devices are used on gas cylinders?

10.15. List ten precautionary measures to be taken with gas cylinders.

10.16. Prepare six questions to be added to the checklist in Fig. 10-7.

CHAPTER 11

Electrical Hazards

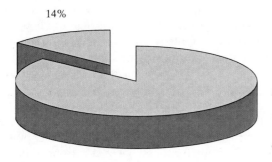

14%

*Percentage of OSHA
General Industry citations
addressing this subject*

Year after year, the National Center for Health Statistics reports approximately 500 to 1000 accidental electrocutions annually in the United States, with about 1 in 4 being industry and farm related. Everyone knows that electrical shock can be fatal, but the mechanism of the hazard is a mystery to most people. The mystery is due in large part to the fact that electricity is invisible. The use of electricity throughout our homes has led to a degree of complacency which is a factor in most electrocutions.

ELECTROCUTION HAZARDS

The first step toward safety from electrocution is to overcome the myth that "ordinary 110-volt circuits are safe." The truth is that ordinary 110-volt circuits can easily kill, and actually do kill, many more people than do 220- or 440-volt circuits, which nearly everyone respects. But the myth about 110 volts persists because almost everyone has sustained an electrical shock around the home or on the job without serious injury. An accident like this leads victims to the false conclusion that, although a 110-volt shock can be startling, it probably will not be fatal. Although they know that others have been killed by such shocks, they may somehow feel resistant or too strong to be seriously injured.

It is true that some persons are more resistant to electrocution hazards than others, but a far more important factor is the set of conditions surrounding the accident. Wet or damp locations are known to be hazardous, but even body perspiration can provide the dampness that can make electrical contact fatal. Another important condition is the point of contact. If current flow enters the body through the fingers and passes out through a contact at the elbow, no vital organs receive direct exposure. But if the flow is from a hand through the body to the feet, vital organs such as the heart, chest muscles, and diaphragm are affected, with possibly fatal results. Contact by the body torso to complete a circuit can also produce vital exposure to electrical current. Another factor can be the presence of wounds in the skin, which can result in a much higher current flow if contact is made where the skin is broken.

Physiological Effects

The central nervous system of our bodies is the conduit of signals between our brains and our muscles, including muscles of vital organs such as the heart and diaphragm. These signals are tiny electrical voltages that tell our muscles when to contract and when to relax. An external electric shock can send currents through the body that are many times greater than the tiny natural currents within our nervous systems. These larger currents can cramp or freeze muscles into a violent contraction—one that will not allow the victim to let go of the object contacted, or one that will stop breathing or stop the heart.

The heart is obviously our most important muscle. Its function is a rhythmic contraction and relaxation, which is timed by natural electrical pulses. The heart is thus very vulnerable to any pulsating electrical current. Common electric utility power supplies alternating current that cycles at a frequency of 60 hertz. It is ironic that 60 hertz is one of the most dangerous frequencies to which the heart can be exposed. This frequency tends to cause the heart to convulse weakly and irregularly at a rate too rapid to accomplish anything, a phenomenon known as *fibrillation*. Once fibrillation starts, death is almost a certainty, except that fibrillation has sometimes been stopped by controlled electric shocks to the heart muscle. The controlled electric shocks reestablish the heart's natural rhythms. Unfortunately, a defibrillation device is rarely available soon enough to save the life of an electrocution victim.

Stopped breathing from electric shock is due to cramped muscles responsible for respiration, such as the diaphragm and those controlling rib cage expansion. The first-aid remedy is artificial respiration, the same as for near drowning or other respiratory crises.

Just how much electrical current is fatal? There is no set answer to this question, but Figure 11.1 summarizes the opinions of several experts. The horizontal scale is logarithmic and is in units of milliamps or thousandths of an ampere. To put the chart in perspective, an ordinary table lamp with a 60-watt bulb draws about 500 milliamperes of current, far more than is needed to be fatal. An ordinary house circuit of 20 or 30 amperes will not trip the circuit breaker until there is a current flow of 20,000 to 30,000[1] milliamperes, respectively, about 100 to 1000 times as much as the lethal dose.

With such lethal potential available from an ordinary 110-volt house circuit, it would appear that almost no one could survive an electrical shock from such a circuit. But the body, especially the skin, has resistance that limits the flow of electric current

---

[1]1 ampere = 1000 milliamperes.

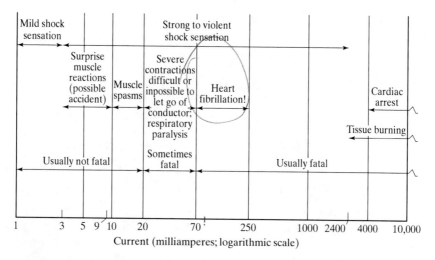

FIGURE 11.1

Effect of alternating electric current on the human body.

when exposed to 110-volt potential. To understand this resistance, some fundamentals of electricity may need review.

Ohm's Law

The basic law of electric circuits is *Ohm's law*, stated as

$$I = \frac{V}{R} \qquad (11.1)$$

where I = current in amperes
R = resistance in ohms
V = voltage in volts

The law can be rewritten as

$$V = IR \quad \text{or} \quad R = \frac{V}{I}$$

Wattage is a measure of power and can be computed from known quantities of current and voltage or resistance as

$$W = V \times I \quad \text{and} \quad W = I^2R \qquad (11.2)$$

where *W* is the power in watts.

Of principal concern are alternating-current (ac) circuits, which are the predominant type in both domestic and industrial use. Standard ac circuits cycle 60 times per second (in the United States and Canada), as shown in Figure 11.2. Alternating currents are more convenient to generate and distribute than are direct currents. But computations of current, resistance, and voltage using Ohm's law are somewhat awkward

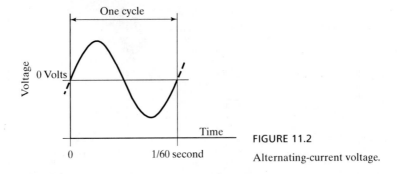

FIGURE 11.2

Alternating-current voltage.

for ac circuits because the voltage varies from zero to positive, back to zero, to negative, and back to zero again every cycle. For convenience, an "effective" current for an ac circuit is computed as a value somewhat less than the current peaks. A direct current operating through a given load is found to generate as much heat as an alternating current that has peak currents 41.4% higher than the direct current. Thus, the ratio of effective current to peak current is computed as follows:

$$\frac{\text{Effective current}}{\text{Peak current}} = \frac{100\%}{100\% + 41.4\%} = 0.707 = 70.7\%$$

Effective voltages are computed by the same ratios as effective currents since they are related by Ohm's law. An ordinary 110-volt circuit then has an effective voltage of 110 volts, even though peaks of voltage over 150 volts occur every cycle.

The current drawn by an ordinary 60-watt lamp bulb can be computed by arranging Equation (11.2) as

$$I = \frac{W}{V} = \frac{60 \text{ watts}}{110 \text{ volts}} = 0.55 \text{ ampere}$$

Since the wire and other parts of the circuit would consume some power, a fair approximation to the current flow in the 60-watt table lamp is $\frac{1}{2}$ ampere, or 500 milliamperes, as stated earlier.

Returning now to the question of why more people are not killed by ordinary 110-volt circuits, we can use Ohm's law to determine how much the skin can limit the flow of electric current through our bodies. Human skin, if it is dry enough, is a good insulator and may have a resistance of 100,000 ohms or more. By using Ohm's law, a 110-volt exposure then would result in only a tiny current:

$$I = \frac{V}{R} = \frac{110 \text{ volts}}{100,000 \text{ ohms}} = 0.0011$$

$$= \text{approximately 1 milliampere}$$

From Figure 11.1, it can be seen that such a tiny current will probably not even be noticed. But add any perspiration or other moisture to the skin, and the resistance drops sharply. Due to perspiration alone, the skin resistance can be reduced 200 times, to a level of about 500 ohms with good contact with the electrical conductor. Once inside the

ry low and the current flows almost unimpeded. If the
y 500 ohms, the current is calculated as

$$\frac{110 \text{ volts}}{00 \text{ ohms}} = 0.22 \text{ ampere}$$

$$= 220 \text{ milliamperes}$$

t an alternating current at this level passing through
most likely be fatal. Therefore, if you have ever rest of us have, you can be glad that you were not per-
have a good enough contact, or that the path of the
r body, or that you were poorly grounded, or that
current. Otherwise, you would have been killed by
atter how resistant you think you are to electrical
of the electrocution hazards of ordinary house cur-
11.1 and 11.2

ASE STUDY 11.1

cular saw to cut extruded aluminum strips in the
He is holding the workpiece firmly in his left
ight hand. Aluminum is an excellent conductor
making solid electrical contact with ground. In
tly, the worker accidentally saws the electrical
le consequences in the following three sets of

rough the third prong of the electrical plug.
ated.

ong plug that is connected through an adapter to
is ungrounded.

Case A. Current will flow through the metal case of the saw handle into two paths,
one through the grounding circuit, and the other through the worker's right hand,
through his body, crossing through his torso and through his left hand into the well-
grounded workpiece. Although the resistance through each of these paths might be
relatively low, the resistance through the third prong grounding conductor should
be the lower of the two, on the order of 2 to 3 ohms. A resistance as low as 3 ohms
would immediately trip a 15- or 20-ampere circuit breaker, the type one would expect to find on such a circuit, as can be confirmed in the following calculation using
Ohm's law:

$$I = \frac{V}{R} = \frac{110 \text{ volts}}{3 \text{ ohms}} = 36 + \text{amperes}$$

The current flow just calculated would be in addition to whatever a current might flow through the man's body and other paths to ground, including perhaps some flow through the tool itself before the accident completely severs the cord. The total current would therefore easily trip any reasonable circuit breaker and interrupt the flow of current, protecting the worker.

Case B. A double-insulated tool would have a nonconducting housing, resulting in no flow through the handle and the worker's body. The breaker would likely still be tripped as the metallic blade would make contact with both the hot wire and the well-grounded neutral. In addition, if the blade was cutting the aluminum workpiece at the time of the accident, another excellent path to ground would be through the metallic blade and into the grounded workpiece, causing an overcurrent to trip the breaker.

Case C. With no double insulation to protect the worker and no grounding conductor to trip the breaker, conditions might be present to cause the common accident to result in an electrocution. The well-grounded left hand of the worker would permit a substantial flow of current through his upper torso, the danger zone for heart and lung exposure. A reasonable value for the resistance in a well-grounded path through the worker's left hand and the aluminum workpiece would be 600 ohms. The current in such a grounding circuit would be calculated as follows:

$$I = \frac{V}{R} = \frac{110 \text{ volts}}{600 \text{ ohms}} = 0.183 \text{ ampere}$$

The current just calculated, only a small fraction of an ampere, would have no effect on a normal 15- to 20- ampere circuit breaker. However small a 183-milliampere current may be for breaking the circuit, it is a very large and dangerous current to flow through the worker's upper body. Such a current is shown by Figure 11.1 to represent a strong to violent, usually fatal, shock capable of producing heart fibrillation. The metallic blade of the saw might provide a good grounding path through the severed neutral or the well-grounded workpiece, accommodating an overcurrent that would trip the breaker and save the worker's life. But such a grounding through the metallic blade would be dependent upon chance; without such grounding the accident would likely be fatal.

CASE STUDY 11.2

A worker uses a trouble light suspended from the hood of an automobile while he repairs the engine. He leans across the fender of the car as he works so that his chest makes firm contact with the metallic fender, although that contact is resisted somewhat by a thin T-shirt he is wearing and slightly, by the paint on the fender of the automobile. The light, which has been through many years of severe usage, has developed a worn connection at the point at which the flexible cord is connected to the lamp socket. As the worker adjusts the light's position the worn connection results in accidental contact between the worker's index finger and the hot wire. Current passes through the man's finger and arm, continuing through multiple paths through his torso, most of it flowing to ground through his chest and the fender of the automobile and some through his feet and shoes. The contact between the hot wire and man's finger is only partial, and the electrical resistance of the skin in the man's finger at the point of contact is about 800 ohms. If this resistance represents about half the effective total resistance in the short circuit, how much current would flow through the man's torso? Would the circuit breaker, rated at 15 amperes, be tripped? Would the shock likely be fatal?

Solution

In this situation the current would flow through many parallel paths through the man's body, but for purposes of considering the total current flow due to the short circuit, one can consider the path to be equivalent to one effective path with a resistance of twice 800 ohms, or 1600 ohms. Using Ohm's law, we find that

$$I = \frac{V}{R} = \frac{110 \text{ volts}}{1600 \text{ ohms}} = 0.069 \text{ amphere}$$

$$= 69 \text{ milliamperes}$$

Such a current flow is much too small to trip the 15-ampere breaker, even if combined with the current flow through a 60-watt lighted lamp, which was calculated earlier in this chapter to be 0.55 ampere. If the entire 69- milliampere short circuit passes through the central part of the man's body, he is in critical danger of electrocution. Figure 11.1 reveals that 69 milliamperes is in the region of "sometimes fatal" and "respiratory paralysis." The victim may survive if an alert bystander is trained in cardiopulmonary resuscitation and applies artificial respiration, and if the victim is fortunate enough to avoid heart fibrillation.

Grounding

In the previous discussion, the term *grounded* was used. Just what does this electrical term mean? A requirement for electrical current to flow is that its path make a complete loop from the source of electrical power through the circuit and back again to the power source. We understand this loop as we connect a lantern bulb to the posts of a lantern battery, as shown in Figure 11.3. Disconnection of the circuit at any point in the complete loop stops the flow of current. This means that there must always be two conductors: one to carry the current to the device (usually called the "load") that uses it and another to carry the current from the load back to the electrical source. However, a trick makes the long trip back to the electrical source very simple in most applications of electrical power.

The earth for the most part is a fairly good conductor of electricity. Besides this, it is so massive that it is difficult for a human-made source of electricity to affect it much one way or another. Thus, no matter what we do on the surface of the earth, the earth

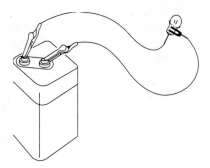

FIGURE 11.3

An electrical circuit makes a complete loop.

maintains a relatively even potential or charge. This means that if we drive two stakes firmly into the earth, even at great distances from each other, we may consider the resistance between them to be nil. The current flow may not be directly from one stake to the other because there are millions of electrical contacts to the earth at all times. Some of these contacts are positive and some are negative, but the total result is zero or earth potential. Thus, any electrical conductor driven into the earth immediately assumes the zero reference potential of the earth. This is a very convenient characteristic of the earth because it enables us to use it as one great common conductor back to the source of power. Figure 11.4 illustrates the use of the ground as a return conductor.

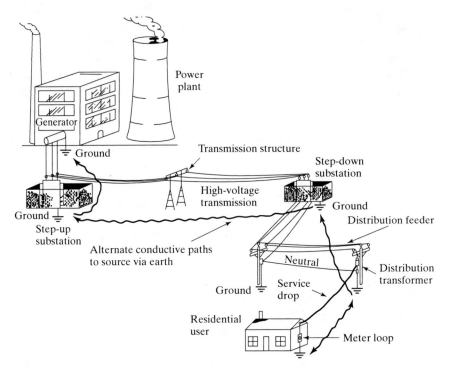

FIGURE 11.4

Alternative conductive paths to source through earth.

A careful examination of Figure 11.4 reveals that the power company provides a separate neutral conductor for the completion of the circuit back to the source. There are conditions that make dependence on the common potential of the earth somewhat unreliable. A very dry season, for instance, may make the surface of the earth lose its conductivity. This is especially a problem if the area is dry around the grounding conductor stake that has been driven into the ground. The neutral conductor then ensures the completion of the circuit regardless of conditions.

The use of ground in electrical circuits is so advantageous as to be considered indispensable. However, the very convenience and proximity of the ground everywhere present a hazard. If a person contacts an energized conductor and at the same time is in contact with the ground or some other object that has a conductive path to ground, that person completes the electrical circuit loop by passing electric current through his or her body. A major portion of the *National Electrical Code*[®2] is devoted to prevention of this hazard.

The principal way in which persons are protected from becoming a part of the path to ground is by insulation of conductors. In addition, exposed conductive surfaces are given a good connection to the ground, usually by means of the ground wire, so that opportunity for a person's body to be the path to ground is minimal. Paradoxically, in some rare instances, the *National Electrical Code*® takes exactly the opposite approach. For some systems, it makes more sense to *isolate* the entire structure from ground. If the structure is isolated, workers are protected by not being in contact with conductors that could connect them with ground.

Wiring

A typical 110-volt circuit has three wires: *hot, neutral,* and *ground.* Sometimes the neutral is called the "ground*ed*" conductor, in which case the ground is called the "ground*ing*" conductor. The purpose of the hot wire (usually a black insulated wire) is to provide contact between the power source and the device (load) that uses it. The neutral (usually a white insulated wire) completes the circuit by connecting the load with ground. Both the hot and the neutral normally carry the same amount of current, but the hot is at an effective voltage of 110 volts with respect to ground, whereas the neutral is at a voltage of nearly zero with respect to the ground.

The third wire is the ground wire and is usually either green or is simply a bare wire. The purpose of the ground wire is safety. If something goes wrong so that the hot wire makes contact with the equipment case or some other conductive part of the equipment, the current in its path to ground can bypass the load and take a shortcut, commonly called a *short.* Since the load is bypassed, the short is a very low-resistance path to ground and by Ohm's law draws a very high current. This high current in a properly protected circuit will almost immediately either "blow" a fuse or "trip" a circuit breaker, depending on the type of overcurrent protection provided in the circuit, and stop all flow of current in the circuit.

---

[2]The National Electrical Code®, commonly abbreviated NEC, is published regularly by the National Fire Protection Association (NFPA), 470 Atlantic Avenue, Boston, MA, 02201.

It is possible, of course, to have a short without a ground wire. The equipment may be naturally grounded by its location or installation, or the hot wire can somehow contact the neutral. Sometimes the short to ground is only partial because there is considerable resistance in the short path to ground. Such a short may go undetected because the short flow of current is of insufficient amperage to cause the total circuit current to trip the overcurrent protection in the circuit. In this case, current will continue to flow, and equipment loads will continue to operate in the presence of these shorts, or *ground faults*, as this type of short is sometimes called. Such ground faults can be especially dangerous on construction sites. This hazard is the basis for ground-fault circuit-interruptor (GFCI) devices on construction sites. The GFCI protection is in addition to overcurrent protection such as circuit breakers or fuses.

Figure 11.5 explains how a GFCI works. Whenever the current flow in the neutral is less than the current flow in the hot wire, a ground fault is indicated, and the current flow is stopped by a switch that breaks the entire circuit. Building codes have required the installation of GFCI circuits in residential bathrooms. GFCI electrical receptacles have small, red "RESET" buttons, as shown in Figure 11.6. One difficulty with GFCIs is that some leakages to ground are almost impossible to prevent, especially when conditions are wet or extension cords are extremely long. This causes the GFCI to trip even when no hazard exists, a condition known in the construction industry as "nuisance tripping." An alternative to GFCIs is for the employer to test, inspect, and keep records of the condition of equipment grounding conductors.

One misconception about shorts is the idea that a good fuse or circuit breaker is sufficient to stop the flow of a dangerous short through a person's body. A reexamination of Figure 11.1 shows that a person will almost certainly be killed by exposure to a current that would not blow even the smallest popular household fuses (i.e., 15- or 20-ampere fuses). A fuse or breaker rated at 15 amperes will handle up to 15,000 milliamperes before blowing, several times as great as the fatal current shown in Figure 11.1. The beauty of the third wire or grounding wire is that it provides a very low-resistance, high-current short to ground, which will trip the fuse or breaker immediately, before *other* short paths to ground (such as through a person's body) can do their damage.

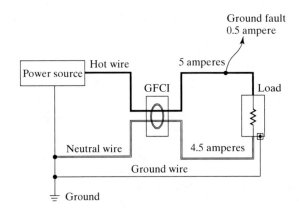

FIGURE 11.5

Ground-fault circuit interruptor (GFCI). The 0.5-ampere fault to ground causes a current flow imbalance between the hot and the neutral. This imbalance triggers the GFCI to break the circuit.

FIGURE 11.6

An electrical receptacle equipped with a GFCI.

Double Insulation

Unfortunately, less than half of the electric hand tools in actual use are properly grounded. Studies of equipment returned to the factory for repair have shown that a large
number of units have been altered so that the grounding system is no longer intact. A
common alteration is to cut off the third prong of the plug so that it can be plugged into
an old two-wire receptacle. To counter this practice, the use of "double-insulated" tools
is permitted in lieu of equipment grounding. A second covering of insulation gives an
extra measure of protection to the operator of double-insulated tools in case of a short
to the equipment case.

Most double-insulated tools have a plastic, nonconductive housing, but this is
not a fully reliable indication that the tool is double insulated. The second covering of
insulation must be applied according to precise specifications before the tool can
qualify to receive the designation "double insulated." Qualifying tools have the manufacturer's mark "double insulated" or a square within a square ▭ to indicate double insulation.

Miswiring Dangers

In the original wiring job, electricians sometimes make mistakes or use slipshod practices that increase hazards. One of these practices is to "jump" (connect) the ground
wire to the neutral wire. Actually, this is a trick that will work, and usually no one will
be the wiser, but the practice does cause hazards. Figure 11.7 shows how a circuit is correctly wired, revealing that both the neutral and grounding wire are connected directly
to ground. So in Figure 11.8, in which it is shown that the ground is jumped to the neutral, a third wire is not used in the wiring system.

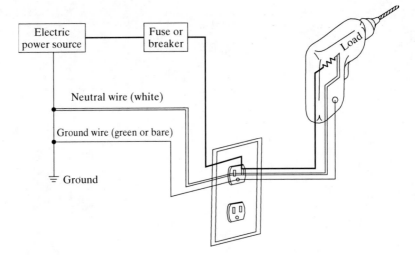

FIGURE 11.7

Correctly wired 110-volt circuit.

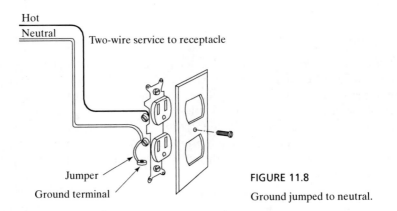

Jumper

Ground terminal

FIGURE 11.8

Ground jumped to neutral.

The main hazard in jumping the ground to neutral is that it can create low voltages on exposed parts of equipment. The equipment case or housing is connected to the ground wire. Since no current normally flows through the ground wire, it serves as an excellent method of keeping the voltage on the equipment case close to zero with respect to ground. But the neutral does carry considerable current. By using Ohm's law, it can be determined that this large current on the neutral may cause it to have a low voltage with respect to ground, especially if the neutral wire must travel a long distance back to the ground at the meter. If the circuit is carrying a current of 20 amperes and the resistance of the neutral wire is $\frac{1}{2}$ ohm, the voltage on the equipment case is calculated to be

$$V = IR = 20 \times \tfrac{1}{2} = 10 \text{ volts.}$$

This is a low voltage, but is theoretically capable of producing a fatal current through a person's body if conditions are just right (or rather, wrong). The real hazard, though, is that a loose or corroded connection somewhere in the neutral circuit would increase its resistance, perhaps to 4 or 5 ohms, causing the voltage to increase several times.

Another common wiring mistake is *reversed polarity*, which simply means that the hot and neutral wires are reversed. This is another subtle problem because most equipment will operate perfectly well with reversed polarity. One hazard of reversed polarity is that the designated leads (black lead, hot; white lead, neutral) become reversed, and the confusion could bring on an accident to an unsuspecting technician. Another hazard is that a short to ground between the switch and the load could cause the equipment to run indefinitely, independent of whether the switch is on or off. (See Figure 11.9.) Finally, bulb sockets can become hazardous when the polarity is reversed. In Figure 11.10(a), a correctly wired socket shows the screw threads to be neutral. But in a reversed-polarity socket, as shown in Figure 11.10(b), the exposed screw threads become hot, and the button, which is naturally more protected at the bottom of the socket, becomes neutral.

Perhaps the most common wiring mistake of all is to fail to connect the ground terminal to a ground wire, a condition known as *open ground*, or *ground not continuous*. This is another error that can easily go unnoticed because equipment attached to

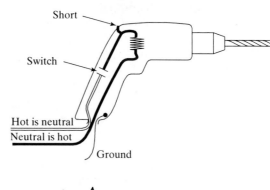

FIGURE 11.9

Reversed polarity. A short in the position indicated in the circuit for this drill will cause the drill to operate continuously, independent of the switch.

FIGURE 11.10

Hazards of reversed polarity in lamp socket: (a) correctly wired socket; (b) reversed-polarity socket.

circuits miswired in this way will usually operate normally. But if an accidental short to the equipment case occurs, the worker is in danger of electrocution.

The three cases of miswiring discussed in this chapter are not the only mistakes that can be made in wiring electrical circuits; they are not even the most hazardous. But because they permit electrical circuits to "work normally," they go unnoticed by uninformed users of equipment attached to such circuits. Because the errors are not immediately crippling to the function, they are frequently committed. Some simple checks with inexpensive testers can easily demonstrate the problems. These testers will be examined later.

FIRE HAZARDS

Most people think of electrocution when they think of electrical safety, but electrical codes have as much to do with fire hazards as they do with electrocution. Many systems, such as fuses or circuit breakers, protect against both fire and electrocution, but their primary function is fire prevention.

Wire Fires

One of the most common causes of electrical fires is wires that become overheated because they conduct too much current. Wire diameters (gauges) must be properly sized to handle the expected current load, and overcurrent protection (fuses or breakers) must ensure that these loads are not exceeded. Substitution of fuses with copper pennies is a common method of defeating the overcurrent protection so that the circuit will handle larger loads. If no fuse is present to burn in two, the wire itself may act as the next weakest link. If the wire becomes hot enough to burn in two, any contact with combustible material along the wire run is likely to produce a fire.

Arcs and Sparks

Whenever two conductors make a physical contact to complete a circuit, a tiny (or not so tiny) electric arc jumps the air gap just prior to contact. This arc may be so small as to be undetectable, but it is usually hot enough to ignite explosive vapors or dusts within their dangerous concentration ranges.

When the electric arc is an instantaneous discharge of a statically charged object, it is sometimes called a *spark*. Such sparks are capable of igniting an explosive mixture, the spark plug of an automobile engine being ample testimony. Sparks are prevented by electrically connecting, or "bonding," two objects that may be of different static charge. This is especially important when pouring flammable liquids from one container to another.

The arc that occurs when an ordinary electrical circuit is completed is virtually impossible to prevent. This means that switches, lights, receptacles, motors, and almost any electrical device, even telephones, are a source of ignition to hazardous concentrations of explosive vapors or dusts. Since the arc is impossible to prevent, some means must be used to separate it from the hazardous concentrations in the air. This is done by using wire, conduit, or equipment that is either vapor tight or strong enough to contain and prevent the propagation of an explosion inside the conduit or equipment. This is an expensive undertaking, and it is tempting to take shortcuts. The *National Electrical Code*® has a strict code for electrical wiring and equipment designed for hazardous locations. The safety and health manager should be able to identify the operations or hazardous locations within the plant that require special wiring and electrical equipment. Accordingly, this identification scheme is discussed next.

Hazardous Locations

One of the most difficult tasks in the field of industrial safety is the definition of various industrial locations that require special wiring and equipment to prevent explosions. Industrial processes are so diverse as to defy a general definition. In addition, the ignition mechanisms are different for different materials. For instance, the hazard of heat buildup on electric equipment housings and bearings coated with ignitable dusts is altogether different from the hazard of spark ignition of explosive vapors derived from flammable liquids. Difficult as the problem is, it must be dealt with because some industrial locations are just too dangerous to allow exposure to electric ignition sources.

The *National Electrical Code*® meticulously defines various conditions to classify hazardous locations roughly into six categories. Within these classifications are various groups that identify the substance group that is causing the hazard.

The major classification is according to the physical type of dangerous material present in the air and is designated *Class*. The next classification is called *Division* and relates to the extent of the hazard by considering the relative frequency with which the process releases hazardous materials into the air. The criteria for "Division" are subjective, not quantitative, except around paint spray areas. This subjectivity introduces problematic gray areas.

Figure 11.11 is a decision chart that attempts to simplify the complicated process of the classification of hazardous locations. The chart is approximate only because strict definition would require enumeration of pages of exceptions and conditions, many of which would overlap. The thing to remember is that the "Class" is the material and the "Division" is the extent of the hazard. Thus, one can state that Division 1 locations are more hazardous than Division 2 locations, but cannot state absolutely that Class I locations are more hazardous than Class II or III locations.

Since classification is so complex, industry often relies on examples common in similar industries to decide whether a location is Division 1 or 2 or not of sufficient hazard to classify at all. Examples of some common hazardous locations are listed in Table 11.1.

Equipment qualifying for hazardous locations usually qualifies for both Division 1 and 2. When in doubt, most industries want to install equipment approved for Division 1 in order to be prepared for the worst. Most violations of code are not for selection of Division 2 equipment when Division 1 should have been selected; most violations are from the use of thin-walled conduit and conventional electrical equipment in Division 1 or 2 locations.

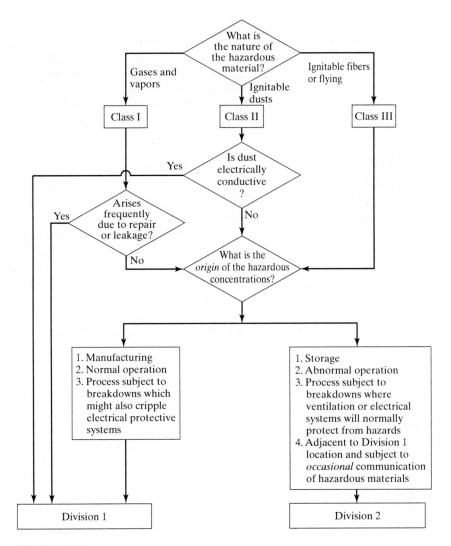

FIGURE 11.11

Decision chart for classifying hazardous locations that are dangerous from the standpoint of ignition of materials in the air.

"Approval" of electrical equipment for use in hazardous locations means that the manufacturer's design has been tested and approved by a recognized testing laboratory such as Underwriters' or Factory Mutual. A label must be on the equipment designating its classification if that equipment is to be used in hazardous locations.

Figure 11.12 shows several examples of *explosion-proof equipment* approved for Class I, Division 1 locations. Explosion-proof conduit looks more like pipe than conventional thin-walled conduit, which looks more like tubing. Explosion-proof junction boxes are castings, as opposed to conventional formed sheet metal boxes. The complicated

TABLE 11.1   Classification of Common Hazards.

Description	Classification
Paint spray areas (flammable paint)	Class I, Division 1
Areas adjacent to, but outside of, paint spray booth	Class I, Division 2
Areas of open tanks or vats of volatile flammable solvents	Class I, Division 2
Storage areas for flammable liquids	Class I, Division 2
Inside refrigerators containing open or easily ruptured containers of volatile flammable liquids	Class I, Division 1
Gas generator rooms	Class I, Division 1
Grain mills or processors	Class II, Division 1
Grain storage areas	Class II, Division 2
Coal pulverizing areas	Class II, Division 1
Powdered magnesium mill	Class II, Division 1
Parts of cotton gin locations	Class III, Division 1
Excelsior storage areas	Class III, Division 2
Closed piping for flammable liquids (piping has no valves, checks, meters, or similar equipment)	Not classified

structures for telephones and even light switches make obvious the fact that explosion-proof equipment costs several times as much as conventional equipment.

In Division 1 locations, it is recognized that there is no way to ensure that the vapors will be kept out of the conduit and equipment. During maintenance, installation, or other open periods, vapors will enter the system. Therefore, the electrical equipment designer assumes this inescapable reality and designs the Division 1 equipment to withstand an internal explosion and cool the explosion gases as they escape before they can ignite the entire area in a devastating explosion.

By contrast, Division 2 electrical equipment enjoys some isolation from dangerous explosive vapors *most* of the time. Therefore, if the Division 2 equipment can be properly sealed with gaskets to make it vapor tight, it will be safe. Class I, Division 2 equipment is characterized as vapor tight, whereas Class I, Division 1 equipment is *not* vapor tight but is explosion proof. Of course, if equipment is classified as Class I, Division 1 (explosion proof), it is also acceptable for use in Class I, Division 2 areas even though the equipment is not vapor tight.

The foregoing comparison of Division 1 and Division 2 equipment and locations acknowledged the generalization that any equipment approved for Division 1 locations is also acceptable for Division 2 locations *of the same classification*. However, it should be noted here that equipment approved for Class I locations is not necessarily approved for Class II or III. The hazard mechanisms of ignitable Class II dusts or Class III fibers are somewhat different from the hazards of Class I vapors. Dusts and fibers can settle on warm equipment, insulating it from necessary heat dissipation during operation. Such insulation can cause a substantial heat buildup on the equipment that can result in a smoldering dust ignition and subsequent explosion.

A common error when selecting electrical receptacles for hazardous locations is to mistake weatherproof electrical outlets for approved equipment. Ordinary weatherproof outlets, as shown in Figure 11.13, are not approved for any type of hazardous locations in either Division 1 or 2. The spring-loaded cover protects the receptacle from

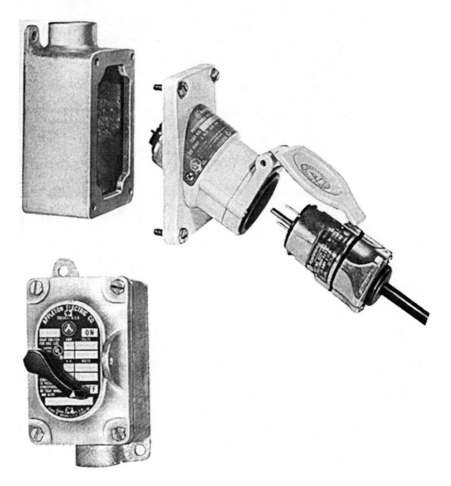

FIGURE 11.12

Explosion-proof electrical equipment approved for Class I, Division I hazardous locations. Note heavy-duty, machined components. (a) Electrical outlet plug and receptacle; (b) wall switches (*Source:* Courtesy of Appleton Electric Co.).

FIGURE 11.13

Ordinary weatherproof outlets not approved for hazardous locations.

weather when the receptacle is not in use, but when a plug is inserted into the receptacle, the receptacle is exposed as much as any conventional one.

The safety and health manager may be baffled when reading equipment labels to find that equipment is classified and labeled by Class and *Group*, rather than Class and *Division*. Like the Class designation, the Group designation identifies the type of

TABLE 11.2   Groups and Classes.

Class	Group	Description	Examples	Industries
I	A		Acetylene	Welding fuel generators
	B	Highly flammable gases and some liquids	Hydrogen	Chemicals and plastics
	C	Highly flammable chemicals	Ethyl ether, hydrogen sulfide	Hospitals, chemical plants
	D	Flammable fuels, chemicals	Gasoline	Refineries, chemical plants, paint spray areas
II	E	Metal dusts	Magnesium	Chemical plants
	F	Carbon, coke, coal dust	Carbon black	Mines, steel mills, power plants
	G	Grain dusts	Flour, starch	Grain mills and elevators

material present in the atmosphere, but the Group classification is more detailed. Four of the Groups belong to Class I and three to Class II and are summarized in Table 11.2.

A typical classification label will state "approved for Class I, Groups A and B," omitting the "Division" designation. When the "Division" is omitted, the classification is invariably acceptable for both Division 1 and 2 locations. If the equipment is merely vapor tight and approved only for Division 2, the "Division" designation should be displayed on the label. Class I equipment is usually either approved for Groups C and D or is approved for all four Class I Groups: A, B, C, and D.

TEST EQUIPMENT

Pursuant to general electrical safety, there are a few inexpensive items of test equipment that the safety and health manager should have access to for occasional in-house inspections. Brief descriptions of these items follow.

Circuit Tester

A circuit tester (Figure 11.14) simply has two wire leads connected by a small lamp bulb, usually neon. Whenever one of the leads touches a hot wire and the other lead touches a grounded conductor, completing the circuit, the bulb glows. The tester works only for a given voltage range, but most are able to handle both 110- and 220-volt circuits. The circuit tester is somewhat of a safety device in itself, enabling maintenance workers to be sure that power is turned off before touching hot wires. The circuit tester can also be used to determine whether various exposed parts of machines or conductors are *live* or *energized*.

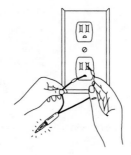

FIGURE 11.14

Circuit tester.

Receptacle Wiring Tester

One of the simplest and most widely used test devices is the receptacle wiring tester, which can be carried around in one's pocket. (See Figure 11.15). No battery or cord is required. The user simply plugs the device into any standard 110-volt outlet and interprets the arrangement of indicator lights to determine whether the receptacle is wired improperly. Note carefully the use of the word *improperly* instead of the word *properly* in the preceding sentence. Only certain errors will be detected, and a "correct" indication of the lights means only that those certain errors were not found. The receptacle could still be wired incorrectly.

Figure 11.16 reveals that the receptacle wiring tester is nothing more than three simple circuit testers combined into one tester. The tabular portion of the figure shows types of wiring errors that can be interpreted from the indicator lights. One of the most common wiring errors—"ground jumped to neutral"—is shown by the tester to be wired correctly.

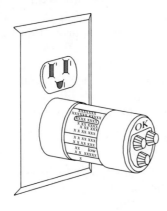

FIGURE 11.15

Receptacle wiring tester.

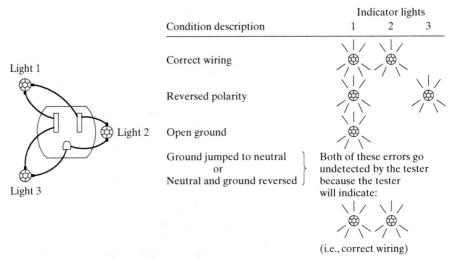

FIGURE 11.16

Schematic of receptacle wiring tester.

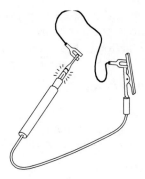

FIGURE 11.17

Continuity tester

Continuity Tester

It is sometimes useful to check a dead circuit simply to see whether all the connections are complete or whether a break in a conductor has occurred. Figure 11.17 illustrates a simple continuity tester, which is similar to a circuit tester except that a small battery is included to provide power for the light. The continuity tester also has much less electrical resistance than the circuit tester because it is used only on dead circuits. If the continuity tester is used on a live 110-volt circuit, it will immediately blow a fuse or throw a breaker in the circuit.

An important application for a continuity tester is to check the path to ground. One terminal of the tester can be connected to the exposed equipment case of a machine in question and the other terminal to a known-grounded object. If the lamp lights, the machine is known to be grounded. If the lamp does not light, there is a break somewhere in the path to ground.

FREQUENT VIOLATIONS

Having been versed in the principles of electrical hazards, the safety and health manager should know what to look for when making an inspection. But for review, the remainder of this chapter will describe frequently cited violations of the *National Electrical Code*®.

Grounding of Portable Tools and Appliances

It should come as no surprise that the most frequently cited electrical code violation is for grounding. This is the code cited for ungrounded electric drills, sanders, saws, and other portable hand-held equipment. Nonportable equipment, such as refrigerators, freezers, and air conditioners, must also be grounded. Special attention should be given to the use of portable electric tools used in damp or wet locations and, of course, to plugs that have the ground pin broken off.

Exposed Live Parts

Almost as frequent as ungrounded portable equipment is the existence of exposed live parts. If the actual equipment conductors cannot be insulated and terminals covered, locked rooms should be used to prevent exposure to workers. One of the most frequent observations of exposed live parts is sloppy electrical installations in which covers are left off junction boxes or receptacle cover plates are missing. A switch box, fuse, or breaker box in which the door is open also constitutes "exposed live parts."

Improper Use of Flexible Cords

Makeshift or temporary electrical installations are prohibited as are substitutions of flexible cords for fixed wiring. Obvious instances are flexible cords run through holes in the walls, ceilings, floors, doorways, or windows.

Marking of Disconnects

This is an easy thing to correct. The disconnect box or switch panel for motors and appliances must be identified so that equipment can be quickly and confidently disconnected. Also, the origins of branch circuits, such as in the breaker box, must be labeled to indicate their purposes. If the location or arrangement of the disconnect makes it obvious which machines or circuits it controls, marking may not be necessary. Very few of the disconnect marking violations are designated as "serious."

Connection of Plugs to Cords

Here is another extremely simple item. When repairing a plug to an extension cord, appliance cord, or any other flexible cord, be sure to tie a knot in the cord or do something that will prevent a pull on the cord from being transmitted directly to joints or terminal screws. This is just a basic principle of electrical maintenance.

SUMMARY

This chapter began with some sobering thoughts of what electricity, even in small amounts, can do to the human body. The greatest hazard is with 110-volt circuits, not 220-volt or higher circuits. This is because of the popularity of 110-volt circuits and the complacency of the people who use them. Besides electrocution hazards, electricity also presents fire hazards, not to speak of burns and other electrical exposure hazards.

Simple testers can demonstrate quickly some of the frequent wiring mistakes that might otherwise go undetected in normal operations. But some of these testers are too simple and overlook common errors such as "ground jumped to neutral."

Providing for electrical equipment in industrial processes that produce flammable vapors, dusts, or fibers is a difficult and expensive task. The definitions and codes for hazardous locations with explosive atmospheres are also complicated and tricky. The safety and health manager is advised to look for required markings on electrical equipment installed in hazardous locations to be sure that the equipment is approved for the "Class" and "Division" of the location in which it has been installed.

Violations of electrical code are often for conditions that are easy to correct. The largest single item to remember is grounding—grounding of both portable and fixed equipment and the circuits that serve them. Of less frequency, but of great seriousness, are the OSHA citations for unapproved conduit and electrical equipment used in explosive atmospheres of flammable vapors or dusts.

EXERCISES AND STUDY QUESTIONS

11.1 What are the two principal hazards of electricity?

11.2 Approximately how many people die each year of electrocution in the United States?

11.3 Compare 110-, 220-, and 440-volt hazards of electricity.

11.4 At approximately what current levels through the heart and lungs does the sustained flow of electricity become fatal?

11.5 What part does grounding play in an electrical circuit? Why do safety regulations require equipment to be grounded?

11.6 Compare the functions of hot, neutral, and ground wires.

11.7 What is a GFCI, and where is it used?

11.8 Explain the term *double insulation*.

11.9 What are the hazards of reversed polarity?

11.10 Compare electrical "arcs" and "sparks."

11.11 Explain the difference between Class I, II, and III hazardous locations.

11.12 What do the terms *Division* and *Group* mean in the classification of hazardous locations?

11.13 Explain the difference between a continuity tester and a circuit tester.

11.14 Name some of the most frequent violations of electrical code.

11.15 A certain string of Christmas tree lights has eight bulbs, each rated at 5 watts. If there is no ground fault, how much current flows through the hot wire at the receptacle plug? How much flows through the neutral?

11.16 In Exercise 11.15, if all the current flowing through the hot wire would pass through a person's heart muscle, would the current likely be fatal?

11.17 A maintenance worker wires a 110-volt electric lamp without disconnecting the circuit. With no load energized in the circuit, the worker accidentally contacts the bare hot wire. What will probably happen? Under what conditions would the worker likely be killed?

11.18 In Exercise 11.17, suppose the wire that was contacted was the neutral wire. What would probably happen? Are there conditions under which the worker would be killed?

11.19 In Exercise 11.17, suppose the wire that was contacted was the equipment ground wire. What would probably happen?

11.20 Portable "trouble lights" used in automobile repair have been involved in many fatalities. Explain probable hazard mechanisms.

11.21 Explain the difference between a GFCI and an ordinary circuit breaker.

11.22 Explain why it is so difficult to detect the wiring defect "ground jumped to neutral."

11.23 A worker was electrocuted when he drilled through a wall and the drill bit contacted an electrical wire inside the wall by cutting through its insulation. The ground pin of the electric plug for the drill was broken off. Describe several ways in which this fatality could have been prevented.

11.24 The broken-off ground pin represented a code violation in the fatality case described in Exercise 11.23. How did this contribute to the hazard? What would probably have happened had the ground pin been intact?

11.25 It can be said that "grounding" with respect to electricity can be both good and bad. Explain the "good" and the "bad" about electrical grounding.

11.26 Explain the distinction between the terms "grounded conductor" and "grounding conductor."

11.27 For each of the following situations, explain the nature of the hazard and describe probable outcomes:

   (a) A worker brushes his pant leg across a 120-volt terminal strip with screw terminals exposed. Every other screw is hot, with neutral screws intervening.

   (b) A worker's boot contacts a 440-volt bus bar. A ground path occurs through the worker's foot and the nails in the sole of the boot to the concrete floor. The resistance of the ground path is 10,000 ohms.

   (c) A worker wires a 220-volt circuit "hot" using a wood-handle screwdriver. The screwdriver slips, and the shaft of the screwdriver makes a direct short across the hot terminal and the adjacent neutral.

   (d) A worker changes a 120-volt wall receptacle in a garage while standing on a concrete floor. The circuit is energized, but the worker is careful not to touch both the hot wire and the neutral wire at the same time.

11.28 A right-handed worker is repairing a 120-volt lamp socket using a screwdriver with an insulated handle. He is wearing a short-sleeve shirt, and his bare right arm is braced against a water pipe. A bare hot wire contacts the metal housing of the socket assembly the worker is holding in his hand while he is using the screwdriver in his other hand. A ground path occurs with total resistance of 600 ohms. Calculate the current flow and describe its probable path. Will the breaker likely be tripped? Is there a risk of electrocution? If so, what factors contribute to the risk?

11.29 Describe the phenomenon of fibrillation and its probable effect.

11.30 What characteristic about electric utility power aggravates the hazard of fibrillation?

11.31 Calculate the peak voltage for an effective line voltage of 240 volts ac.

11.32 An ac circuit has peak voltages of ±80 volts. Calculate the effective voltage.

11.33 An ac circuit has peak voltages of ±170 volts. Calculate the *effective* current flow in this circuit if the total circuit load operates at 60 watts of power. Calculate the peak current flow.

11.34 Explain why it is so important for the resistance to be low in the "third-wire" path to ground. (*Hint:* "Electricity follows the path of least resistance" is not the correct answer to this question.)

11.35 Explain how a "shorted-out" electric tool may continue to operate. There are at least two different sets of conditions that will lead to this phenomenon.

11.36 Explain why the common wiring defect "open ground" easily goes undetected.

11.37 Is it okay to use Division 1 approved equipment in Division 2 hazardous locations? Why or why not? Is it okay to use Class I approved equipment in Class II hazardous locations? Why or why not?

11.38 **Design Case Study.** In an actual case history of an electrocution fatality, Figure 11.18(a) illustrates the way the chuck key for a hand-held electric drill was conveniently attached to the power cord so that it would always be readily available for operator use in changing bits. The fatality occurred when the twisted wire wore through the cord insulation after continued use. Figure 11.18(b) illustrates a much safer way to connect the chuck key. What other factors probably contributed to this fatality and how could it have been prevented? Suppose that the ground pin had been broken off the plug for this drill. How would this code violation have affected this fatality?

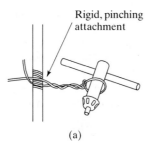
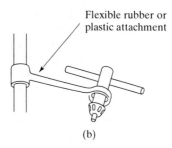

FIGURE 11.18

Cause of electrocution fatality: chuck key secured to cord by twisted wire tie. (a) Unsafe, improvised attachment of chuck key. Wire or tape will eventually damage cord insulation. (b) Safer method of attaching chuck key.

11.39 Design Case Study. An architectural design and engineering firm seeks advice regarding federal safety standards for wiring for a new process being set up to manufacture dyestuff. The process uses chlorobenzene and releases ignitable concentrations in the vicinity of the process equipment. Specify the appropriate Class, Division, and Group classification for wiring and electrical equipment located in this area.

11.40 Design Case Study. In the case study of Exercise 11.39, suppose an alternate supplier of process equipment proposes a completely closed system in which releases would only occur during repair or in event of a leak. Such occurrences arise frequently out of a need to regularly clean the in-feed mechanism. Would the closed system have an impact on safety and on the prescribed wiring system?

RESEARCH EXERCISES

11.41 Use the Internet to find out who publishes the *National Electrical Code*. What other aids for electrical safety are available from this organization?

11.42 Check recent statistics to determine the number of electrocutions annually in the United States. What percentage are "on the job"? Is the annual number of electrocutions increasing or decreasing?

11.43 OSHA citation frequencies change somewhat from year to year. Check enforcement statistics to determine the top five most frequently cited electrical standards. Are they the same as the ones identified in this chapter?

STANDARDS RESEARCH QUESTIONS

11.44 This chapter concludes those related to the General Industry standards. If the reader has been studying the chapters of this book sequentially, then at this point he or she should have a great deal of familiarity with the OSHA General Industry standards and the NCM database tool for examining inspection statistics for these standards. In previous chapters, this text has assigned specific questions for "STANDARDS RESEARCH QUESTIONS." In this chapter, however, rather than address specific questions for research related to electrical standards, it is suggested that the reader go "browsing" in the OSHA General Industry electrical standards, using the OSHA website. Try to relate the standards to topics that were discussed in this chapter. Try to pick out particular provisions in the OSHA standard that you reason would be frequently cited. Check whether your theories are correct by querying the NCM database for your selected provisions to see whether they are indeed frequently cited. Try to pick out standards that OSHA would cite as "serious" violations in many cases. Check the NCM database to determine whether your intuitions about these standards are correct.

CHAPTER 12

Welding

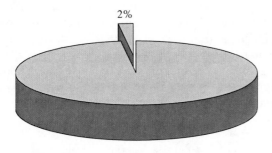

2%

***Percentage of OSHA
General Industry citations
addressing this subject***

After as broad a subject as machine guarding, it may seem ridiculously specific to address a field as narrow as welding. However, it may surprise some to learn that welding processes present some of the greatest hazards to both safety and health. In terms of breadth of hazard, this chapter encompasses even more than the chapter on machine guarding, and for that matter, more than any other chapter of this book.

The term *welding* is to be taken in a very broad sense to include gas welding, electric-arc welding, resistance welding, and even related processes such as soldering and brazing, which technically are not welding processes at all. Welding processes are so diverse, that before addressing the hazards of these processes, it is necessary to name them and to provide the necessary background in welding process terminology.

PROCESS TERMINOLOGY

The key to understanding welding hazards is to know how the process itself works, and unless safety and health managers have this knowledge, their credibility with their manufacturing and operations counterparts will be minimal. Everyone knows that welding requires that material melt or fuse to form a rigid joint. The first question to ask to determine the process is "What material melts?" If the melted material is of the parts to be joined themselves or of like filler material, the process is *welding*. If the material is some other material of lower melting temperature, the process is *brazing* or *soldering.* The breakpoint between brazing and soldering is 800°F (427°C), with brazing above and soldering below 800°F.

Since welding requires materials to be melted, heat is required, usually applied intensely, to meet the demands of high melting points of welding materials. The method of applying this intense heat usually identifies the process. Excluding the unusual and exotic processes, such as thermit and laser processes, the three basic categories of conventional welding are as follows:

- Gas welding
- Electric-arc welding
- Resistance welding

Gas welding is typified by the familiar oxyacetylene torch process, in which the very hot burning acetylene gas is made to burn even hotter by supplying pure oxygen to the flame. For welding materials with lower melting points, alternate and safer gases such as natural gas, propane, or MAPP gas (a trade name) can be used. These alternate gases are often used for brazing and soldering.

The safety and health manager should be careful not to confuse gas welding with some types of electric-arc welding that use an inert gas to facilitate the process. Indeed, some of these processes have names such as "gas metal arc welding" or "gas tungsten arc welding," but they are not gas welding. The telling feature of gas welding is that the gas must be used as a fuel for the process, not as an inert gas.

Even more diverse than the types of gas welding are the various types of *electric-arc welding*. Arc welding requires a small gap between electrodes, one of which is usually the workpiece itself. The intense heat is provided by the electric arc that forms between the electrodes. The process that typifies electric arc is *stick electrode* or shielded metal arc welding (SMAW),[1] shown in Figure 12.1. This highly portable and most popular operation is seen in welding structural steel for buildings, in repair of steel components, and in a wide variety of manufacturing processes. The *stick* is a piece of *welding rod* that is held by a gripper and is consumed by the process. The stick consists of a filler metal surrounded by a *flux*, a term to be explained later. Similar to SMAW welding is *flux-cored arc welding* (FCAW), in which the flux is on the inside of the rod, reminiscent of acid- or resin-core solder. Sometimes the welding process does not consume the electrode, a good example being the process commonly called TIG (tungsten inert gas) or GTAW (gas tungsten arc welding) shown in Figure 12.2. In a related process, GMAW (gas metal arc welding), the electric arc consumes a *flexible* electrode that is spooled on a reel and is continuously fed to the arc during welding.

The terms *flux* and *inert gas* have been used earlier and need some explanation. The extremely hot melting temperatures of steel and other metals make these metals very vulnerable to oxidation, which is harmful to the weld. Flux is typically a chemical compound that combines with impurities and with oxygen to prevent harmful oxidation of the hot metals. After combining with impurities while the flux is in the molten state, the resultant molten liquid is called *slag*, which later solidifies and must be removed from the finished weld. With some processes, one of the inert gases, such as

---

[1]American Welding Society recommended abbreviation.

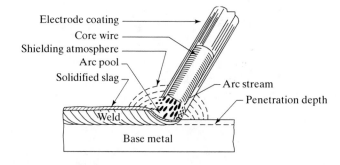

Electrode coating
Core wire
Shielding atmosphere
Arc pool
Solidified slag
Arc stream
Penetration depth
Weld
Base metal

FIGURE 12.1

Stick electrode or SMAW (shielded metal arc welding).

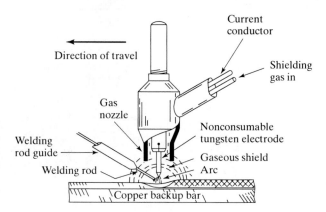

Current conductor
Direction of travel
Shielding gas in
Gas nozzle
Nonconsumable tungsten electrode
Welding rod guide
Gaseous shield
Welding rod
Arc
Copper backup bar

FIGURE 12.2

TIG (tungsten inert gas) welding or GTAW (gas tungsten arc welding).

argon or helium, is used for the same purpose. The inert gas displaces the air ambient to the weld and thus keeps harmful oxygen away from the hot metals. Unfortunately, this inert gas also sometimes keeps the oxygen away from the *welder*, an obviously undesirable characteristic that will be explored subsequently in the section on hazards mechanisms.

One other electric-arc process should be mentioned at this point: *submerged arc welding*, or SAW. In this process, the flux is granular and, as can be seen in Figure 12.3, the electric arc is hidden under the pile and puddle of granular and melted flux, respectively. This has great safety and health advantages, and submerged arc is growing in popularity. Automatic welding machines are often programmed to apply flux automatically and move the electrode over a long, straight path in the manufacture of large structural steel beams or plate girders. However, SAW welding in overhead positions is a problem because the granular flux will fall by gravity instead of covering the weld.

Resistance welding (Figure 12.4) is one of the least hazardous welding processes. It is widely used in mass-production manufacturing. However, resistance is generally restricted to relatively thin sheets of material. The concept of resistance welding is to pass electrical current *through* the material to be welded, enabling the heat so generated to melt the material. Physical pressure is also applied at the point of the weld. The attractive thing about resistance welding is that the melting generally occurs only where the mating surfaces meet. The outside and adjacent surfaces that are exposed to atmospheric contaminants harmful to the weld do not reach melting point, and damage

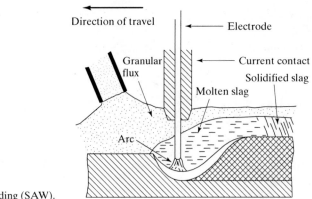

FIGURE 12.3

Submerged arc welding (SAW).

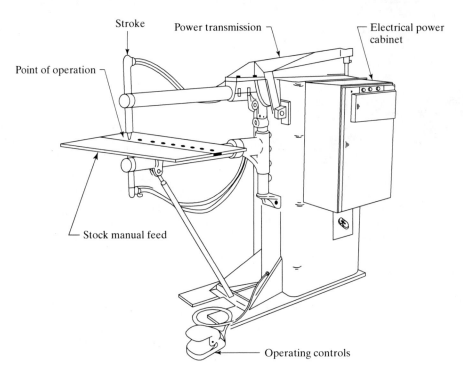

FIGURE 12.4

Resistance spot welder.

to the material is minimal. This fact also precludes the need for a flux or inert gas to complicate both the production process and the safety and health aspects.

Resistance spot welding (RSW) is widely used to join sheet metal coverings, housings, guards, and shields on such products as space heaters and grain bins. Another important industry for spot welding is the automobile industry. Seam welding (RSEW) is generally preferred over spot welding for watertight seals because a pair of rollers apply continuous pressure and a series of electrical pulses make, in effect, a seam of overlapping spot welds.

Some of the more unusual or exotic processes should be mentioned because, although they may rarely be used or seen by the safety and health manager, the nature of their hazards may be entirely different. The *thermit* method of welding (TW) employs a chemical reaction to produce the welding heat. Thermit is good for awkward applications or perhaps where the welding to be done is remote from convenient electrical power or gas sources. *Laser beam welding* (LBW) uses a concentrated laser light beam to generate the welding heat. Lasers pinpoint the weld so precisely that they are used for almost microscopic applications on tiny parts.

GAS WELDING HAZARDS

The myriad of different processes for welding should give some clue as to why the breadth of welding hazards is so great. We now examine these hazards, beginning with gas welding because it has given safety and health managers the most problems.

Acetylene Hazards

Gas welding cylinders are so familiar that it is difficult to keep in mind their devastating destructive power. Acetylene gas, the fuel gas for most gas welding, is so unstable that its pressurization in manifolds to pressures greater than 15 psig (30 psia) is prohibited. Contrast this low pressure with the familiar oxygen, nitrogen, or other ordinary compressed-gas cylinder, which contains pressure greater than 2000 psi.

There are tricks to avoid the instability hazards of acetylene gas; the most popular one is to dissolve the gas in a suitable solvent, usually acetone. Then the pressure can be raised to around 200 psi. As the acetylene gas is used from the acetylene cylinder, the pressure is lowered slightly, permitting a greater quantity of gas to bubble out of the solution, resulting in equilibrium at a pressure suitable for welding. In this fashion, a relatively large quantity of acetylene can be stored in a reasonably portable cylinder.

Figure 12.5 shows the inside of an acetylene cylinder. Most people do not know that the cylinder contains a solid absorbent filler material for the acetone–acetylene solution. The contents are more liquid than gas, and this gives rise to a hazard mechanism. Acetylene cylinders should be kept valve end up both while in storage and while

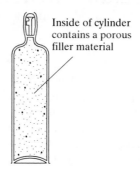

Inside of cylinder contains a porous filler material

FIGURE 12.5

Acetylene cylinder.

in use. There is no harm in tilting cylinders slightly, and in fact this is common practice in the use of hand trucks to handle cylinders connected for use. Good advice, however, is not to tip acetylene cylinders to an angle more than 45° from vertical.

If the cylinders are stored horizontally or valve end down, liquid acetone could enter the valve passages instead of the intended acetylene gas. Then later, when the valve is opened, the welder could get an unexpected flow of highly flammable liquid acetone instead of acetylene gas. Since the purpose of opening the valve is usually to ignite the torch with a sparking source, it is obvious that it would be easy to ignite the liquid acetone accidentally. A burning quantity of spilled acetone is difficult to control and is quite dangerous.

Another way to get liquid acetone through the cylinder valve is to use the cylinder when it is nearly empty. Acetone coming through the valve or leaking elsewhere is easy to detect. The principal active ingredient in nail-polish remover is acetone, the odor of which is familiar to most everyone.

Acetylene cylinders have been known to leak around the valve stem, causing what welders call "stem fires." Another place to check for leaks is from the plug in the bottom of the cylinder. In one incident, fortunately not a serious accident, the welder was perplexed by occasionally hearing a small explosion, audible but causing no damage. The mystery was finally solved when it was discovered that the explosions were occurring in the small concave area beneath the bottom of the cylinder. The little explosions were harmless, but imagine the hazard that could have accumulated if there had been no ignition, and the defective cylinder had been allowed to slowly release acetylene, as in overnight storage.

It is important to be able to turn off the fuel flow quickly in an emergency, especially when the fuel is acetylene. Some acetylene cylinder valves are designed to accept a special wrench, but ordinary hammers and wrenches are in general inappropriate for opening cylinder valves. The special wrench should be kept available for immediate use.

A carbide "miner's lamp" burns on acetylene by dropping lumps of calcium carbide into water. The resulting chemical reaction is as follows:

$$CaC_2 + 2H_2O \rightarrow Ca(OH)_2 + C_2H_2 \uparrow$$

Thus, acetylene gas slowly bubbles out of the water solution and fuels the lamp. The same chemical reaction can be used for generating acetylene gas for welding by means of an acetylene generator. This process avoids the hazards of large-scale storage of acetylene cylinders. But the process of storing acetylene in cylinders has been so perfected, so commercialized, and made relatively safe, that acetylene generators are rarely seen anymore. The cylinder supplier has a large acetylene generator somewhere, but this is of no concern to most safety and health managers.

Before leaving the subject of acetylene hazards, we should consider alternative fuel gases. If a safety and health manager really wants to win the approval of top management, he or she will offer a production innovation that will make the workplace safer, reduce the company's legal vulnerability, and cut production costs—*all at the same time!* It is difficult to do, but not impossible, and the selection of welding fuel gas presents a potential opportunity. It takes some "homework" and particular diligence to pursue the issue, but the rewards to the company and to everyone involved can be dramatic.

MAPP gas, natural gas, and propane were mentioned earlier as possible alternatives to acetylene. The first objection that the safety and health manager will hear to the idea of using these gases is that they do not burn hot enough. It is true that acetylene excels when a very hot flame is needed, but many industrial applications do not need temperatures as high as welders want for *some* applications. Alternate gases are certainly hot enough for brazing and soldering, as well as being hot enough for some welding applications.

One reason that halfhearted attempts to switch to alternate gases do not work is that welders attempt to switch gases while using the same torch tips they used with acetylene. Special torch tips may be the secret to making the new idea a success. Welders may also need to be taught how to adjust their torches to achieve a "neutral flame" with the proper burning characteristics.

Case Study 12.1 will illustrate how one safety and health manager had a positive economic impact on his company by making a suggestion that improved safety while reducing production costs.

CASE STUDY 12.1

REDUCING A HAZARD BY SUBSTITUTION

The safety and health manager of a manufacturing plant noticed that a production operation was using conventional gas welding equipment to perform a brazing operation. The conventional gas welding setup is a portable cart with a torch connected to oxygen and acetylene cylinders. However, in a production operation in which the process stays in one place within the plant, there is no need for the welding equipment to be on a portable cart and use fuel gases supplied in expensive portable bottles or tanks. Furthermore, since the operation was brazing, not welding, a much lower temperature was needed to do the job, which gave the safety and health manager the idea that perhaps dangerous and expensive acetylene gas, with its characteristic hot flame, might not be needed. The cheapest alternative welding fuel of all, natural gas piped into manifolds in the plant, was suggested as an alternative to acetylene. Unfortunately, public utility supplies of natural gas are at very low pressures, approximately 4 oz/in^2 and welders scoffed at the idea, saying that the natural gas pressures were too low to be effective in this production process. Not giving up easily, the safety and health manager negotiated an arrangement with the supplier utility to supply the natural gas to the plant at higher pressures than is normally used for other gas customers. The result was a very successful brazing operation using natural gas as a fuel substitute for the much more expensive acetylene gas. By following through with his idea, this safety and health manager gained prestige with the plant manager and throughout the plant by demonstrating that he was a problem solver with an eye for production cost and efficiency as well as for safety. At the same time, he succeeded in reducing the plant's exposure to OSHA citation for some of the most frequently cited OSHA standards ever.

Oxygen Cylinders

We have seen the hazards of highly unstable acetylene, and by comparison oxygen is much more stable; in fact, it is almost completely safe *if* it is kept away from fuel sources. But ironically, oxygen cylinders are more dangerous than acetylene cylinders. The reason for this danger is the extremely high pressure contained by the oxygen cylinder. Figure 12.6 depicts the familiar oxygen cylinder; note its resemblance to the shape of a bomb or a rocket. It is difficult to comprehend the energy that can be released by the sudden rupture of the valve on an oxygen cylinder containing 2000-psi pressure. There have been numerous accounts of cylinders becoming airborne and crashing into brick walls, demolishing the walls. If a cylinder valve ruptures while the cylinder is confined in a relatively small room, it may ricochet off walls until it kills anyone unfortunate enough to happen to be in the same room when the valve breaks. Consider the hazard of a heavy cylinder flying wildly around the room like a rapidly deflating balloon.

Workers often unwittingly drop oxygen cylinders onto the ground or bang them violently together. Oxygen cylinders are often seen standing alone and unsupported. Even though they are quite heavy, their small bases make them easy to tip over, with the resultant danger of knocking off the valve. The temptation to leave oxygen cylinders standing alone and unsecured needs to be dealt with in safety training sessions.

Another temptation with oxygen cylinders is that they seem to make perfect rollers for supporting and moving heavy items about. No matter whether the cylinders are full or "empty" (even a spent cylinder is not completely empty), use of cylinders as rollers or support can damage the cylinder and perhaps the valve. Furthermore, the large, heavy cylinders used as rollers present a problem of *control*. Once a heavy load begins to roll on a set of welding cylinders, it can even *run over* an unsuspecting victim.

A perennial problem is keeping track of the valve protection cap, which must be removed to use the cylinder, but which also must be screwed back into place when the cylinder is in storage. This cap protects the important valve from damage, and if the cylinder is ever moved about without it, there is a risk of the cylinder falling and knocking off the valve, with disastrous results.

When an oxygen cylinder is strapped to a wheeled cart or hand truck along with its companion acetylene cylinder and the regulator assembly is in place for welding, the

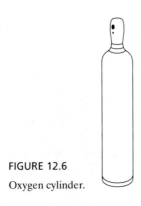

FIGURE 12.6

Oxygen cylinder.

cylinder is generally considered to be in operational status, not in storage. Therefore, industry practice says that the valve protection caps do not have to be in place in these situations.

By looking carefully at the valve protection cap in Figure 12.6, a somewhat odd-looking vertical slot can be seen; actually, there are two, but one is hidden in this view. These slots have a definite engineering purpose, but not the purpose most people think. If the valve comes off while the protection cap is screwed into place, the escaping gas will impact at high velocity on the closed top portion of the cap, tending to counter the force of the gas escaping at the valve. The slotted parts on the sides of the cap permit the gas to escape, but in directions exactly opposite to each other, balancing forces and leaving the cylinder relatively at rest.

Unfortunately, the existence of the slotted openings on the cap are an invitation to their misuse by the worker who is attempting to handle the cylinder. Cylinders are heavy and unwieldy, especially to the worker who has had to handle a lot of them in one day. Furthermore, in cold weather these cylinders have a tendency to become frozen to the ground, to a slab, or even to each other. The worker will want to find a means to break them apart from each other or from the slab to which they are frozen. The slotted opening on the cap seems to be an ideal place to insert a pry bar to obtain some leverage. But this is *not* the purpose of the slots, and misuse in this fashion is what can lead to a broken or damaged valve.

As if the extreme pressure hazards were not enough, oxygen presents additional hazards due to its chemical properties. As stated before, it is relatively stable in the absence of fuel sources, but the fire hazard of pure oxygen under pressure in the presence of a combustible substance is extraordinary. A substance as benign as ordinary grease can suddenly become explosively combustible in the presence of pure oxygen under pressure. A worker will often hold his or her hand over the valve opening when first opening the valve to test the cylinder. If the hands or gloves are greasy, an explosive combustion can follow in which a hand can easily be lost.

We have examined the separate hazards of acetylene and oxygen, but when oxygen and acetylene cylinders are stored together, the hazards are multiplied. There is always the possibility that one or more cylinders will leak. The reader will perhaps recall the earlier account describing small explosions from a leaking plug in the bottom of an acetylene cylinder. Acetylene is already highly flammable, and the presence of pure oxygen makes the situation about five times as serious. A noncombustible barrier at least 5 feet high must separate oxygen and acetylene cylinders, or they must be moved apart at least 20 feet.

Torches and Apparatus

Because of their vital role in safety, torches, manifolds, regulators, and related apparatus must be "approved," usually by a recognized testing laboratory, such as Underwriters' or Factory Mutual.

The familiar torch, illustrated in Figure 12.7, is a more sophisticated piece of engineering than most people realize. The torch is often taken to be simply a handy double tube-and-valve assembly for delivering both oxygen and fuel gas to the weld flame, but it

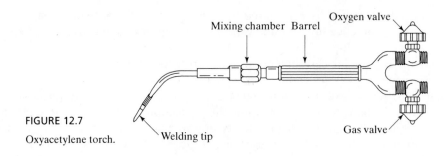

FIGURE 12.7

Oxyacetylene torch.

is more than that. Note in the figure that it has a *mixing chamber*. The torch is designed so that the mixing takes place at the right time and in the correct *total* volume. The welder controls the *proportion* of volumes of the mix by adjusting the torch valves for oxygen or acetylene, an oxidizing flame being oxygen rich and a reducing flame being fuel rich, but the total volume of the mixture is determined by the torch itself. The mixing chamber is mated to the various correct apertures for the approved torch tips, and this also is an important balance. If the balance is disturbed, flow rates may also be disturbed, and the flame may begin to travel back up the mixture stream and begin to burn *inside* the torch! This is really not all that uncommon; all welders know this phenomenon and commonly call it *flashback*. A popping or snapping sound is a warning that flashback is about to occur. Once the flashback begins, a distinctive humming sound can be heard. The heat being generated inside the torch will soon ruin it, and it also presents a safety hazard. The dangerous situation is alleviated by turning off both torch valves quickly.

Even with approved torches and tips, flashback can occur because of the deterioration of the equipment, especially the tips. The tips are close to the heat and naturally become brittle or burned and crack, or pieces may break off. If the tip is not replaced, flashback is likely.

Despite the importance and sophistication of the torch and tip, it is not uncommon to see the torch used as a hammer or chisel! This temptation arises due to the formation of a slag, a waste product of the flux mentioned earlier. This hard coating of slag generally covers the weld and sticks to it. To finish the job, the welder or helper must chip the brittle slag off the finished weld. The torch and tip are so handy for this purpose (take note of shape in Figure 12.7) that welders will often take the shortcut of using the torch as a chipping tool. This is a good way to ruin an expensive piece of apparatus and at the same time increase the likelihood of flashback due to a damaged torch or tip.

The torch assembly is expensive and may be owned personally by the welder. Even when the company owns the torch, the individual welder to whom it is assigned may rightfully be very possessive because of the importance of care of the apparatus. This can cause another safety problem. Welders may want to keep their torches in their locked toolboxes, but the danger here is that almost all toolboxes contain at least some grease or oil materials. Grease or oil on the torch is dangerous because of the oxygen hazards discussed earlier. Case Study 12.2 illustrates a related hazard, locking welding torches in personal lockers.

CASE STUDY 12.2

WELDING TORCH SAFETY

Welding torches are valuable pieces of equipment, and welders are reluctant to leave them unsecured at the end of a work day. Personal lockers for personal valuables are sometimes designed so that welding torches can be locked inside while the torches remain connected to the hoses that in turn remain connected to the welding fuel and oxygen cylinders used by the welder. In the state of Iowa, a welder once locked his torch inside his personal locker in this way. The welder closed his torch valves before leaving work, but he did not close the cylinder valves on the welding cart. The torch valves leaked a small amount of acetylene gas and oxygen, which overnight built up an explosive mixture in the confined space inside the locker. The next morning the welder opened his locker and was apparently smoking a cigarette at the time. The acetylene–oxygen mixture inside the locker ignited in a powerful explosion that decapitated the welder.

The next most abused piece of welding apparatus is the hose for delivering gas to the torch. To be practical, this hose must be flexible, and it is thus subject to the physical hazards of wear and tear and deterioration to which such materials are generally susceptible. Multiple hoses can easily become entangled, and because of this, welders commonly wrap the acetylene and oxygen hoses together with tape simply to keep them more orderly, but such taping practices may hide defects in the hose. It is a good idea to keep at least 8 of every 12 inches uncovered.

Manifolds are the rigid tubing networks that enable one or more cylinders to supply one or more torches. Manifold setups are sometimes found when a regular production operation requires long-term, regular use of welding gas. The principal purpose of welding manifolds is to increase gas welding volumes, but safety is also usually enhanced by the more permanent arrangement. An example manifold setup was described in Case Study 12.1.

Service Piping

Manifolds, described in the previous section, are not to be confused with *service piping*, an even more permanent arrangement. Some plants use so much welding gas that it becomes practical to pipe the gas to the workstation, which can present some problems. The piping for acetylene must be either steel or wrought iron because copper might react with the acetylene to produce copper acetylide, a dangerous explosive. A danger with oxygen piping is again the possibility of contact with oil or grease. Fittings and pipe must be checked before assembly and thoroughly cleaned if necessary. A solution of hot water and caustic soda or trisodium phosphate is suggested for this purpose. A modern solvent such as chlorothane (1,1,1-trichloroethylene) is recommended by some engineers today. Oxygen piping systems should be purged after assembly by blowing them out with oil-free nitrogen or oil-free carbon dioxide. Chlorothane should be used to be sure that every trace of oil is removed.

Flashback can occur in service pipe systems, too, and flashback protection devices are specified, as are check valves in appropriate positions. One design for flashback protection devices involves a simple water lock. But if the water freezes, the system will not work, so antifreeze protection is needed.

The things that can go wrong with a service piping system for welding are numerous and sometimes subtle. These problems involve inadequate emergency venting, improper joints, mistakes in installation in tunnels, and other items too numerous to mention here. The purpose of this book is to alert the safety and health manager to the potential problems accompanying these systems so that he or she can be sure that personnel obtain and follow the appropriate standards for installing these systems.

ARC WELDING HAZARDS

Arc welding is a more popular process and is in many ways even more hazardous than is gas welding, even with its more stormy safety record. This is one of the ironies of the subject. The major hazards of arc welding are health hazards, fires and explosions, eye (radiation) hazards, and confined space hazards, but they also appear to a lesser degree in gas welding and other welding. Therefore, these subjects are addressed in later sections. Before such arc welding hazards are covered, however, the equipment used in arc welding should be understood.

Equipment Design

Industrial arc welding manufacturers do all they can, by means of federal standards they have helped to write and in other ways, to promote their equipment to the exclusion of lesser and cheaper models that might compete. But there is a logic to their efforts other than the profit motive. Small and relatively inexpensive models of arc welding machines are available that operate off ordinary household 110-volt current. But there are physical disadvantages with welding that uses ordinary household current. Welding requires large amounts of electrical power in the form of low-voltage, high-amperage circuits. Since household circuits are rated for amperages insufficient for effective welding, the small household machines make up in voltage what they lack in amperage. The high-voltage hazards of these small welding machines are admittedly difficult to understand because the industrial welding machines are supplied by much higher voltages—typically 240 to 480 volts! The key to this paradox is that the industrial machines step down the high voltage to less than 80 volts while raising the amperage to effective levels.

Grounding

Even with machines operating at proper voltages, the welder or other personnel can receive an electrical shock from contact with the machine if something goes wrong.

The protection for this is to be sure that the frame of the welding machine is properly grounded. Thus, if there is a dangerous short to the frame of the machine, the overcurrent protection mechanism on the circuit will be tripped, protecting personnel. Welding machine grounding needs to be strong, both physically and electrically, to meet the demands of the current that may be applied to it. This is an especially important consideration for portable machines.

Operation

In the case of welding equipment, safety and health training will pay dividends in longer service lives on the equipment, a point sometimes overlooked. Welding cable carries so much electrical current that it can overheat and damage the insulation. Coiling the cable, although convenient, contributes to this hazard. Coiled cable should be spread out before welding. Splices in the cable are not permitted within 10 feet of the electrode holder. The splices themselves must be properly insulated. Some judgment is required to determine when welding cables should be replaced. Certainly, damage to the extent that some conductors have bare spots is cause for replacement.

Care must be taken by the welder to prevent the wrong items from becoming a part of the welding circuit, either during welding or while the electrode holders are not in use. Voltage is not so much the danger as is heat produced by the potentially high amperages. Compressed gas tanks or cylinders must not be part of the electrical circuit, regardless of the flammability of their contents. The heat buildup caused by a high-amperage current through the conducting metal cylinder can cause pressure buildup in the cylinder that can exceed its design limits.

Some types of arc welding are safer than others, and they are gaining in popularity. This is especially true with respect to the hazards of fume generation and radiation, which will be discussed later.

RESISTANCE WELDING HAZARDS

The cleanest, most healthful, and probably safest form of welding is resistance welding. There are still hazards from electrical shock, but more important are the mechanical hazards surrounding the point of operation.

Shock Hazards

As in the spark coil of an automobile, many resistance welding machines build up electrical energy in a bank of capacitors for sudden release when the weld is made. The voltage may reach hundreds or even thousands of volts at peak. These voltages are not the empty variety seen in discharges of static electricity collected by walking on a thick carpet. The voltages may be at the same level, but the welding machine voltages carry with them the capacity to deliver a burning current. The capacitors that store this electrical energy should have interlocked doors and access panels. Not only must the inter-lock stop the power to the machine, it must also short-circuit all capacitors. Without this short-circuiting, the capacitors could deliver a lethal shock even with the power *disconnected*. The short-circuiting of welding machine capacitors when the machine is turned off is an example of the concept of "zero mechanical state," and of the general fail-safe principle.

Guarding

Spot and seam welding machines apply pressure to the materials when the weld is made. For spot welding machines, this pressure makes the machine analogous to a power press, and the operator can be injured from the mechanical hazards alone. The reader may want to refer back to Figure 12.4 to study the operation of the spot welder.

Seam welding machines are not like power presses, but they, too, have point-of-operation hazards. The nature of the hazard for seam welders is that the opposing rotation of the rollers produces a pair of in-running nip points both above and below the material being welded. The hazards of seam welders do not seem to be as pressing as those of spot welders because seam welding is more often a part of an automatic or mechanized production operation, and thus operator exposure is not as great.

FIRES AND EXPLOSIONS

Welding is one of the principal causes of industrial fires. Perhaps even more than for any other welding hazards, the safety and health manager can have an impact on this particular hazard because preventing welding fires is more of a procedural matter than anything else. This means that training becomes a very important element in the hazard prevention strategy. Fortunately for the safety and health manager, there is a wealth of audiovisual aids, literature materials, and case studies on the subject of welding fires.

To use just one case history as an example, one of the most devastating and tragic industrial accidents in the nation's history occurred in Arkansas in the 1960s. A welder's spark started a fire in a missile silo, and 53 workers trapped inside the silo were killed. This accident dramatically illustrates how welding adds to other hazards, such as confined workspaces, flammable and combustible materials, and lack of ventilation. Welding on old oil drums or pipes that have contained asphalt or other petroleum products has resulted in a large number of explosions and senseless fatalities.

Welding, a dangerous operation, and confined spaces, which are dangerous locations, often appear together. We addressed primarily the health hazards of working in confined spaces. When the job to be done in the confined space is welding, both health and safety hazards are compounded. The use of inert gas to protect the weld can cause oxygen deficiency in a confined space. In another scenario, the presence of oxygen and ignition sources from gas welding processes can aggravate the problem of fires and explosions when the welding is in a confined space. Welding is often a repair operation, and unfortunately the location of the necessary repair is in a confined space.

People do not seem to realize the ignition potentials of welding operations. Welding is not safe to watch directly because of the eye hazards, so unfortunately, except for welders themselves or their helpers, few people realize what kind of a fireworks display is really taking place. Some industrial movies are good for illustration of these fireworks. Sparks are flying everywhere—not just the benign variety as seen flying from a typical bench grinder, but visible chunks and spatters of red-hot molten metal that can burn a hole completely through heavy fabric, plastic containers, and cracks in floors. Welders are more likely to know the potential for fires generated by the arcs and sparks generated by the welding process. One would think that the welder would thus hesitate to weld in areas in which the welding sparks could cause fires. The subtlety lies in the fact that welding is often a short repair operation, and the temptation is to take a few chances because of the short duration of the hazard. This temptation often leads to the type of tragedy described in Case Study 12.3.

CASE STUDY 12.3

WELDING IN A CONFINED SPACE

An employee of a trailer service company entered a 8500-gallon cargo tank to weld a leak on the interior wall of the tanker. Despite the presence of strong fumes of lacquer thinner (the material previously carried in the tanker), the welder decided to proceed with the repairs even though the written company safety policy required the use of an explosion meter at that point. When he began welding, an explosion occurred. The employee was removed from the tank and taken to a nearby hospital, where he was declared dead by the attending physician (ref. Preamble).

Welding Permits

Even before federal standards required permits for entering certain confined spaces, the advantages of a permit system for welding operations were recognized. There is sometimes a tendency to ignore the short-term hazards of welding repair operations and proceed to get the job done quickly. The safety and health manager is wise to counter this natural tendency by instituting a system of requiring approval and written permits to do welding operations, even for quick repairs. There are so many special precautions to take that a signed checklist is a good idea. The responsible party is usually the supervisor of the area in which the welding is to take place, but in some instances the welder can make the necessary checks and sign the form. The safety and health manager's responsibility is to set up the permit system and ensure that it is executed properly by actually checking permits occasionally when welding is seen to be taking place in areas of potential hazard. Any responsible party will give the matter some conscientious attention before signing a welding permit form, especially if personnel have received safety training that exposes them to the devastating hazards of welding fires such as the one that killed 53 workers in Arkansas. Such training will certainly make the supervisor or welder think twice before signing the form.

Judgment should be exercised to attempt to set up a permit system that will be considered reasonable by welders and plant personnel alike. The key to this reasonableness will be to set up blanket permits or exemptions from the permit system in those areas of the plant in which fire hazards are minimal. Welding done in the welder's own welding shop, for instance, should be his or her responsibility, and for the safety and health manager to attempt to impose a permit system in the welding shop would obviously constitute unwise interference. For some plants, the entire plant might be reasonably safe from welding fires, and no permit system may be needed, except for confined spaces. Hazard identification surveys and advance planning for exactly when and where the permit system is really needed will go a long way toward the establishment of a reasonable system.

EYE PROTECTION

Eye protection comes under the topic of personal protective equipment, but eye protection for welding operations is so important that this chapter on welding would not be complete without a section on this subject.

Note the careful reference in the preceding paragraph to welding operat*ions*, not welding operat*ors*. The welders themselves need protection, of course, but it is easy to forget about welding helpers and others in the area. Almost every welder has received an eyeburn at some time during his or her career and knows to be careful to wear eye protection as much to prevent pain and discomfort as to prevent long-range eye injury. But less experienced personnel may need more supervision and administrative controls to ensure protection.

A summary of minimum appropriate eye protection shades is shown in Figure 12.8. In selecting eye protection, one should remember that the darker shades (higher shade numbers) provide more protection than do the lighter (lower shade number) shades. The trade-off is visibility. Some shades are so dark that the user can hardly see the workpiece until the arc is turned on. To get the maximum protection, the darkest shade consistent with adequate visibility should be used. The various arc welding methods produce much more intense radiation and thus require higher shade numbers than does gas welding. The radiation from arc welding, except submerged arc methods, is so intense that a helmet is necessary to protect the entire face area from painful burns. Gas welding is typically done while wearing goggles.

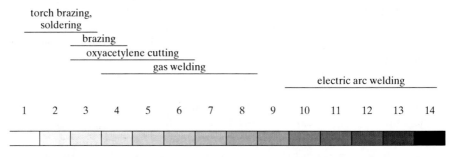

FIGURE 12.8

Summary of recommended shade numbers for various welding, cutting, brazing, and soldering operations (adapted from OSHA standard 1910 Subpart I, Appendix B).

PROTECTIVE CLOTHING

Proper clothing is serious business to the professional welder. Virtually every experienced arc welder has, some time in his or her career, sustained a "sunburn" from the ultraviolet rays produced by the welding arc. Such a welder does not need to be told to use protective clothing to cover all skin areas that would otherwise be exposed to the arc rays. But ultraviolet burn is only one of several hazards against which protective clothing is intended. Hot, burning sparks or small pieces of molten metal can fall into openings around shoes or between pieces of clothing. Even when the clothing is seamless or when openings are well shielded, a hot piece of molten metal can be trapped in a fold and burn its way through to the welder.

Leather is the traditional favorite material for welding gloves, aprons, and leggings because of its superior thermal protective qualities. Wool is also very durable. But Nomex and other synthetic materials are also becoming popular for welders' protective clothing. Cotton fabric is attacked by the radiation and soon disintegrates even if it escapes ignition by the sparks.

Hazards to the welder from falling sparks and weld metal are greatly increased when the welding must be done overhead. The welder is virtually taking a shower in welding sparks. All clothing openings must be carefully shielded, and even under the helmet, the welder's head must be protected from such misfortunes as a welding spark in the ear.

GASES AND FUMES

There are two extremes in degree of concern over welder breathing hazards. One extreme, call it position A, is taken generally by welders themselves, who often have no concern at all over chronic exposure to welding "smoke." Some welders even enjoy the smell of welding fumes in the air. The other extreme, position B, is the occasionally overzealous industrial hygienist who can find a hazard somewhere in almost all welding fume situations. Both extremes are only partially correct and can lead to dangerous errors in safety and health strategies.

The principal error in position A is that persons taking this extreme position are usually overlooking the long-term effects of chronic exposure. These persons tend to believe that if the welding smoke does not make them nauseated, dizzy, or give rise to some other acute symptom, the fumes are safe. The chronic exposures can actually be the most dangerous because of their adverse effects on worker health.

Position B exaggerates the effects of tiny exposures to dangerous contaminants. It is terrifying to realize that some welding releases phosgene gas, the same gas that has been used in chemical warfare. But the exposures are generally very low and can be controlled by appropriate procedures. In the final analysis, no epidemiological studies have shown welding to be an extremely dangerous occupation. From a health standpoint, welders do not have significantly shorter life spans than workers in general. Having considered this perspective, let us categorize the hazards of welding atmospheres and rationally examine what should be done about them.

Contaminant Categories

Figure 12.9 diagrams the major kinds of welding atmosphere contaminants: particulates and gases. The particulates are dust particles or even tinier smoke particles. Metal fumes in the welding atmosphere are tiny particles of metal that have been vaporized by the arc and then resolidified into particles as they cool. The gases may be either already present, as in inert shielding gases, or they may be chemical reaction products of the process.

The term *pneumoconioses* in Figure 12.9 is merely a general term that literally means "reactions to dust in the lungs." Everyone's lungs must deal with dust to some extent, and some welders' pneumoconioses are no more hazardous than would be caused by sweeping the floor. Some welding dusts are more hazardous, however, because they cause *fibrosis*, the building up of useless fibrous tissue in the lungs. The most harmful dusts are those in which the microscopic particles have the shape of fibers instead of more rounded particles. Asbestos and silica are examples of such dusts.

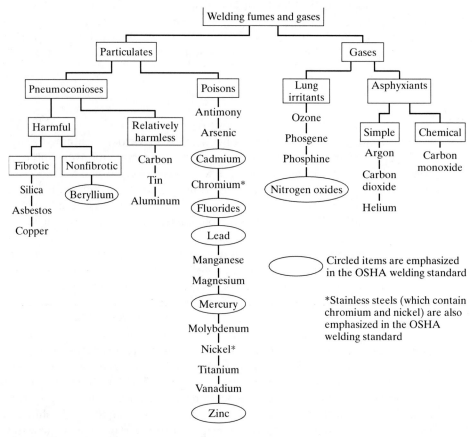

FIGURE 12.9

Classification of welding fumes and gases by hazard.

The "pulmonary irritants" are simpler in that they attack the lungs directly, whether the irritants be particulate or gas. The more insidious hazards, though, are from those particulates or gases that do not irritate the lungs directly, but through the lungs gain access to the rest of the body, where they act as systemic poisons.

It would be nice to have quantified tables of expected contaminant levels for various atmospheric constituents for various types of welding. There have been some experimental attempts at this (see refs. Fumes, Welding), but there are so many variables to be controlled that it is almost impossible to obtain reliable predictions of weld fume content. The best strategy is to be aware of potential hazardous contaminants and to know what conditions are most likely to produce these contaminants. Atmospheric sampling can then be used in suspect situations to establish whether contaminant levels are indeed excessive.

Hazard Potentials

The biggest contributor to atmospheric contaminants around welding is the coating or condition of the surfaces to be joined. It is true that welding on clean iron or ordinary construction steel produces fairly large concentrations of iron oxide fume, but fortunately siderosis, the pneumoconiosis resulting from iron oxide, is not really a very dangerous disease when it occurs alone. If the surface of the metal has a coating of material containing asbestos, however, this coating must be removed to prevent asbestos contamination of the air.

Even the act of cleaning the metal surfaces to be welded can result in secondary hazards. If chlorinated hydrocarbons, such as trichloroethylene, are used to clean the metal, these solvents must also be removed thoroughly before the welding takes place. The energy of the welding arc can cause decomposition of the solvent into dangerous phosgene gas.

Galvanized is a term referring to a zinc coating on the metal to prevent rust. Welding on galvanized steel needs extra caution and good ventilation because the welding arc can produce fumes of zinc or zinc oxide. Zinc is not as dangerous as its relative, lead, but it can cause a brief but uncomfortable "metal fume fever." Daily exposure results in a sort of immunity, but this immunity is lost in a few days, even in just a week-end away from exposure. The next Monday morning the nausea and chills are back again, causing this disease to be known as "Monday morning sickness," although admittedly there are other things about Mondays that often make workers "sick."

Plating metals are usually much more dangerous to weld than the iron or steel on which the plating is used. Cadmium is a plating metal for which welding fumes are considered very dangerous. This is one fume that has been known to be fatal in a single acute exposure. Even worse, acute exposures to cadmium usually do not display warning symptoms. Chronic exposures have been associated with emphysema and kidney impairment.

Stainless steel is one of the most dangerous materials to weld because of its high chromium content. Chromium trioxide is formed by the oxidation triggered by the welding heat and reacts with water to produce chromic acid. Ample sources of water can be found on human skin and the mucous membranes, resulting in chromic acid ulceration of these surfaces.

Welding in confined spaces complicates the atmospheric contamination problem. In confined spaces, the hazards of gases increase dramatically. Nitrogen and argon are inerting agents for the protection of the weld, but they are also simple asphyxiants to the welder. Another simple asphyxiant in welding atmospheres is carbon dioxide. Contrasted with the simple asphyxiants is the chemical asphyxiant carbon monoxide, also present to some extent in welding atmospheres, especially for gas welding.

Nitrogen is not as inert as argon or helium, mentioned earlier as inerting agents, although it is true that nitrogen is a relatively stable element. But nitrogen can be oxidized, especially in the extremes of welding temperatures, creating oxides that can be harmful. Since there are several oxides of nitrogen and they are somewhat difficult to isolate, industrial hygienists often refer to them as a group, naming them "NO_x." Nitrous oxide, N_2O, sometimes called "laughing gas," was once considered harmless and was even used as a dental anesthetic. Much more harmful are its dangerous cousins, nitric oxide (NO) and especially nitrogen dioxide (NO_2). According to Sax (ref. Sax), NO_x in concentrations of 60 to 150 ppm can have a delayed effect after the initial irritation of nose and throat. After breathing fresh air, the irritation goes away and the victim may feel all right. However, some 6 to 24 hours later, the following chain of symptoms can begin: tightness and burning sensation in the chest, shortness of breath, restlessness, air hunger, cyanosis, loss of consciousness, and, finally, death. Welding atmospheres are usually not this concentrated, but it should be noted that 100 ppm is only 0.01%.

Lead and mercury are well-known systemic poisons, and airborne fumes are the prime avenues for entry of these poisons into the body. Most welding does not involve these two metals. Soldering is used widely with lead alloys, but the low temperatures of soldering render the lead fumes relatively harmless.

Beryllium is a very useful alloy metal used in steel, copper, and aluminum. Unfortunately, the presence of the beryllium alloy in the material makes the metal very dangerous to weld. Since beryllium fume (particulate) hazards are both acute and chronic, most welders are wary of beryllium dangers.

Fluorine and fluorine compounds, usually fluorides, enter the welding atmosphere through welding flux or coverings. The popular shielded metal arc welding (SMAW) process is subject to hazards of fluorine compounds. The principal hazard is chronic, not acute, exposure, and long-term exposures cause abnormalities in the victim's bones. Other cleaning compounds and fluxes may also be hazardous, and personnel should check ingredients and heed manufacturer's instructions.

Before leaving the subject of welding gases and fumes, an important point is to be emphasized: None of the toxic materials or hazardous conditions described in this section is so dangerous as to prohibit welding. Welding atmospheres can be made safe by local or general exhaust ventilation or by personal protective equipment. The key is to recognize the potentially hazardous conditions, test atmospheres for excessive contaminant levels, and take corrective action if required.

SUMMARY

Welding represents a microcosm for the study of the entire field of occupational safety and health. It involves mechanical hazards, fire hazards, air-contamination hazards, personal protective equipment considerations, and almost every other subject addressed in this book. Welding processes are many and varied, and most safety and health managers know little about the technical aspects and terminology. A little study of the basics of welding, however, can open up opportunities for revision or substitution of processes that can enhance health and safety and at the same time improve efficiency and cut production costs. No other subject area seems to offer so much opportunity for safety and health managers.

EXERCISES AND STUDY QUESTIONS

12.1 What are the three basic categories of conventional welding? Which of the three is the cleanest and most healthful?

12.2 What distinguishes soldering and brazing from welding?

12.3 What distinguishes soldering from brazing?

12.4 What is the commonly used name for the most popular process of arc welding? What is the official AWS designation for this process?

12.5 Identify the following welding processes:

    (a) GTAW

    (b) GMAW

    (c) SAW

    (d) RSEW

    (e) RSW

12.6 Why should acetylene cylinders be stored valve end up?

12.7 Why are oxygen cylinders charged at so much higher pressures than acetylene cylinders?

12.8 In what ways are greasy gloves of particular hazard to the oxyacetylene welder?

12.9 Describe a way in which gas welding can sometimes be modified to cut production costs and at the same time avoid hazards.

12.10 Why are valve protection caps important to safety? Explain the purpose of the slots in the caps. How are the slots often misused?

12.11 Explain the phenomenon of flashback in welding operations.

12.12 How can taping welding hoses together to keep them orderly result in a hazard?

12.13 Which of the following materials should be avoided in pipes used for delivering acetylene to the work station: steel, wrought iron, or copper? Explain.

12.14 How can small arc welding machines that use ordinary household current be more dangerous than industrial arc welding machines.

12.15 Why should welding cables be uncoiled before using?

12.16 What is the principal hazard of allowing metal tanks to become a part of a welding circuit?

12.17 What arc welding process is gaining popularity because it is more healthful than other arc welding processes? What big disadvantage does it have?

12.18 What is the principal mechanical hazard of spot welders?

12.19 Give at least two reasons why people are psychologically inclined to risk the chance of welding fires.

12.20 Against what principal hazard are welding permits aimed?

12.21 Which of the following welding operations requires the most eye protection: SMAW, SAW, or RSEW? Explain.

12.22 What is the best natural material for welders' protective aprons, gloves, and leggings?

12.23 Name the pneumoconiosis resulting from exposure to iron oxide fume. Is it a severe hazard?

12.24 Why is it difficult to provide accurate tables of welding fume content?

12.25 What distinguishes welding fumes from toxic gases produced by the welding process?

12.26 Describe some workplace material characteristics that, when present, make welding fumes and gases more dangerous to the welder.

12.27 Consider the conditions narrated in Case Study 12.4 (obviously contrived), and describe apparent hazard mechanisms along with potential consequences.

CASE STUDY 12.4

A welder has constructed a manifolding arrangement for an assortment of oxygen and acetylene cylinders stored together lying on the floor. The manifold pressurizes the gaseous acetylene and depressurizes the oxygen to 50-psig for both. The room smells strongly of nail-polish remover. The welder is wearing greasy gloves and is chipping welding slag from the weld using his torch tip. The welding torch is connected to the manifold by two flexible hoses that are carefully wrapped together with duct tape, completely covering the hoses.

12.28 Nitrogen is a gas very widely used in welding operations, except gas welding. Explain.

12.29 In parts per million, calculate the approximate concentration of nitrogen in normal breathing air. How can nitrogen in breathing air be a hazard?

12.30 Acetylene is an unstable gas. Describe steps taken to make it safe to containerize and handle.

12.31 Discuss the principal hazards associated with oxygen cylinders used for welding.

12.32 Name some alternative fuels for acetylene in welding processes. In what way is acetylene superior to these fuels?

12.33 Explain why some people exaggerate the hazards of welding operations. Also explain why some people overly minimize the hazards of welding.

12.34 If items to be welded are cleaned with a solvent before welding, what dangerous gas may be generated if the solvent is not thoroughly removed before welding commences?

12.35 Describe the welders' illness "Monday morning sickness." What causes it?

12.36 Is exposure to welding flux an acute or chronic hazard? What adverse effect does welding flux have on the body?

RESEARCH EXERCISES

12.37 Examine the relative dangers of the various oxides of nitrogen, generically labeled NO_x. Which ones have both acute and chronic effects?

12.38 Look up records of industrial disasters involving welding.

12.39 Check the Internet home page for the American Welding Society. What sources of information there are valuable to the safety and health manager?

STANDARDS RESEARCH QUESTIONS

12.40 This chapter made a point about separating oxygen cylinders from acetylene cylinders in storage either by distance or by a noncombustible barrier at least 5 feet high. Search the OSHA standards for a provision dealing with this problem. Check the NCM database to determine whether this is a frequently cited standard.

12.41 Suppose your company is comparing processes to decide whether to use an arc welding process or a gas welding process. Do some research on the OSHA standards to compare these two types of welding. How do they compare with respect to the generation of OSHA citation activity?

C H A P T E R   1 3

Confined-Space Entry

The danger of work in confined spaces is well known and not new. Suruda et al. report that "the danger of work in confined spaces has been written about since Roman times, when the Emperor Trajan was noted to have sentenced criminals to clean sewers, an occupation considered one of the worst."[1] In 1556, Agricola wrote that stagnant air in mines impaired breathing, and mine fires soon killed those who came to work there. In 1906, The Pittsburgh Survey shocked America. This Russell Sage Foundation study of safety in the workplace in the Greater Pittsburgh area counted 526 work-related deaths and 500 seriously and permanently disabled workers in one year's time. Asphyxiation at work in industries such as steel making was cited in this study as one of the causes of injury and death. In 1925, Alice Hamilton wrote that decomposing organic matter in vats, tank, and manholes emitted hydrogen sulfide, resulting in death by asphyxiation.

NIOSH published a Criteria Document in 1979 containing recommendations for working in confined spaces.[2] In this document, 276 confined-space incidents were analyzed. Of the 193 fatalities, 78 (40 percent) resulted from atmospheric hazards. An Alert: Request for Assistance in Preventing Occupational Fatalities in Confined Spaces was published by NIOSH in 1986.[3] This was followed by a worker's guide in 1987.[4]

The National Institute for Occupational Safety and Health (NIOSH) studied fatalities related to confined-space entry during the period from December 1983 to December 1989.[5] NIOSH used data from a surveillance project called "Fatal Accident Circumstances and Epidemiology" (FACE), which was designed to collect descriptive data on selected fatalities to identify potential risk factors for work-related death, to develop recommended intervention strategies, to disseminate important findings, and to reduce the risk of fatal injury in the workplace. They reviewed 55 confined-space events which resulted in 88 deaths. Only three of the workers who died had received any training in confined-space safety, and only 27 percent of the employers had any type of written confined-space entry procedures. The mean age of the fatality was 35. All were men. Sixty-six percent were workers who were engaged in activities relating to water, wastewater, and sewerage repair, cleaning, inspection, etc. Thirty-five percent of the victims had supervisory duties. The cause of death was: asphyxiation (47 percent), drowning (21 percent), toxicity from chemical exposure (19 percent), blunt-force trauma (10 percent), electrocution (2 percent), and burns (1 percent). Three underlying factors were common to most of these deaths: (1) Failure to recognize the hazards associated with confined spaces, (2) failure to follow existing, known procedures for safe confined-space entry, and (3) incorrect emergency response. Before, during, and after this data-gathering period, attempts were made to advise industry of the dangers involved in confined spaces.

A study published in 1989 of OSHA investigations of asphyxiation and poisoning conducted in 1984 through 1986 showed 188 deaths in confined spaces.[6] Of these, 42 were from mechanical hazards such as engulfment by loose materials, and 146 were from oxygen deficiency or poison gases or chemicals. These confined-space fatalities constituted 4 percent of the fatalities investigated by OSHA during that period of time. The confined-space classification did not include deaths from trench cave-ins (190), electrocutions, or explosions, which occurred in confined spaces.

Finally, on April 15, 1993, OSHA issued a regulation entitled "Permit-Required Confined Spaces" as part of the Code of Federal Regulations, 29 CFR 1910.146. This regulation, because of its broad definition of a confined space, is applicable to an estimated 300,000 facilities with over 12 million employees.

In 1994, NIOSH published a summary of NIOSH findings about worker deaths in confined spaces, using the National Traumatic Occupational Fatalities (NTOF) surveillance system database.[7] NIOSH reviewed death certificates for 1980–1989 in which "injury at work" was indicated. There were 585 separate fatal incidents in confined spaces, with 670 fatalities. Seventy-two (12 percent) involved multiple victims, 61 involving 2 persons; 9, 3 persons; and 2, 4 persons. The confined-space death rate was 0.08 per 100,000 workers per year. In the mining/oil/gas industry that rate was 0.7, in agriculture it was 0.3, and in construction 0.2. Forty-five percent of the deaths were accounted for by asphyxiation, 41 percent by poisoning, and 14 percent by drowning. Clearly, this is a persistent problem.

WHAT IS A CONFINED SPACE?

There are two important definitions regarding confined spaces in the United States. First, in 29 CFR 1910.146 a *confined space* is an enclosed area which (1) is large enough to enable an employee to enter and perform assigned work, (2) has limited or restricted means for entry or exit, and (3) is not designed for continuous employee occupancy.[8] The second definition, as follows, is a subset of the first. In 1910.146, a *permit-required confined space* is a confined space with one or more of the following characteristics: contains or may contain a hazardous atmosphere, contains a material with the potential for "engulfment" of an entrant (such as sawdust or grain), has an internal configuration or shape such that an entrant could be trapped or asphyxiated, or contains any other recognized serious safety or health hazard.

Confined Space

The regulation's definition of a "confined space" is broadly inclusive. The first criterion indicates that a space that cannot be completely entered by an employee is not a confined space. The second criterion is less precise. It includes tanks, vessels, silos, storage bins, hoppers, vaults, and pits, because these have limited means of ingress and egress. Open-topped spaces can be difficult to ingress or egress. ANSI Z 117.1-1977 listed as one criterion for a confined space an open-topped space more than 4 feet in depth.[9] NIOSH says that "Confined spaces include but are not limited to storage tanks, compartments of ships, process vessels, pits, silos, vats, wells, sewers, digesters, degreasers, reaction vessels, boilers, ventilation and exhaust ducts, tunnels, underground utility vaults, and pipelines."[6] It is evident that confined spaces can be found in many, if not most, industries. The third criterion does not effectively limit the domain of confined spaces because it does not spell out the elements of design that must be included for continuous employee occupancy.

Permit-Required Confined Space

The criterion for permit-required confined space that it contains or has a known potential to contain a hazardous atmosphere includes chemicals, sludge, or sewage. "Hazardous atmosphere" means an atmosphere that may expose employees to the risk of death, incapacitation, impairment of ability to self-rescue (escape unaided), injury, or acute illness from one or more of the following causes:

1. Flammable gas, vapor, or mist in excess of 10 percent of its lower flammable limit (LFL);
2. Airborne combustible dust at a concentration that meets or exceeds its LFL;
3. Atmospheric oxygen concentration below 19.5 percent or above 23.5 percent;
4. Atmospheric concentration of any substance for which a dose or a permissible exposure limit is published in Subpart G, Occupational Health and Environmental Control, or in subpart Z, Toxic and Hazardous Substances, of 29 CFR part 1910, and which could result in employee exposure in excess of its dose or permissible exposure limit; and
5. Any atmospheric condition recognized as immediately dangerous to life or health (IDLH).

If a confined space contains a material that has the potential for engulfing an entrant, it is a permit-required confined space. "Engulfment" means the surrounding and effective capture of a person by a liquid or finely divided (flowable) solid substance that can be aspirated to cause death by filling or plugging the respiratory system or that can exert enough force on the body to cause death by strangulation, constriction, or crushing.

If a confined space has an internal configuration or shape that could trap an entrant or contribute to the asphyxiation of an entrant, it is a permit-required confined space. A confined space with inwardly converging walls or a floor which slopes downward and tapers to a smaller cross section is an example of such a potentially dangerous configuration for an entrant.

Finally, a confined space that contains any other recognized serious safety or health hazard is a permit-required confined space. The suggestion to this author is that if an employer has a serious accident or injury in a confined space, unless that accident or injury is unforeseeable, that space should have been a permit-required confined space. The key is prevention of that undesired event, which can be costly and embarrassing to the employer. The employer is under an obligation to recognize serious safety or health hazards before accidents or illnesses occur, and when these are recognized in a confined space, that becomes a permit-required confined space. These hazards can include physical, electrical, mechanical, chemical, biological, radiation, temperature extremes, and structural hazards.

ATMOSPHERIC HAZARDS

NIOSH has developed a classification scheme for atmospheric hazards in confined spaces. It is based on the oxygen content of the air, the flammability characteristics of gases or vapors, and the concentration of toxic substances present. These are shown in Figure 13-1. Classification is determined by the most hazardous condition present.

This classification scheme is useful in considering entry procedures and work practices in confined spaces. It is used in this way in NIOSH's "Criteria for a Recommended Standard: Working in Confined Spaces," 1979.[2]

CHARACTERISTICS

CLASS A
Immediately dangerous to life
   Oxygen: 16 percent or less* (122 mm Hg) or greater than 25 percent (190 mm Hg)
   Flammability: 20 percent or greater of lower flammable limit (LFL)
   Toxicity: Immediately dangerous to life or health (IDLH)

CLASS B
Dangerous, but not immediately life threatening
   Oxygen: 16.1percent to 19.4 percent* (122–147 mm Hg), or 21.5 percent to 25 percent (163–190 mm Hg)
   Flammability: 10–19 percent LFL
   Toxicity: Greater than contamination level, re: 29 CFR Part 1910 Subpart Z (IDLH)

CLASS C
Potential hazard
   Oxygen: 19.5 percent–21.4 percent* (148–163 mm Hg)
   Flammability: 10 percent LFL or less
   Toxicity: Less than contamination level, re: 29 CFR Part 1910 Subpart Z

* Based upon a total atmospheric pressure of 760 mm Hg (sea level)
Table adapted from *Worker Deaths in Confined Spaces*, NIOSH, 1994[106]

FIGURE 13–1   Confined-Space Classification   Table adapted from *Worker Deaths in Confined Spaces*, NIOSH, 1994.[7]

PHYSICAL HAZARDS

Physical hazards include those associated with the unwanted flow of energy in confined space. These include mechanical, electrical, and hydraulic energies; engulfment; communication problems; noise; and the size of ingress and egress openings.

Engulfment hazards often are associated with bins, silos, and hoppers used to store and transfer grain, sand, gravel, or other loose materials. These materials can behave unpredictably and entrap and bury a person in a matter of seconds. The flow path of a bottom-emptying bin forms a funnel shape, with the material at the center of the bin moving faster than elsewhere. The flow rate can become too great for a worker who is caught in the flow path to be able to escape. Material can cling to the sides of a container or vessel that is being emptied from the bottom, forming a "bridge." The bridge may collapse suddenly and without warning upon workers below. Engulfment can happen in seconds.

Activation of mechanical and electrical equipment (agitators, blenders, stirrers, fans, augurs, pumps, machinery with moving parts, etc.) can cause injury to workers in confined spaces. Release of material into or out of confined space can be life threatening to those who are within. Fluids under pressure pose a hazard. Objects falling into confined space present the entrant with the hazard not only of the object but also of limited evasive potential if the object is detected. Slippery surfaces (sometimes made slick by material residue), hot and cold extreme temperatures, inadequate lighting, limited work space, excessive noise, and sources of electrocution all are physical hazards that exacerbate confined-space entry and work.

CHEMICAL, BIOLOGICAL, RADIATION

Chemical hazards of industrial processes are varied and myriad. Hazardous wastes and useful materials that are threatening to life and health abound. There are threats not only of acids, corrosives, and toxics, but also of inert materials that displace oxygen and of materials that reduce oxygen content in confined spaces.

Biological hazards from infectious microorganisms and biological wastes are found in waste streams, pools and ponds, sludge pits, and sewers. Some industrial processes and research efforts involve this hazard intensely and are especially susceptible to its problems. The control of bacteria is a growing area of public health concern. Where these threats are potential within a confined space, entry to that space for work must be made with care.

Radiation potential in both nonionizing and ionizing forms where confined-space entry might occur requires special attention.

MANAGEMENT RESPONSIBILITIES FOR CONFINED SPACES

It is essential that employers have a well-defined and implemented confined-space program. In the United States this program must comply with the requirements of federal and state regulations. It is not the purpose of this text to restate regulations. General program guidelines are provided by NIOSH (1994), without the distinction between "confined space" and "permit-required confined space" given in the federal regulations. These guidelines for elements in a comprehensive, written confined-space entry program are given below.[7]

The program should include, but not be limited to, the following:

- identification of all confined spaces at the facility/operation
- posting a warning sign at the entrance of all confined spaces
- evaluation of hazards associated with each type of confined space
- a job safety analysis for each task to be performed in the confined space
- confined-space-entry procedures
  - initial plan for entry
  - assigned standby person(s)
  - communications between workers inside and standby
  - rescue procedures
  - specified work procedures within the confined space
- evaluation to determine if entry is necessary—can the work be performed from the outside of the confined space?
- issuance of a confined-space-entry permit—this is an authorization and approval in writing that specifies the location and type of work to be done, and certifies that the space has been evaluated and tested by a qualified person and that all necessary protective measures have been taken to ensure the safety of the worker
- testing and monitoring the air quality in the confined space to ensure that
  - oxygen level is at least 19.5 pecent by volume
  - flammable range is less than 10 percent of the LFL (lower flammable limit)
  - all toxic air contaminants are absent
- confined-space preparation
  - isolation/lockout/tagout
  - purging and ventilation
  - cleaning processes
  - requirements for special equipment and tools
- safety equipment and protective clothing to be used for confined-space entry
  - head protection
  - hearing protection
  - hand protection
  - foot protection
  - body protection
  - respiratory protection
  - safety belts
  - lifelines, harness
  - mechanical-lift device—tripod
- training of workers and supervisors in the selection and use of
  - safe entry procedures
  - respiratory protection

- lifelines and retrieval systems
- protective clothing

- training of employees in confined-space-rescue procedures
- conducting safety meetings to discuss confined-space safety
- availability and use of proper ventilation equipment
- monitoring the air quality while workers are in the space.

Safe work in confined spaces is teamwork. It requires a trained confined-space team which includes:

- the entrant(s), the person(s) who does (do) the work
- the attendant, who stays outside while the entrant is inside the confined space
- the person who authorizes permits, and
- the rescue team.

A person may perform more than one of these tasks. For example, the person who authorizes the permits may also be trained to do one of the other tasks. The National Safety Council has prepared educational materials which outline the duties of this team.[10]

The entrant does the work assigned to be done in the confined space. The entrant:

- reviews the permit before entry; wears/uses appropriate personal protective clothing and equipment;
- uses, attends and appropriately responds to monitoring equipment;
- is sensitive to and appropriately responds to personal physical reactions that may indicate unsafe conditions;
- maintains communications with the attendant and obeys evacuation orders;
- signals the attendant for help as appropriate and leaves the confined space promptly.

The attendant is responsible to make sure the entrant remains safe. This responsibility is discharged by:

- reviewing the permit before any entry,
- constantly keeping track of the personnel in the confined space,
- keeping unauthorized persons out of the area,
- maintaining continuous communication by sight or voice with all persons in the confined space,
- making sure the ventilation equipment, if any, is working,
- monitoring the atmospheric testing equipment,
- tending the lifeline of the entrant,
- tending the air line, if any, to prevent tangles and kinks,
- remaining alert for signs of trouble,
- watching for hazards outside and inside the space,

- maintaining clear ingress and egress to the space,
- notifying the entrant and ordering evacuation if conditions warrant, or the permit limits expire,
- being prepared to call for emergency help,
- remaining at the entry point unless relieved by another trained attendant.

The person in charge of issuing the permits:

- plans each entry
  - describes the work to be done
  - identifies the workers involved
  - evaluates the hazards of the space
  - performs or oversees atmospheric testing and monitoring
  - develops rescue plans

- ensures the permit is properly completed
- determines equipment needs
- ensures appropriate atmospheric testing
- verifies that all necessary procedures, practices, and equipment for safe entry are in effect
- cancels the permit and terminates the work if the conditions are not acceptable
- trains (or provides training) for all workers on the confined-space entry team
- Keeps records on training, safety drills, test results, equipment inspections, and equipment maintenance
- cancels the permit and secures the space when the work is done
- determines if a written rescue plan is necessary for a particular confined-space entry
- verifies that emergency help is available and that the method of summoning assistance is operable.

Members of the rescue team may be from within the plant or from an arrangement with an outside rescue team. The team members, if from within the plant, must be trained in appropriate personal protective equipment, be trained as authorized entrants, drill at least once every twelve months (by rescuing mannequins from simulated confined spaces), and at least one member must have a current CPR and first aid certification. Regardless of the rescue arrangements, the team should be able to respond quickly to the site with the necessary equipment in proper working order. They should be cross-trained, and preferably all should have current CPR and first aid certification. Several should be trained in advanced first aid and first responder.

BIBLIOGRAPHY

[1] A. J. Suruda, D. N. Castillo, J. C. Helmkamp, and T. A. Pettit, "Epidemiology of Confined-Space-Related Fatalities," In *Worker Deaths in Confined Spaces*, National Institute for Occupational Safety and Health, Jan. 1994.

[2] National Institute for Occupational Safety and Health, *Criteria for a Recommended Standard: Working in Confined Spaces,* DHHS (NIOSH) 80–106, 1979.

[3] National Institute for Occupational Safety and Health, *Request for Assistance in Preventing Occupational Fatalities in Confined Spaces,* DHHS (NIOSH), 86–110, 1986.

[4] T. A. Pettit and H. E. Linn, eds., *A Guide to Safety in Confined Spaces,* National Institute for Occupational Safety and Health, DHHS(NIOSH), 87–113, 1987.

[5] J. C. Manwaring and C. Conroy, "Occupational Confined-Space-Related Fatalities: Surveillance and Prevention, *Journal of Safety Research,* Vol. 21, pp. 157–165, 1990.

[6] A. Suruda and J. Agnew, "Deaths from Asphyxiation and Poisoning at Work in the United States 1984–6," *British Journal of Industrial Medicine,* Vol. 46, 1989, pp. 541–546.

[7] NIOSH, *Worker Deaths in Confined Spaces: A Summary of NIOSH Surveillance and Investigative Findings,* National Institute for Occupational Safety and Health, 1994, 273 pp.

[8] Code of Federal Regulations, 29 CFR 1910.146 [1993], *Permit-Required Confined Spaces,* U.S. Government Printing Office, Washington, D.C.

[9] American National Standards Institute, *Safety Requirements for Confined Spaces,* American National Standard, Z-117.1, New York, 1977.

[10] National Safety Council, *Confined Spaces: Training the Team,* Chicago, 1991.

EXERCISES

13.1. How many facilities are covered by the 1993 OSHA regulation, "Permit-Required Confined Spaces"? How many employees are in these affected facilities?

13.2. 1994 NIOSH reviewed death certificates of occupational fatalities for the 80's decade. How many fatal incidents were there? With how many fatalities?

13.3. Name some of the spaces included by NIOSH as confined spaces.

13.4. Name the criteria for permit-required confined space.

13.5. Name each class and describe the various characteristics used in the classification of confined spaces according to atmospheric hazards.

13.6. Name the elements in a comprehensive, written confined-space entry program for the entrant, attendant, and permit issuer.

13.7. Can the rescue team be from within the plant?

CHAPTER 14

Buildings and Facilities

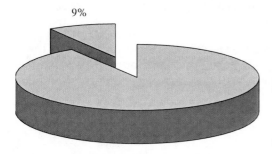

9%

Percentage of OSHA General Industry citations addressing this subject

We now turn to the business of examining hazards in various categories, highlighting applicable standards and suggesting methods of bringing about change to eliminate or reduce hazards. Most enterprises begin with a building in which to conduct operations, and this is an appropriate beginning for the examination of hazards. The enterprise is fortunate if its management considers hazards and applicable safety and health standards during its building design stages.

Safety standards for buildings, whether they be municipal, state, or federal, are usually called *codes*. For the most part, building codes apply to the construction of new buildings or to their modification. Thus, although building codes change constantly, those buildings built or remodeled before a particular change in the code are not required to be torn down and rebuilt or remodeled according to the new code. Needless to say, most buildings in existence do not meet the latest provisions of current building codes.

Some federal standards for buildings have been applied to all buildings, regardless of age. The standards have included matters of relative permanence such as floors, aisles, doors, numbers and locations of exits, and stairway lengths, widths, riser design, angle, and vertical clearance. Industry's objection has been that such standards are unfair, not only because they apply to existing buildings, but also because they are vague and generally worded. But despite these problems, industries have undertaken a large number of retrofit programs to update their buildings and facilities to satisfy federal standards.

In the defense of federal standards for buildings and facilities stands the fact that some of the most frequent categories of worker injuries and fatalities arise from improper building design, lack of guardrails, and problems with exits. Building equipment is designed and built without sufficient thought about the worker who must have access to this equipment to clean, maintain, repair, replace light bulbs, or otherwise service the buildings or facilities. Some workers are even in locations where they would be unable to escape in event of fire. Aisle widths are often set up arbitrarily, without giving thought to clearance between moving machinery and personnel.

Federal standards pertaining to buildings and facilities include the following categories:

- Walking and working surfaces
- Means of egress
- Powered platforms, manlifts, and vehicle-mounted work platforms
- General environmental controls

A few provisions of these standards generate almost all of the problems. This chapter will now single out those individual provisions and analyze each to determine what the safety and health manager should do to alleviate hazards and conform to standards.

WALKING AND WORKING SURFACES

One does not normally call a floor a *walking* or *working surface*, so why do the standards writers select such a complicated bit of jargon? This question is answered by reflecting on the hazardous locations in which people work. To be sure, many accidents, especially slips and falls, occur on floors, but consider the other walking and working surfaces—for instance, mezzanines and balconies. Then there are the even more hazardous platforms, catwalks, and scaffolds. Not to be forgotten are ramps, docks, stairways, and ladders.

Guarding Open Floors and Platforms

The most frequently cited standard in the walking-and-working-surfaces subpart is indeed one of the most frequently cited standards in all of the OSHA standards. It is repeated here in its entirety, due to its importance.

OSHA standard 1910.23—Guarding floor and wall openings and holes

(c) Protection of open-sided floors, platforms, and runways
  (1) Every open-sided floor or platform 4 feet or more above adjacent floor or ground level shall be guarded by a standard railing [or the equivalent as specified in paragraph (e)(3) of this section] on all open sides, except where there is entrance to a ramp, stairway, or fixed ladder. The railing shall be provided with a toeboard wherever, beneath the open sides,
    (i) Persons can pass,
    (ii) There is moving machinery, or
    (iii) There is equipment with which falling materials could create a hazard.

To many people, 4 feet seems an innocuous height, but the reason for this illusion is that they are thinking of jumping, not falling. Almost everyone has *jumped* without injury from elevations of more than 4 feet, but few adults experience a *fall* from that height without injury. A surprising number of *fatalities* result from falls at heights of only 8 feet. National Safety Council estimates place falls third, after workplace violence, as one of the leading causes of work-related fatalities (ref. Accident).

The illusion of safety of platforms in the range 4 to 14 feet has led to complacency on the part of building and facility designers as well as of safety and health managers. To stand on the extreme point of a precipice overlooking the Grand Canyon without a guardrail would seem foolhardy to the average person. But many "average persons" would think nothing of standing on the unguarded top of a tank 10 feet high. An unexpected event in such a situation can easily result in the worker taking a reflex action that results in a fatal fall.

The top of a tank, in the example just cited, was considered a *working surface* to be reckoned with by the facility designer. This is an important thing to remember. Even if the surface is the top of a tank, or even the top of a piece of equipment that is in the process of being manufactured, it may act as a temporary walking and working surface. But in unusual temporary situations, there are other ways to provide temporary fall protection for workers.

Another problem area is the protection of personnel from falls from loading docks. A few loading docks are slightly less than 4 feet high, and the issue is thereby avoided. Some safety and health managers have had the area immediately adjacent to the dock built higher to comply with standards, but this is of dubious value in preventing injuries. Others have installed temporary, removable railings, and some have used chain-type gates. The chain-type gates do not qualify as "standard railings," but have sometimes been accepted as a practical substitute in an attempt to deal with the hazard in the face of a difficult situation.

A rooftop is, of course, a walking and working surface for roofing workers. This raises the question of whether guardrails, fall protection, or some other type of protection is needed for perimeters of rooftops on which persons are working. A provision of the OSHA Construction Standard specifies *catch platforms*, unless

1. The roof has a parapet.
2. The slope of the roof is flatter than 4 inches in 12 inches.
3. The workers are protected by a safety belt attached to a lifeline.
4. The roof is lower than 16 feet from the ground to the eaves.

The term *standard railings* mentioned in the platform guarding standard is further clarified by federal standards, and salient features are shown in Figure 14.1. Certain reasonable deviations from the specifications shown in Figure 14.1 are permitted. For instance, some other material in place of the midrail is permitted, provided that the alternative material provides protection equivalent to the midrail. Also, the height of the railing does not have to be exactly 42 inches. Railings of 36-inch height are acceptable if they do not present a hazard and are otherwise in compliance. This avoids the necessity of tearing down good railings and rebuilding to meet current codes, as has actually been done by some employers, as shown in Figure 14.2.

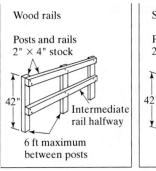

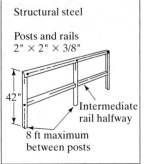

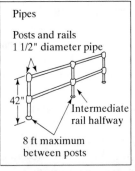

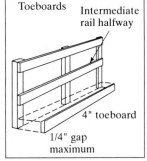

FIGURE 14.1

Standard railings (*Source*: NIOSH).

FIGURE 14.2

New guardrails. Some employers tore down their guardrails and rebuilt them 3 or 4 inches higher just to meet OSHA's standard in the early years of OSHA enforcement. Note the paint marks on the wall where the old guardrail had been attached. OSHA has since relaxed its rule somewhat.

One type of railing that is definitely not standard, but still can afford reasonable protection in some cases, is lines of parallel ductwork or pipes along the otherwise exposed sides. In many cases, parallel ductwork or pipes completely eliminate the hazard of the otherwise open-sided floor, platform, or runway. In fact, one might argue that such a floor, platform, or runway is not even "open-sided," provided that the parallel structure is sufficiently rigid.

In OSHA standard 1910.23(c)(1) quoted earlier, three conditions are enumerated, any one of which calls for a *toeboard*. Toeboards are vertical barriers along the exposed edges of the walking or working surface to prevent falls of *materials*. A standard toeboard is 4 inches high and leaves no more than a 1/4-inch gap between the floor and the toeboard. If the toeboard is not of solid material, its opening must not be greater than 1 inch.

Although 4 feet is the maximum height for open platforms in general, special situations require protection *regardless* of the height of the walking or working surface. Examples are open pits, tanks, vats, and ditches. When the hazardous opening size is small, it may be more practical to place a removable cover over the opening than to place a guardrail around it. Some safety and health managers have saved their firms a great deal of money by calling attention to this alternative. Another special situation is walking and working surfaces adjacent to dangerous equipment, where standard railings are appropriate.

Floors and Aisles

Judging by the level of OSHA enforcement activity, the most important consideration for floors and aisles is not how they are built, but how they are maintained. Federal standards for housekeeping require areas to "be kept clean and orderly and in a sanitary condition." The obvious question is "How is the safety and health manager to know what constitutes 'clean and orderly and in a sanitary condition'?" There is no clear-cut answer to this question, but some information can be gleaned from past cases of OSHA citations.

Example 14.1

In the railroad yard area of a steel manufacturing industry, piles of debris such as railroad ties and cables were lying about close to the track and presented tripping hazards to employees who must work in the area of the tracks. A complicating factor was that some of the debris was hidden by weeds.

Example 14.2

Dangerous accumulations of grain dust were found in many locations in a grain elevator. The dust was sufficiently concentrated so as to represent a health hazard to cleanup personnel and present a serious explosion hazard. Since the condition had been cited before, the citation was established as "serious and repeat," and the penalty was set at $10,000.

Example 14.3

A cluttered workshop had obstructions that some of the employees had to step over or go around to do their jobs.

Example 14.4

Leaking hydraulic cylinders dripped oil on the floor in a work area. No one was responsible for cleaning up the leaked oil.

Some conditions might *look* bad, but not represent a hazard. In one example, an OSHA compliance officer wrote a citation for piles (approximately 2 feet high) of sawdust around a planer and jointer in a woodworking shop. But the company resisted the citation because few employees would be in the area, and those few would be more inconvenienced than endangered. The company won its case.

It is also recognized that it is necessary in the course of many jobs for objects and materials to lie about in the work area. This is especially true of repair and disassembly work, and also of construction. What is generally considered excessive is material accumulation in the immediate work area in quantities in excess of what is actually required to do the given job, or scrap material lying hazardously about the work area in excess of a day's accumulation.

A prime measure of whether a housekeeping program is inadequate is the number of accidents such as trips and falls occurring in the area. Note that the preceding sentence was worded negatively in that too many accidents suggest an inadequate program, but "no accidents on record" does not prove that the work area is *free* of hazards. For every accident that is on file in the plant, the wise safety and health manager will have documented what steps have been taken to remove or reasonably reduce the offending hazard, whatever that hazard has been determined by analysis to be.

Finally, safety and health managers can look to their own industries for guidance. Any reasonable person knows that the definition of "clean and orderly and in a sanitary condition" is different in a foundry than in a pharmaceuticals plant. If the industry has any work practice guidelines, as put forth by trade associations, for instance, these guidelines would be very helpful in illustrating what is reasonable for a given industry.

The general housekeeping standard is targeted at a very common hazard and a very frequent source of workers' compensation claims: slips and falls. So important is this hazard to insurance companies that they sometimes have research facilities to study tribology (ref. Lorenzi). "Tribology" is the study of the mechanisms and phenomena of friction and applies to the study of trips and falls as well as to lubrication and wear of contact surfaces (ref. Lopedes).

Water on the floor is a problem in many industries, and constant surveillance becomes necessary to assure that the floor is kept clean and dry. In the design phase of buildings and facilities, attention to the problem of wet processes will suggest slopes and floor drainage systems to alleviate the problem. Another helpful device is to use a false floor or mat to provide a dry standing place for the worker who must work in a wet process.

Some buildings are not built to facilitate cleaning. The floors in others not only are poor from a cleaning standpoint, but also present trip hazards, such as protruding nails, splinters, holes, or loose boards.

Trip hazards due to uneven floors can result in serious injury. In one case in a steel mill, a difference of 1 to 3 inches existed at a point where a grating and a plate came together in the floor. The employee who worked in the area had the job of guiding red-hot steel butts from the end of a roller line. A fall could have brought the employee into contact with the red-hot butts of steel.

Aisles are important, and standards for aisles specify that permanent aisles be kept clear of hazardous obstructions and that they be appropriately marked. Ironically, the more clearly the aisles are marked, the more noticeable will be clutter or materials allowed to accumulate in the aisles. Conversely the more materials or obstructions are kept clear for forklifts or other travel, the more obvious will be the misuse of an aisle that is not appropriately marked.

There is a lesson to be learned from the irony just described. There is a tendency among safety and health managers to go out all over the plant, indiscriminately laying out aisles, and then to take pride in marking them according to appropriate standards. It is human nature for some managers to want to show everyone that they are taking positive action to enhance safety and comply with established standards. The unfortunate result is that aisles can become too regimented and so much time then spent policing them that production efficiency is lost. In fact, the effect on safety and health can thus become negative, with employer and employee alike wanting to say, "Do we really need that safety and health manager in the plant?" Aisle-marking procedures are a prime illustration of the principle that overzealous safety and health action can do more harm than good. Every time a decision is made to mark an aisle, the safety and health manager should stop and ask the question, "Can we keep this aisle free of material or other obstructions?"

Conspicuously absent from federal standards for aisles is a specific minimum width for aisles. State codes that reflect the National Fire Protection Association's Life Safety Code often specify a minimum exit access width of 28 inches. But the federal code is silent on this point except to use the language "sufficient safe clearances shall be allowed." Aisles in forging-machine areas receive special attention: "sufficient width to permit the free movement of employees." But this standard also does not specify an actual minimum width dimension. These two standards are therefore good examples of "performance standards."

The OSHA aisle-marking standard has left a mark of its own on industry. The term "appropriately marked" originally meant black or white or combinations of black and white for aisles. Untold thousands of dollars were spent by industries switching from the yellow stripes widely used for aisles to OSHA-acceptable white stripes. However, the white striping used was not as durable, and frustrated facilities superintendents would return in desperation to the more durable yellow stripe in order to maintain any stripe at all. The black-and-white rule became more and more unpopular until OSHA finally revoked the aisle color code as superfluous. In summary, the safety and health manager should be sure that aisles are well marked, but the choice of color for the marking stripe is of little importance. Thus, the aisle-marking standard was formerly a specification standard but is now a performance standard.

The discussion about floors thus far has concerned guarding of openings, surfaces, maintenance, and appropriate markings. Nothing has been said about the structural design of the floor itself or whether the floor can withstand the loads applied to it. One is reminded of the eight-story vehicle parking building in which the eighth floor collapsed on the seventh. The seventh floor was well constructed but was unable to withstand the shock load of the falling eighth floor, and from then on, all the floors came down like dominoes. An even more grim reminder was the Kansas City hotel tragedy of 1981. Almost no one really pays attention to whether a floor is overloaded. Earlier editions of this book referred to structural collapse of buildings to be so remote and rare that few people ever worry about the problem. Sadly, that statement will never again be true after the tragic events of September 11, 2001, when terrorist attacks caused the collapse of the twin World Trade Center towers in New York City.

Federal standards require marking plates for floor loads approved by the "building official." One of the chief complaints from industry safety and health managers is that the floor-loading standard does not explain its use of the term *building official*. Confusion over this term has led to phone calls to various agencies in attempts to identify some *public* official to come to the facility to make an engineering determination to use as a basis for the floor-load marking plates. Since the term "building official" is not defined, a better course of action for the safety and health manager is to secure the services of a competent professional engineer either inside or outside the company. This would show a good-faith effort to comply with the standard and would virtually eliminate the possibility of a hazard.

Floor-load marking plates are of little value if they are ignored by employees. Adherence to floor-load limits is an administrative or procedural matter and thus calls for vigilance in order to maintain compliance. A good system of records and inventories can make weights and locations part of the database of an overall management information system. If this system is computerized, the computer can monitor loads at all times and print out a warning message in the unlikely event that a distribution of inventories exceeds a floor-load limit.

Such a computerized system may seem to be an overreaction to the problem, and in fact it would be an overreaction for most companies small to medium in size. But in a large-scale computerized warehouse system, the floor-load monitoring system would represent such a small sideline to the overall computerized operating monitor that it would require only a few seconds of computer time per month. The system could be programmed to print out status reports monthly or on an exception basis whenever loads exceed or perhaps approach limits. The monthly status reports would be preferable to the exception reports because the monthly status reports would provide evidence of positive adherence to approved standards.

A word of caution is in order here. If there actually exists a violation of floor-load limits in the plant, no fancy computerized information system is going to hide it. Manual calculations can be used to determine whether a floor-load limit has been exceeded, and symptoms such as crushed, bent, or cracked floor members can be as embarrassing as they are hazardous.

The whole problem of floor and aisle design and maintenance is magnified by the use of mechanical handling equipment such as forklift trucks. Forklifts both aggravate the problems and at the same time become more of a hazard themselves whenever problems with floors exist.

Stairways

Building codes and standards for stairs are well established, but many factories and businesses have stairways that do not meet code. If the stairways have four or more risers, they need standard railings or handrails and must be kept clear of obstructions. Note the use of the words *handrail* and *railing*. **They are not the same**. A handrail, as used in this standard, is a single bar or pipe supported on brackets from a wall to furnish a handhold in case of tripping. A railing, however, is a vertical *barrier* erected along the exposed sides of stairways and platforms to prevent falls. A handrail and railing may of course be combined into the same unit, but the two terms are not interchangeable.

The OSHA standard is very flexible on the subject of the placement of stairway landings, using such language as "avoid" (long flights of stairs), and "consideration should be given to."

The placement of stairway landings is a safety consideration. Most people think that the purpose of stairway landings or platforms is to give the climber a chance to rest, and it is true that this is a supplemental purpose. However, the main purpose of the stairway landing is to shorten the distance of falls, and thus landings play an important role in building and facilities safety. Extremely long flights of stairs are obviously more dangerous than stairs interrupted by landings. To be effective, landings must be no less than the width of the stairway and a minimum of 30 inches in length measured in the direction of travel.

Ladders

Ladders are not the simple devices most people think they are. Design is critical—the construction should be neither too strong nor too weak. A weak ladder is obviously dangerous, but a ladder that is overdesigned is difficult or impossible to handle safely. A long, heavy ladder can be as much a hazard when it is carried as when it is climbed. It is easy to see why ladders must be manufactured to exacting standards.

Most firms buy ladders from reputable ladder manufacturers, and the safety and health manager can be quite sure that the ladders were constructed properly in the first place. What is more important to industrial safety is how the ladders are used and maintained. Defective ladders must be either repaired or destroyed, and while awaiting either fate, they must be tagged or marked "Dangerous; Do Not Use." Personal interviews with safety and health managers have indicated that they often saw defective ladders in half rather than risk the possibility of a defective ladder being returned to service. When a job needs to be done and there is no regular ladder in sight, the temptation is too great for maintenance or other personnel to remove the danger tag and make immediate use of a defective ladder. At best, a repair job on a portable ladder usually does not look very good and will likely arouse suspicion even if the ladder is safe. It takes a good engineer to convince anyone that the repaired ladder is just as good as new, even if the engineer has been able to convince himself or herself.

Portable metal ladders share common hazards with portable wooden ladders; a major difference, however, is the fact that metal ladders conduct electricity. Many workers are aware of the increased hazards of electrocution present when using metal ladders. Rubber or otherwise nonconducting feet are a good precaution on metal ladders, but the hazard is still present. The rubber feet should not be allowed to give rise to complacency.

Whether the portable ladder is made of wood or metal, it is the way in which the ladder is used that will chiefly determine its safety. Almost everyone knows the admonition that it is unsafe to ascend or descend a ladder with the climber facing away from the ladder. Less obvious is the fact that portable ladders are typically not designed to be used as platforms or scaffolds, and they become very weak if used at angles close to horizontal.

A common error in the use of ladders is to use ladders that are too short. For instance, when accessing a roof, the ladder needs to extend at least 3 feet above the upper point of support. For ordinary stepladders, the top should not be used as a step. Another foolish practice is to place ladders on boxes, barrels, or other unstable bases to obtain additional height. Some people even try to splice short ladders together to make longer ones.

The first consideration in the use of a portable ladder is its condition, especially the rungs. Next to the hazard of broken rungs, the greatest hazard probably is a ladder that slips or tips because it is insecurely positioned. The proper slant is 4 feet vertical to 1 foot horizontal. A safe practice is to tie off the ladder at the top so that it cannot tip or slide down. This is not always practical, however, and alternative solutions can solve the slipping problem. Sometimes a ladder can be made stable by positioning it where the structure of the wall or building limits its movement and makes the ladder safe. Another solution is to use nonslip bases, but this method may not work on some surfaces, such as oily, metal, concrete, or slippery surfaces. Metal ladders in particular may be subject to slipping and need to be equipped with good safety shoes. Safety shoes are as much to prevent slipping as they are to prevent electrocution. Even spikes may be useful on some surfaces to make the footing secure. If the ladder is used without safety shoes on a hard, slick surface, the ladder needs a footladder board to prevent slipping.

Fixed Ladders

From a safety and health standpoint, fixed ladders require a somewhat different approach than portable ladders. With portable ladders, the emphasis is on care and correct use, as just discussed. With fixed ladders, the emphasis is on design and construction. It is beyond the scope of this book to specify all of the details of fixed-ladder design. If fixed ladders need to be constructed, the designer should follow the detailed specifications laid out in established standards, not this book.

This book seeks only to alert safety and health managers to problems they may encounter with existing fixed ladders. Some fixed ladders may have been constructed long ago or perhaps without the benefit of standards. It is the duty of the safety and health manager to alert the company if fixed ladders are found to be incorrectly constructed. The safety and health manager can then recommend that design details be followed when the ladders are rebuilt.

Some knowledge of fixed-ladder design principles is necessary, however, if the safety and health manager is to know how to recognize common problems found. For brevity, this book selects some easy-to-observe problems with fixed-ladder design, illustrated in Figure 14.3. The rung offset is to prevent the foot from sliding off the end of the rung. Other means, such as siderails, would also be acceptable.

Long unbroken lengths of fixed ladders are dangerous, and ladder standards prescribe breaking the long lengths and separating successive lengths of the ladder by an offset equipped with a landing platform. Such offsets are required every 30 feet of

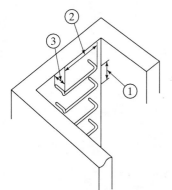

1. Distance between rungs not more than 12 inches and uniform.
2. Minimum rung length is 16 inches.
3. Back clearance minimum is 7 inches. This dimension is the most frequently violated, according to frequency of OSHA citation.

FIGURE 14.3

Easy-to-recognize problems with fixed ladders; all three are required by OSHA. Note the rung offset to prevent the foot from slipping off (based on OSHA standards).

unbroken length. When the fixed ladder is more than 20 feet long, but less than 30 feet long, protective cages are needed. But many safety and health managers do not realize that there is an alternative to installing ladder cages. On tower, water tank, and chimney ladders over 20 feet in unbroken length, ladder safety devices may be used in lieu of cage protection. Ladder safety devices usually take the form of a combination of fixed equipment on the ladder and personal equipment worn by the climber. One type uses a trolley that moves along a fixed rail. The trolley is attached to the climber's belt. The trolley moves easily up or down the rail when the climber ascends or descends, but a brake engages that stops the trolley in event of a fall. One thing to watch carefully with a rail-and-trolley device is to ensure that the device is equipped to deal with ice on the rail if the ladder is located in a climate where ice is a possibility (most outdoor locations in the United States). The safety problem with ice on the rail is somewhat indirect; the trolley simply cannot move along the ice-covered rail, making the system useless. But this is when the safety device is most needed. The problem is not without solution because there are deicing devices for trolley systems. Safety and health managers should choose their protection systems with care, however, being sure to consider all factors, including the problem of icing, in order to avoid later embarrassment and wasted investment on the part of the company. An example rail-and-trolley ladder safety device system is illustrated in Figure 14.4.

Dockboards

A dockboard, or bridge plate, provides a temporary surface over which loads can be transported, particularly during the loading or unloading of a cargo vehicle. One of the main safety hazards with these boards is that they may shift while in use. It is also possible that the surfaces connected by the dockboard can shift, such as when the cargo vehicle itself moves. Finally, the dockboard itself may not be strong enough to carry the load.

FIGURE 14.4

Example of ladder safety device system.

EXITS

Exits are usually considered doors to the outside and from a safety standpoint are considered a means of escape, especially from fire. Such thinking is accurate, but incomplete. The safety and health manager should enlarge the concept by using the more general term *means of egress* to include the following:

1. The way of exit access
2. The exit itself
3. The way of exit discharge

By considering means of egress instead of simply exits, the safety and health manager can analyze the entire building to determine whether every point in the building has a continuous and unobstructed way of travel to a public way. In this way, one must think of such building facilities as stairways, intervening rooms, locked interior doorways, and limited-access corridors. Outside the building one must think of yards, exterior storage of materials, fences, courtyards, and shrubbery. One thinks of shrubbery and landscaping as affecting neither safety nor health. However, employees might escape a burning building (or perhaps a building with a ruptured chlorine gas line) through an exit door, only to find outside that the exit empties into a courtyard tightly confined by a fence, dense shrubbery, or other obstruction.

Almost every safety and health manager at some time during his or her career encounters the embarrassment of an exit that is *locked*. This can be a two-edged problem because many safety and health managers are also responsible for plant security. In many cases, the only practical solution is to provide panic bars or other mechanisms for locking doors from outside entry while maintaining free and unobstructed egress from the inside. Where unauthorized exit can be as much a security problem as unauthorized entry, the automatic-alarm-sound type of door may be the only alternative. Facilities designers are turning more and more to the use of unlocked, automatic-alarm-sounding emergency exit doors. Even more frequently encountered than locked exits are exits that are cluttered or blocked by obstructions or impediments. Stacks of material obstructing the door or way of travel defeats the purpose of the exit.

If anyone ever doubted the importance of the OSHA requirement to keep exits unlocked and clear, that doubt was swept away by the tragedy that occurred in Hamlet, North Carolina, the morning of September 3, 1991. In one of the worst industrial accidents in U.S. history, 25 people were killed and another 56 were injured in a fire that swept through the Imperial Foods poultry processing plant (ref. Labar, 1992). The inferno was put out in only 35 minutes, but it had already done its damage. The 30,000-square-foot building, a converted 1920s vintage ice cream plant, was virtually windowless, and when the lights went out soon after the outbreak of the blaze, the 90 workers present were scrambling through a maze of production processing equipment in the dark trying to find a way out. To prevent product theft and to keep out flies, reportedly seven of the nine exit doors were routinely locked or bolted from the outside. The tragedy closed the plant permanently, and three members of top management were indicted for 25 counts each of involuntary manslaughter. The three indicted were the owner of the company, which is now bankrupt; the owner's son, who was working in the plant as operations manager; and the plant manager.

The entire nation will ever be more acutely aware of the importance of exits and building egress after the tragedy of September 11, 2001, when both colossal towers of the World Trade Center collapsed.

Americans with Disabilities Act

Attention to buildings and facilities assumed increased significance with passage of the Americans with Disabilities Act (ADA) in 1990. This law mandated that employers make reasonable accommodation for handicapped employees rather than deny them employment. This means that many changes to walking and working surfaces, exits, drinking water fountain levels, rest rooms, and other facilities became mandatory instead of voluntary. Often, the safety and health manager has been assigned the responsibility for compliance with ADA, if for no other reason than the fact that he or she has been accustomed to dealing with compliance problems with other federal regulations, such as OSHA standards.

ADA is being taken seriously by industry and public institutions as well. Expert consultants in building compliance for handicapped access can be retained to conduct an audit of facilities. Some of these consultants are themselves handicapped and derive their livelihood by visiting facilities in their wheelchairs and touring the building to check facilities for handicapped access. When a handicapped person in a wheelchair attempts to gain access to a building or its facilities, such as water fountains or rest rooms, and is unable to do so, a convincing case can be made to justify capital improvements in buildings and facilities. At the same time, the Safety and Health Manager should assure that OSHA as well as ADA standards are considered in the redesign of buildings and facilities.

ILLUMINATION

The subject of lighting was mentioned earlier. Lighting, or the lack of it, can be a safety hazard, but there is no code for minimum safe lighting except for specialized areas. For instance, if forklift trucks are operated in the plant area, the minimum general lighting level is two lumens per square foot unless the forklift trucks themselves have lights. Every exit sign should be suitably illuminated by a reliable light source giving a value of not less than five footcandles on the illuminated surface. This is not to say that the exit sign must be the kind that is *internally* lighted. An alternative to be considered is artificial lighting *external* to the sign. Also, there is nothing wrong with relying on *natural* illumination (sunlight) on the exit sign in an amount not less than five footcandles. Natural illumination can be a problem, however, if the area is accessed on second or third shifts. Incidentally, five footcandles is not very much illumination. Most plant areas are normally lit by much greater levels of illumination.

In the General Industry standard adopted as the national consensus standard in the early days of OSHA, there was no general lighting standard. However, the omission seems to be an oversight on OSHA's part. More than a decade later, OSHA promulgated a standard for "Hazardous Waste Operations and Emergency Response," commonly known as the HAZWOPER standard. The HAZWOPER standard focused on special emergency operations, but a little-known provision of this standard had to do with minimum illumination levels. Table 14.1 delineates these minimum illumination levels and is taken directly from the HAZWOPER standard. Review of the table clearly reveals that it was originally conceived to be a general table of illumination levels, not just a special table for HAZWOPER operations. For instance, the table specifies levels for "warehouses," "general shops," "barracks," "dining rooms," and "offices," all of which describe areas that might be associated with general employment, not only "emergency response" operations. OSHA has not seen fit to attempt to promulgate a general illumination standard for all workplaces. Instead, the agency has adopted such a standard within specific standards only. Another example standard that contains the Table 14.1 illumination minimums is the OSHA Construction standard.

TABLE 14.1   Minimum Illumination Intensities in Footcandles

Footcandles	Area or operations
5	General site areas.
3	Excavation and waste areas, accessways, active storage areas, loading platforms, refueling, and field maintenance areas.
5	Indoors: warehouses, corridors, hallways, and exitways.
5	Tunnels, shafts, and general underground work areas; (Exception: minimum of 10 footcandles is required at tunnel and shaft heading during drilling, mucking, and scaling.) Mine Safety and Health Administration approved cap lights shall be acceptable for use in the tunnel heading.
10	General shops (e.g., mechanical and electrical equipment rooms, active storerooms, barracks or living quarters, locker or dressing rooms, dining areas, and indoor toilets and workrooms.)
30	First-aid stations, infirmaries, and offices.

(*Source*: OSHA standard 29 CFR 1910. Subpart H, Table H-1.)

MISCELLANEOUS FACILITIES

Maintenance Platforms

The importance of planning for maintenance activities when constructing a new building was pointed out earlier in this chapter. Many modern buildings have built-in, safe suspension systems for exterior window cleaning and other exterior maintenance. Maintenance workers for buildings not so equipped are less fortunate and typically work from suspended scaffolds of the same type as construction scaffolds. Not only are the maintenance workers less fortunate, but so are the employers of these workers and the safety and health managers who must worry about the safety of the scaffolds, the proper securing of scaffolds on the roof of the building, and other items governed by applicable standards.

Safety and health managers who do find that their buildings are equipped with powered platforms for exterior maintenance should direct most of their attention to how these platforms are being used and maintained, not how they are made. The manufacturer of such equipment would normally be very careful to adhere strictly to standards when fabricating the powered maintenance platform. Typical problems with these platforms are missing guardrails, missing toeboards, missing side mesh, disabled safety devices, and inadequate inspections or records of inspections.

Regarding the equipment itself, some companies have been tripped up for not having load-rating plates on the platform. The load rating must be stated in letters at least $\frac{1}{4}$ inch in height. The wire rope suspending the platform must also be marked with a metal tag stating its maximum breaking strength and other data, including the month and year the ropes were installed.

Workers on some types of powered platforms need to wear safety belts; on other types, they are safe without the belts. A platform supported by four or more wire ropes can be so designed that the working platform will maintain its normal position even if one rope fails. However, many powered platforms are suspended by only two wire ropes and will tip dangerously if one of the ropes fails. One of the more dangerous types of platform is known as "type T," and workers on these platforms must wear safety belts attached by lifelines. If the platform qualifies as type T, it will upset with a single wire rope failure, but it will not fall to the ground. Therefore, the lifeline may be attached either to the building structure or to the working platform. Compare this to construction industry standards, which require that lifelines be secured to an anchorage or structural member instead of to the scaffold.

Public-utilities workers and tree trimmers often use platforms that are vehicle mounted, such as aerial baskets, aerial ladders, boom platforms, and platform-elevating towers. Again the majority of accidents arise from improper use of the platform rather than from equipment failure or design. This is even more true of the vehicle-mounted platforms than of the building-mounted models discussed earlier.

The most serious hazard with vehicle-mounted platforms is contact with high-voltage power lines, and this kills workers every year. This hazard is so severe that a safety distance must be maintained at all times—except, of course, in the case of electric utility companies who by the nature of their work must approach closer. For safety, the utility companies must insulate aerial devices that work closer than the standard safety distance. For nonutility companies, the accepted standard is a ten-foot distance in the case of a 40-kilovolt line, for example. Different line voltages may need higher or lower safety distances.

Sometimes special sensors called "proximity warning devices" are installed on the boom to warn the operator when the basket is too close for safety. However, these warning devices do not provide positive protection and thus should not be considered an excuse for moving the boom closer to the line than authorized minimums.

Workers in aerial baskets often fail to wear a body belt and lanyard attached to the boom. Adding to the fall hazard is the possibility of unexpected contact with an object that might strike and perhaps sweep the worker out of the basket or off the platform. Echoing the hazards avoidance principles, such unusual hazards point to the importance of training for personnel who work in aerial baskets. Other unsafe procedures are failure to secure the aerial ladder before traveling; climbing or sitting on the edge of the basket; or improvising a work position other than the floor of the basket.

Elevators

Elevators are everywhere, but when can you remember one falling? The catastrophic fall of an elevator is such a horrifying thought that the public long ago set up regulations for safe elevators. Jurisdiction was placed within the states, and most states administer elevator inspections through "labor" or "labor and industry" commissions. Next time you ride in an elevator, look at the certificate of inspection posted inside the elevator car.

Elevators must be inspected both when new (or altered) and periodically thereafter. Many states even require construction permits from the authorized elevator inspection agency before elevator construction is begun. Elevator operating permits and fees are also required by some states. Not every inspector must be an agency official, but state licensing procedures for elevator inspectors may be applicable.

Manlifts are used as elevators, but unlike elevators, there are federal standards for manlifts. Manlifts are much cheaper and more efficient than elevators for many plant operations and are thus sometimes used instead of elevators. As can be seen in Figure 14.5, however, a manlift is inherently more hazardous than an elevator. It is ironic that elevators—which are safer than manlifts—are governed by strict state inspection, licensing, permits, and approvals. With manlifts, though, it is up to the safety and health manager to interpret general standards and identify hazards. It is apparent from Figure 14.5 that the biggest hazards with manlifts are getting on and getting off. Exit is essential because the belt is continuous, and to stay on the belt past the top or bottom floor would be either impossible or extremely hazardous.

Boilers

Steam boilers and pressure vessels are so safe today that most people do not even think about them. It has not always been that way. Although steam boilers are not as popular today for building heating systems, many are still in use; in addition, industrial processes use hundreds of thousands of boilers and pressure vessels. So the lack of familiarity with boiler accidents is not because the boilers themselves are rare—it is the

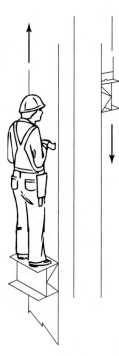

FIGURE 14.5

Manlift: a continuously moving belt on which workers
may ride both up and down.

accidents that are rare. When an accident does occur, the energy released by the explosion is so devastating that it usually produces a catastrophe.

The extreme hazard of an unsafe boiler led to the early regulation and safeguarding of these vessels. As with elevators, the historical development of boiler codes
has placed their jurisdiction within the states. State control has been very effective in
keeping boiler accidents to an absolute minimum.

The safety and health manager needs to ensure that boilers and pressure vessels
in the plant are being inspected and that state procedures are being followed. One
question that immediately comes to mind is "What pressure vessels are covered by the
regulations?" Most states exempt containers for liquefied petroleum gases (LPG), as
these are covered by other regulations. The same can generally be said of vessels approved by the Department of Transportation for public highway transportation of liquids and gases under pressure. Some states also exempt vessels used in connection with
the production, distribution, storage, or transmission of oil or natural gas. Note, however, that the foregoing does not exempt refineries or chemical plants that produce petroleum *products*. In the industry, the term *oil production* refers to the drilling and
extraction, or "mining," of petroleum, not its refining. The only way to be sure about
exemptions in a given state is to check with that state's agency of authority.

The time to stop and think about regulations for boiler and pressure vessel safety
is whenever such a vessel is to be purchased, installed, modified, moved, or sold. Welding on such vessels may weaken them and is scrutinized carefully by the inspector, although welding is not absolutely prohibited. Even hot-water storage containers should
be installed or reinstalled by persons properly licensed to do the work.

SANITATION

The sanitation of lunchrooms seems straightforward and obvious, but sanitation decisions can be trickier than they appear. If a decision is made to allow employees to eat in the plant, principles of hygiene must be observed. The safety and health manager should be sure that a sufficient number of waste receptacles is provided to avoid overfilling. But before going overboard, the safety and health manager should realize that too *many* waste receptacles can be provided also. If too many receptacles are provided, maintenance personnel will become lax about emptying containers that receive little use, resulting in additional sanitation problems.

The presence of toxic materials complicates the whole problem of food service, consumption, and storage. Certainly, food and beverages must not be stored in areas where they will be exposed to toxic materials. This rule may seem obvious, but the safety and health manager should consider not only the plant cafeteria or lunchroom but also the employee who brings snacks from home and stores them in areas in which they could be exposed to toxic materials.

Some toxic materials, such as lead, are particularly susceptible to exposure by ingestion during food consumption. Some toxic materials, such as vinyl chloride and arsenic, are of such concern that there are strict, specific standards for their control.

SUMMARY

Safety and health managers who are willing to plan ahead can save their companies a great deal of money by heeding building and facility codes *before* commencing construction or expansion of plant space. Planning ahead is the key to compliance with standards for floors, aisles, exits, and stairways. Guardrails, ladders, and platforms may be added, but they, too, deserve some advance consideration to ensure that installations meet requirements.

Safety and health managers need to be careful not to get too enthusiastic and provide for too many aisles or exits. An extra aisle or exit that is improperly maintained or marked can easily lead to problems and indeed is not even in the interest of safety.

The subject of buildings and facilities may not be the most exciting topic for the safety and health manager's attention. However, even ordinary matters such as housekeeping and sanitation deserve careful consideration and judgment to promote safety and health at reasonable cost.

EXERCISES AND STUDY QUESTIONS

14.1 What is the height of a standard railing for walking and working surfaces?

14.2 A portable ladder is needed to climb onto a rooftop 14 feet high. How long should the ladder be?

14.3 What are the two principal federal requirements for aisles in industrial plants?

14.4 Explain why the title for a major OSHA subpart is "Walking and Working Surfaces" instead of simply "Floors." Name 10 different walking and working surfaces.

14.5 What is deceptive about the danger of an open-sided floor or platform only 4 feet high?

14.6 Suppose that in your plant, welders must stand on top of a 10-foot-high tank to complete manufacturing operations. What should be done, if anything, to protect them from falling?

14.7 What is the purpose of a toeboard?

14.8 Explain under what conditions, and how, roofing workers should be protected from fall hazards.

14.9 When must an open-sided floor or platform be equipped with a railing?

14.10 When would OSHA require guarding for a service pit for use in vehicle maintenance? How would you guard such a pit?

14.11 Explain how poor housekeeping could result in an OSHA citation that classifies the violation as "serious."

14.12 As a safety and health manager, how would you deal with the problem of housekeeping?

14.13 Explain the danger of marking too many permanent aisles.

14.14 Explain the difference between a handrail and a railing.

14.15 Describe the purposes and requirements for stairway landings.

14.16 Describe important points to consider in safety with portable ladders.

14.17 Under what conditions are ladder cages specified? When may alternative ladder safety devices be used? What are the advantages and disadvantages of these devices?

14.18 Define the term *means of egress*.

14.19 What are the biggest problems with exits?

14.20 What are vehicle-mounted work platforms? What are their chief hazards?

14.21 Explain how either too many or too few waste receptacles can lead to sanitation problems.

14.22 Describe the case history in which locked exits resulted in multiple fatalities, criminal indictments, company bankruptcy, and the permanent closing of a plant.

14.23 The decade of the 1990s saw an increase in the significance of buildings and facilities design. What landmark legislation caused this increase?

14.24 What new responsibility was placed into the hands of many safety and health managers in the decade of the 1990s, and why?

14.25 According to the National Safety Council, how do falls rank as a cause of workplace fatalities?

14.26 Discuss the problem that is associated with promulgation of federal standards for building code issues.

14.27 What is "tribology," and in what way is it important to occupational safety and health?

14.28 Compare the Life Safety Code standard with the OSHA standard for aisle width in industrial plants. Which is worded more in performance language and which is worded more in specification language?

14.29 In what way has OSHA's aisle-marking standard changed from specification to performance wording?

14.30 Explain the purpose of a "footladder board."

14.31 Explain why it is acceptable in general industry to secure the worker lifeline to the scaffold itself if the scaffold is "type T."

14.32 Is it OK for just anyone to install a hot-water tank? Why or why not? Explain.

RESEARCH EXERCISES

14.33 Check the Internet for details about the Imperial Foods disaster in 1991.

14.34 Check the Internet for details about the Triangle Shirtwaist disaster in 1911. What lessons could have been learned from this disaster that would have prevented the Imperial Foods disaster 80 years later?

STANDARDS RESEARCH QUESTIONS

14.35 This chapter referred to "one of the most frequently cited standards in all of the OSHA standards." Find this standard and search the NCM database to determine the frequency of citation. Compare the citation frequency of this standard with the frequency of citation of the General Duty Clause.

14.36 The maintenance of aisles is an important consideration in controlling the hazards of work areas. Find the OSHA General Industry standard for aisle maintenance and determine its citation frequency using the NCM database.

14.37 Search the OSHA General Industry standard for the provision prohibiting locked exits. Determine whether it is frequently cited by searching the NCM database. Are any of the citations for locked exits contested by the employer?

CHAPTER 15

Materials Handling and Storage

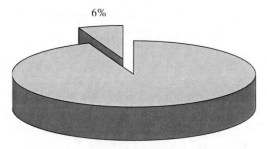

6%

Percentage of OSHA General Industry citations addressing this subject

The usual concept of a factory is a place where things are made or materials are processed, but often the major activity in a factory consists of moving things and materials around. Lifting, a most basic material-handling activity, accounts for most back injuries, one of the largest workplace injury categories of all. At Liberty Mutual Insurance Company, low back pain alone accounts for 33% of the firm's total workers' compensation claims (ref. Lorenzi). Industrial trucks, tractors, cranes, and conveyors all have the simple mission of moving materials, and they all cause injuries and fatalities every year.

The National Safety Council (NSC) charges materials handling with 20 to 25% of all occupational injuries. The size of the problem is emphasized in NSC's *Accident Prevention Manual for Industrial Operations* as follows:

> As an average, industry moves about 50 tons of material for each ton of product produced. Some industries move 180 tons for each ton of product.

In materials handling, masses are usually measured in tons or pallet loads instead of ounces, pounds, or kilograms. The human body is light and frail by comparison, so bulk materials' masses can easily pinch, fracture, sever, or crush its parts. Contributing to the hazards of large masses is the reality that materials handling includes *motion* for these masses.

To illustrate the general *mass/motion* hazards of material-handling equipment, consider the following comparison of processing versus material-handling equipment. To be struck by a moving part of a processing machine may or may not cause injury, depending on the size of the machine, the motion of the moving part, and the shape or surface characteristics of the part. But being struck by an industrial truck or conveyor is almost certain to cause injury. More indirectly, the mass/motion hazards of materials handling can affect safety by impacting facilities such as gas lines or electric lines or by overloading structural components of buildings.

Another general hazard of materials handling is its automatic or remote-control nature. Materials pumps and conveyors are often started automatically on demand or from a manual switch that is located far away. Conveyor accidents are often caused by this remoteness characteristic. In another example, railroad cars often move about a yard, far from the eye of the engineer, or worse yet, they may roll almost silently, coasting independently into position from the momentum of a locomotive's momentary push with no local control at all.

An indirect general hazard from materials handling is fire. This hazard emphasizes the storage aspect of materials handling. Warehouse fires are costly in terms of property loss, but they can also be dangerous to workers.

MATERIALS STORAGE

Materials-handling standards say that bags, containers, or bundles stored in tiers shall be "stacked, blocked, interlocked, and limited in height so that they are stable and secure against sliding or collapse." For general materials, the standard does not explain what constitutes "blocking" or "interlocking" and does not specify height limits for stacks. Some industry practices, however, seem to defy the standard. Since the standard for materials storage is not specific in its requirements but does address results (e.g., "so that they are stable and secure against sliding or collapse"), the standard should be recognized as a performance standard.

Housekeeping is another consideration for materials in storage. Sloppy warehouse practices can lead to trip hazards or fire. Pest harborage can result from certain accumulations of materials and can constitute a hazard. Outside storage can become grown over in weeds and grass, which can be a fire hazard in dry weather.

The safety and health manager should monitor the ups and downs of the company's sales and production fortunes. If there is a recent buildup in production in anticipation or in response to booming sales, there is likely to be a warehousing problem. Additional warehouse space is likely to be added later, after the upturn appears more permanent. Even after an expansion decision is made, a certain amount of lead time is necessary to plan and build add-on warehouse space. Meanwhile, the existing warehouse space becomes crowded and unsafe. Judgmental limits for material stacking are cast aside as creative ideas are explored to squeeze more material into a small space. Some of these new ideas will be good ones; it is not basically unsafe to try to conserve space. But during a period of warehouse crowding, special attention should be given to new hazards that may result from new procedures in the warehouse. Aisle and exit blockage are likely to occur during such periods of warehouse stress, as is the incidence of storage stack collapse. Any accidents that occur during such periods will point to some of the new hazards being generated, and these accidents should be analyzed to eliminate cause.

INDUSTRIAL TRUCKS

This category of material-handling equipment is exemplified by the forklift truck. There is no question that OSHA considers safety with forklift trucks important. OSHA's own estimate of the number of forklift trucks nationwide is over one million (ref. OSHA commits). When you consider that each forklift truck may have more than one employee within the plant authorized to drive it, it is easy to see that forklift truck safety is very important to worker safety. Typically, forklifts either are powered by electric motor or have internal combustion engines. Besides forklifts, there are tractors, platform lift trucks, motorized hand trucks, and other specialized industrial trucks. Not included are trucks powered by means other than electric motors or internal combustion engines. Also not included are farm tractors or vehicles primarily for earth moving or over-the-road hauling.

Truck Selection

"Ignorance is bliss" for most industrial managers who set out to buy a forklift truck. Little known is the fact that there are 11 different design classifications by type of power and by degree of hazard for which approved. These 11 design classifications are distributed over at least 26 different classifications of hazardous locations to which the forklift truck may be exposed.

One can easily wonder why it must be so complicated to select a forklift truck. The basis for this complication is that engines and motors can be dangerous sources of ignition for flammable vapors, dusts, and fibers. To design these engines and motors to effectively prevent ignition hazards is a costly matter, and the marketplace will not support the purchase of an explosion-safe forklift truck for use in an ordinary factory location. Thus, a complicated array of classifications and regulations is set up to permit the specification of the right industrial truck for the right job—no more, no less.

Industry standards for industrial truck classifications and their corresponding hazardous location codes are a maze of abbreviations and definitions. To understand these abbreviations, keep in mind that the objective is safety from *fires and explosions*. Whether the industrial truck is diesel, gasoline, electric, or LP-gas powered, the more fire-safe models are designed to prevent ignition of accidental fires, and thus they are more expensive. A simple summary is contained in Table 15.1. More details are contained in the standards, but most safety and health managers will need only the general idea. Another thing to keep in mind is that it is legal to use a safer, higher classified industrial truck than the minimum required, but of course it usually will not be economical to do so. If a firm already has an EE-approved electric forklift, however, it may be expedient to go ahead and use it instead of buying a new ES- or E-approved unit that would suffice for the given application.

Summarizing these principles and several pages of applicable regulations, Table 15.2 gives the safety and health manager a perspective into the approval classes of various industrial truck designs. The *classes*, *groups*, and *divisions* represent varieties of hazardous locations in which the definitions correspond *roughly* to those of the *National Electrical Code*. *Class* and *group* refer to the type of hazardous material present, and *division* refers to the extent or degree to which the hazardous material is likely to be present in dangerous quantities.

TABLE 15.1 Summary of Industrial Truck Design Classifications

Diesel	Electric	Gasoline	LP gas
D	E	G	LP
Standard model	Standard model	Standard model	Standard model
Cheapest	Cheapest	Cheapest	Cheapest
DS	ES	GS	LPS
Safer model	Safer model	Safer model	Safer model
More expensive	More expensive	More expensive	More expensive
Exhaust, fuel, electrical systems safeguards	Spark prevention Surface-temperature limitation	Exhaust, fuel, and electrical systems safeguards	Exhaust, fuel, and electrical systems safeguards
DY	EE		
Safest diesel	Safer still		
Most expensive diesel	More expensive		
No electrical equipment	All motors and electrical enclosed		
	EX		
Temperature-limitation feature	Safest of all		
	Most expensive electrical truck		
	Even electrical *fittings* designed for hazardous atmospheres		

Source: Summarized from Code of Federal Regulations 29 CFR 1910.178.

There are so many categories of "approvals" for industrial trucks that it is easy to lose sight of the overall objective in the approval process: to prevent fires and explosions from improper use of the wrong truck in a hazardous atmosphere. The authority for approval of industrial trucks is delegated to nationally recognized testing laboratories, such as Underwriters' Laboratories, Inc., and Factory Mutual Engineering Corporation. The prudent safety and health manager will leave the application-for-approval

TABLE 15.2 Allowable Categories for Industrial Trucks for Various Hazardous Locations

Class	Group	Division 1	Division 2
I	A	No industrial truck permitted	DY, EE, EX
	B	No industrial truck permitted	DY, EE, EX
	C	No industrial truck permitted	DY, EE, EX
	D	EX	DS, DY, ES, EE, EX, GS, LPS
II	E	EX	EX
	F	EX	EX
	G	EX	DY, EE, EX, DS, ES, GS, LPX
III		DY, EE, EX	DS, DY, E[a], ES, EE, EX, GS, LPS

[a] Permitted to continue if previously in use.

Source: Summarized from Code of Federal Regulations 29 CFR 1910.178.

process to the manufacturer of the equipment and simply look for the UL or FM approval classification, such as DY, EX, GS, and so on. For nonhazardous locations, even an *unapproved* truck may be used if the truck *conforms* to the requirements of type D, E, G, or LP.

In these days of high energy costs and the search for alternatives, some company managements may desire to convert an industrial truck from one energy source to another. But tampering with the design or altering the truck may invalidate the approval. Industrial truck conversions can be made, but the process is a bit tricky. The conversion equipment *itself* must be approved, and there is a right way and many wrong ways to carry out the conversion.

The hazard of fires and explosions may be the most complicated factor in the selection of forklift trucks, but it certainly is not the only factor. Far more important than the fire hazard rating of the design of the truck are the operations, fueling, guarding, training of drivers, and maintenance—subjects discussed in the next section.

Operations

One of the first items of interest to the safety and health manager should be the refueling or recharging area of forklifts. Smoking is prohibited in these areas, and this fault is found more than any other. Also a problem is the charging of forklifts in a *nondesignated area*. Hazards in the area include spilled battery acid, fires, lifting of heavy batteries, damage to the equipment by the forklifts, and battery gases or fumes. All of these hazards need to be addressed by the safety and health manager in some way.

Federal standards forbid pouring water into acid when charging batteries. Perhaps a sign in the area would achieve compliance with the rule. A better way to promote safety, though, would be to include in an employee training program an explanation of the violent and exothermic reaction that occurs when water is poured into a concentrated strong acid.

Everyone knows that arcs and sparks frequently fly when battery connections are made. What most do not know is that gases liberated during charging processes can reach ignitable concentrations. Fire is little or no hazard when a battery is simply "jumped" to another. But a forklift charging area is a different matter: Large volumes of gases are liberated; therefore, adequate ventilation is essential. In addition to ventilation, personal protective equipment and emergency eyewash and shower should be provided in the battery charging area due to potential exposure to acid.

With hazards of gases and acids in battery-charging areas, the alternative of the internal combustion engine seems attractive. But each of the internal combustion engine choices—diesel, gasoline, and LP gas—emit another dangerous gas: carbon monoxide. Since forklifts usually operate indoors, carbon monoxide gas levels can be a problem. The 8-hour time-weighted-average exposure limit for carbon monoxide is 50 ppm.

If the safety and health manager determines that a carbon monoxide problem exists in the plant and that the forklift trucks are the culprits, several alternatives are possible. The obvious one is to switch to electric forklifts. Another solution might be to alter the building or to install adequate ventilation systems. Perhaps the cheapest solution of all would be to review procedures and operations to determine whether sources of emissions can be reduced or perhaps eliminated entirely. The following are key questions:

1. Are operators leaving engines running unnecessarily?
2. Can the layout of warehouses or plant facilities be revised to reduce concentrations?
3. Are faulty or worn-out lift trucks creating more emissions than necessary?

Although there are no universal general minimum lighting requirements for industrial plants, where industrial trucks are operated, safety demands that the trucks themselves have directional lights if the plant area is too dark. Truck lights are required if the general lighting is less than 2 lumens per square foot. This is really a quite low level of light, since an ordinary 100-watt incandescent bulb can produce 1700 lumens. Even in an all-black room with nonreflective walls, a 100-watt bulb could produce more than 2 lumens per square foot in an 8 by 12 by 16 foot room. Wall or other surface reflections help the overall situation, so the requirement for 2 lumens per square foot is not difficult to meet. A lighting consultant can help in this determination.

Forklift Driver Training

The original National Consensus Standard adopted by OSHA emphasized the proper selection and hazard rating of forklift trucks, as well as the procedures surrounding their operation and maintenance. But far more important to the safety of operators and other workers around forklift trucks is how they are driven. Ironically, only one small general paragraph in the standards required operator training for forklift trucks. Employers were able to show compliance to this very general requirement by merely exposing new forklift drivers to a videotape. The result was a very haphazard approach to forklift driver training and a continued high incidence of fatalities.

Recognizing the gravity of the problem, OSHA promulgated a major change to the Powered Industrial Truck standard in 1999. To safety and health managers in general industry, the most important part of this standard was the dramatic change it brought to the operator training provision of the standard. Responsibility was placed on the employer to ensure that forklift truck drivers are competent. Content of the training must include formal instruction, which can consist of classroom training or videotape training, but this is only part of the requirement. The training must also include practical training, including driving demonstrations, and, perhaps most important of all, evaluation of the operator's performance in the workplace.

The specific content of the formal instruction is outlined in the standard and relates to both the equipment itself and the special hazards of the given workplace in which the equipment will be used. Therefore, it is not enough just to use a standard training program supplied by the equipment manufacturer. The instructor must also be qualified and capable of training the operators to deal with the specific hazards to which they will actually be exposed—for example, ramps that could cause tipping accidents, pedestrian traffic areas within the plant, or narrow aisles and places in which turning and driving will be restricted. These are items that would not be addressed in a general equipment operations manual.

The standard provides for evaluation of the operator's actual driving experience on the job, and if accidents or dangerous near misses occur, the driver must receive refresher training. Additional training may also be required if driving conditions change within the plant, such as those brought about by a remodeling of the work or traffic areas.

The final, clinching requirement of the forklift truck operator training requirement is certification. The employer or employer representative must certify and document the training, the evaluation, the dates of both the training and evaluation, and the identities of both the drivers and the trainers. The certification requirement traces the responsibility for the training and its effectiveness.

There is no doubt that OSHA has stiffened the requirements for forklift truck driver training and has made these requirements more specific. There is also little doubt that OSHA will continue to give this subject a great deal of attention. The problem is a serious one, and resolution will take years to achieve. As recently as the autumn of 2002, more than three years after the new standard on operator training, OSHA was reacting to new reports of large numbers of fatalities from forklift trucks. In one four-state region, 86 fatalities were reported within a 4-year period from forklift truck accidents alone (ref. OSHA Commits).

Just why are forklift trucks so dangerous? Some insight to this hazard may be revealed by considering the special hazards associated with the stability of forklift trucks and the lack of knowledge of this characteristic on the part of forklift drivers.

Many workers feel that because they know how to drive an automobile, they also basically know how to operate a lift truck. Unfortunately, many employers are inclined to take their word for it. But the operation of a lift truck takes a great deal more skill than the operation of an automobile. Compared to an automobile, a lift truck has a much shorter wheelbase, and when the load is lifted the center of gravity is very high. This creates stability problems to which the operator may be unaccustomed. Compounding the stability problem are the small-diameter wheels found on lift trucks, making chuckholes and obstructions more hazardous. When loaded, the center of gravity of the lift truck and load together can be shifted dangerously forward. Picking up and depositing loads require skill in proper manipulation and safe positioning. An off-center load presents a special hazard in which the load might tip in transit even though the truck itself is in a stable position.

Figure 15.1 diagrams the center of gravity of a forklift truck. The center of gravity shifts forward when the forks are loaded. If the load is too great, the center of gravity will shift forward of line BC and the forklift will tip dangerously forward, possibly dumping the load and overturning. Counterweights are added to the back of the forklift to counteract the forward-tipping forces, but if too much counter-weight is attached, the forklift becomes unstable when it is not loaded. Because of the three-point suspension scheme, the forklift may become laterally unstable when traveling while unloaded and tip sideways, especially when traveling on uneven terrain. Recognition of these physical factors facilitates understanding of the special hazards of driving a forklift truck and the need for the training specified by OSHA.

Besides stability problems, visibility can be a problem with lift trucks. The load itself can block the view and necessitate driving with the load trailing. Driving in worker aisles presents problems of pedestrian traffic, especially at corners where visibility is limited. Although lift trucks are not silent, they may seem so in a noisy factory environment. This increases the hazard to pedestrians and the need for greater visibility for lift truck operators.

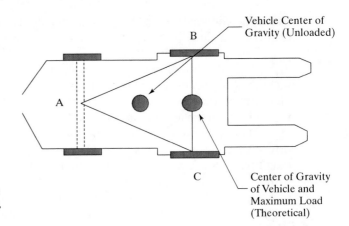

FIGURE 15.1

Top view of forklift truck illustrating the locations of the center of gravity when the forklift is unloaded and when it is loaded to capacity (*Source*: OSHA standard 1910.178, Appendix A).

One of the greatest hazards with forklifts and other industrial trucks is the transition between dock and cargo vehicle. Figure 15.2 shows precautions to be taken. Although a highway truck is shown in the figure, the hazard also exists for loading railroad cars.

Passengers

Passengers on a lift truck can be a hazard in more than one way. For one thing, the truck is often equipped to seat only the driver, and there may be no safe place for a passenger to ride. Hitchhikers also can distract the driver, whose attention is even more important on a lift truck than in an automobile. One practice particularly frowned on is riding on the lift *forks*. The temptation is great to use a forklift truck as a

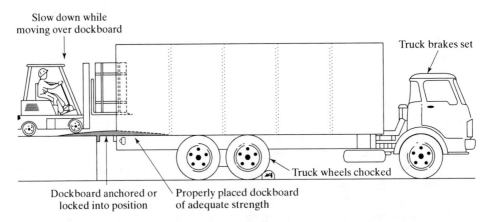

FIGURE 15.2

Preventing forklift hazards: transition from dock to cargo vehicle.

personnel elevator. Actually, this practice can be safe *if* all of the following conditions are obtained:

1. A safety platform is firmly secured to the lifting fork
2. The person on the platform can shut off power to the truck
3. Protection from falling objects is provided if needed

An ordinary wood pallet is not generally considered to be a safety platform, although it is often used for lifting personnel.

Some readers may consider the rule that the person on the platform be able to shut off power to the truck to be unreasonable. This rule also stands in the way of use of an ordinary pallet as a lifting platform. Workers, too, may resist this rule, and the safety and health manager needs to be in a position to counter this resistance with training programs that effectively explain the reasons for the rule. As a rationale for the rule, ask workers to consider the hazard caused by unexpected obstructions. A small obstruction could do any or all of the following:

1. Damage the platform
2. Tip the platform, causing the worker to lose balance
3. Injure the worker on the platform
4. Knock the worker off balance.

The forklift driver is really in a poor position, due to distance or angle, to see all obstructions and to judge their distance from the lifted platform. One might argue that the lift may be entirely clear of any obstructions, but such lifts would be unusual. There is usually no reason for employees to be lifted unless the lift is adjacent to equipment, stacks of material, or building structure. Any of these items can present obstruction hazards.

A variation of the *forklift rider* is the *carpet pole rider.* In carpet warehouses, the lift truck is equipped with a single pole, which is guided into the spool of a roll of carpet to lift the roll and transport it around the plant. Workers have been known to ride these poles rodeo style to gain access to the top of a stack of carpet rolls. Normally, there should be no reason for a worker to ride the pole because the pole can be raised and guided into position by the driver without assistance

When manipulating loads, the forklift is often operating close to observers, supervisors, or assistants giving directions to the operator. A dangerous place to stand is beneath the elevated fork, whether it is loaded or not. Another dangerous position is between an approaching lift truck and a fixed object or bench.

Parking and Maintenance

One thing to check is parked, unattended forklift trucks. The first thing to do is determine whether the lift truck is really unattended. If the operator cannot see the truck, it should be considered unattended. Even if the operator can see the truck, if the truck is more than 25 feet away, the truck is unattended. If the truck is unattended, the motor should be turned off. Even if the operator *is* close by, if the operator is *dismounted*, the fork must be fully lowered and the controls neutralized. The next thing to check is whether the brake is set, and if the truck is on an incline, whether the wheels are blocked. Finally, the horn should be tested.

Federal standards take very seriously the question of maintenance, inspection, and service for industrial trucks. No latitude is permitted concerning defective industrial trucks, to prevent them from being operated until the next regular overhaul. Any condition in a forklift, such as an inoperative horn, a defective brake, or a broken headlight, is cause to remove it from use until it is repaired.

Most people are amazed to learn that federal standards require industrial trucks in use to be inspected *daily* for safety. Compare this rule with procedures for automobile safety inspections, which most states require *annually*. If the industrial truck is used on a round-the-clock basis, safety inspections are required *after every shift*. It would be wise for the safety and health manager to institute some type of procedure or record to ensure that this job gets done and that proof of performance will be kept on file.

A final note on the subject of industrial trucks is the provision of an overhead guard to protect the operator from objects falling from the elevated load. More and more forklifts are being equipped with such guards for protection against falling objects such as small packages, boxes, and bagged material. They are not designed for protection against the impact of a full capacity load. These overhead guards are not to be confused with the much sturdier rollover protective structures (ROPS), although the same structure can be used for both purposes if it is constructed properly. Some loads are unitized, and objects within the load are secured from falling back on the operator. For such applications, the hazard to the operator from falling objects disappears, and the overhead guard becomes unnecessary.

CRANES

An industrial truck is convenient for general material handling of palletized loads. But some material-handling jobs cannot be handled by an industrial truck. Larger, heavier, more awkward loads require the versatility of a crane, especially if the path of travel is complicated.

A crane is a construction industry device that is typically seen lifting heavy steel beams to lofty places. Although this image is accurate, it is incomplete. Cranes are also used extensively in general industry, although they usually take a different form. Cranes in industrial plants are generally limited in travel by a track or overhead runway structure, typified by the *overhead traveling crane* shown in Figure 15.3. Such cranes are popularly called *overhead bridge cranes* or simply *bridge cranes* by the workers who use them. Some models, such as those shown in Figure 15.3, are operated from a cab mounted on the crane itself. Others are operated from the floor by means of a hanging cord control called a *pendant*, or from a fixed remote station called a *pulpit*. *Gantry* cranes have legs that support the bridge above the railway. *Cantilever* gantry cranes have extensions on one or both ends of the bridge; these extensions extend the reach of the crane outside the area between the rails on which the crane travels. One characteristic common to all overhead and gantry cranes is that the trolley, which carries the hoisting mechanism, rides *on top of* the rail on which it travels. Overhead cranes whose trolleys are not so mounted are called *underhung cranes* or *monorails*,

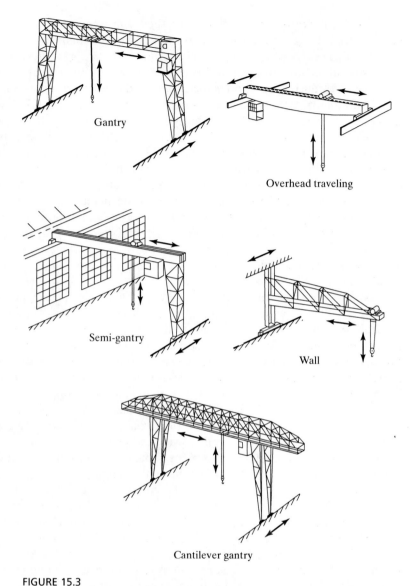

Gantry

Overhead traveling

Semi-gantry

Wall

Cantilever gantry

FIGURE 15.3

Various configurations for overhead cranes (*Source*: ANSI Standard B30.2.0-1976, reprinted with permission of ANSI and ASME).

depending on type or application. Safety standards for overhead and gantry cranes are different from standards for monorails.

The safety and health manager's chief concern with regard to overhead cranes should be that workers will overload the crane. The rated load should be plainly marked on each side of the crane, and if the crane has more than one hoisting unit, each hoist must have its rated load clearly marked. So easily recognized are crane load markings that their absence is conspicuous.

Even if the rated load marking *is* on the crane, workers will sometimes be tempted to exceed the rated capacity. Everyone knows that engineers provide for a safety factor in their designs, so virtually every crane will support more than its rated load, even without damage to the crane. But uncertainties in the actual weight of the load, dynamic loads during transport, shock loads during lifting, variations in crane components, and unavoidable design variabilities can combine to result in a very dangerous situation—even when rated load capacities are exceeded "slightly" or only "occasionally." As with running a stop sign, an alert driver can almost always avoid an accident, but once in a great while, another driver will be approaching the intersection at a high rate of speed, the visibility will be obstructed, or the stop sign violator will be complacent or distracted, and a serious accident will occur. It becomes very difficult for the safety and health manager or anyone else in the plant to police the proper use of cranes within their rated load limits at all times. This is where training becomes important so that workers will understand the risks and consequences of their actions. Another way to control this problem is to take the time to make a big example out of any accident or near accident that occurs as a result of overloading a crane, even if no injuries occur.

Many overhead cranes operate outdoors, where wind can be a hazard. Wind alone is usually not dangerous, but a wind load in combination with a working load can result in dangerous structural damage to the crane. Automatic rail clamps are required for outdoor storage bridge cranes. The purpose of these clamps is to lock the bridge to the rail if the wind exceeds a certain velocity. This idea sounds good because it protects against the types of wind hazards just described and also protects the bridge from unintentional and uncontrolled rolling in a high wind or a brake failure. But like some other devices, the safety device carries with it a hazard of its own. Think about it for a moment: In what mode of crane operation would the tripping device most likely engage the automatic rail clamp? The answer is when the bridge is traveling *at top speed* against the wind. The sudden engagement of the rail clamp when the bridge is traveling at top speed is likely to injure the operator in the cab, dangerously swing the load, damage the crane, or all three. Therefore, the crane needs either a visible or an audible alarm, or both, to warn the bridge operator *before* the rail clamp engages.

If the crane operator rides in a cab mounted on the bridge or the trolley, the operator must somehow have a way to gain access to his or her station. One idea that comes to mind is to use a portable ladder, but this is not such a good idea. Since the bridge travels, the operator, cab, trolley, and bridge may roam far from the point at which the operator mounted. The idle ladder standing far away would be an invitation for someone to remove it for some other use or perhaps just to get it out of the way. A ladder used for crane cab or bridge access should be of the fixed type. Stairs or a platform, or both, can also be used, but must require no step over a gap exceeding 12 inches.

Overhead cranes designed or constructed in-house sometimes do not meet accepted principles for crane design and overlook some of the necessary safety features specified by applicable standards. Besides cab access, there are specifications for footwalks for safe maintenance of the trolley and bridge. These footwalks need standard toeboards and handrails.

Ideally, footwalks will have at least 78 inches of headroom. Sometimes, however, this is not practical because the crane may be near the ceiling of the building. The standards recognize this difficulty and permit less than 78 inches of headroom. However, a footwalk becomes rather ridiculous if the headroom is less than 48 inches and would more properly be called a "hands-and-knees" walk. In these situations, footwalks should be omitted, and a stationary platform or landing stage for crane maintenance workers should be installed.

A critical hazard to the wire rope of a crane or hoist results from drawing the load hook or hook block up too far—to the point at which the load block makes contact with the boom point of the crane or other mechanical assembly for reeving the wire rope. This event is known as *two-blocking*, the term being derived from the physical contact of two blocks in the reeving system. On the incidence of two-blocking, continued travel of the load block causes a severe tensile stress to be immediately imparted to the wire rope, and this stress usually stretches or breaks the wire rope. The blocks may also be damaged.

Two-blocking is a very serious hazard that has resulted in many fatalities. A sudden break in a load-bearing wire rope constitutes an obvious hazard, especially if personnel are under the load or are themselves being hoisted aloft by the crane. As a matter of ergonomics, it can be shown that it is very difficult for a crane operator to be sufficiently vigilant to prevent an occasional dangerous brush with two-blocking, especially for construction cranes. So many fatalities have resulted from two-blocking that crane construction standards now address this hazard, and devices are on the market for the purpose of preventing two-blocking or the damage that can result from it. These mechanisms, usually electromechanical, are commonly called *anti two-block devices*.

An obviously serious hazard associated with the operation of an overhead bridge crane is overtravel. Devices to control overtravel would include trolley stops, trolley bumpers, and bridge bumpers. Bumpers and stops are somewhat different in that bumpers absorb energy and reduce impact, whereas a stop simply stops travel. The stop is simpler and can consist merely of a rigid device that engages the wheel tread. For safety, such a stop needs to be at least as high as the wheel axle center line. Bumpers soften the shock by absorbing energy, but are not as positive as a true stop. For example, bridge bumpers need only be capable of stopping the bridge if it is traveling at 40% or less of rated load speed. If the crane travels only at slow speeds, shock loads are not significant, and bridge bumpers and trolley bumpers are not necessary. There may be other circumstances of operation, such as restriction of crane travel, that eliminate the need for bridge bumpers or trolley bumpers.

Related to bumpers and stops are rail sweeps. If a tool or some item of equipment happens to obstruct one of the rails on which the bridge travels, a catastrophic accident could occur. Therefore, bridge trucks are equipped with rail sweeps, projecting in front of the wheels, to eliminate this hazard. There is nothing magical about the term *sweep*; even part of the bridge truck frame itself may serve as a sweep.

One obstruction that can be encountered by an overhead crane is another overhead crane that runs adjacent to it with parallel side rails. Proper clearance should be provided between the two adjacent bridge structures. Unfortunately, such clearance may make it impossible for one crane to transfer its load to the domain of the adjacent crane. Some factories resolve this problem by using retractable extension arms on the crane. The trouble with these retractable arms is that the operator may inadvertently leave them extended, resulting in a collision between the two adjacent cranes.

Electric shock is a concern with overhead cranes in two principal areas:

- Shock from exposure to current-carrying portions of the crane's power delivery system
- Shock from a shorted connection in a hanging control pendant box. (See Figure 15.4.)

A third area of concern for electrical shock is the accidental contact of live, high-voltage overhead transmission lines. This is a hazard for mobile cranes with booms (discussed in Chapter 18) because of their wide use in the construction industry. Exposed live parts in the crane's power delivery system are usually protected by their remoteness or "guarded by location." Some older models might present hazards and need modification.

A greater hazard is the possibility of shock from a pendant control. The electrical conductors can be strained if they are the sole means of support for the pendant. The control station must be supported in some satisfactory manner to protect against such strain. If there is a failure, it is likely to occur at a connection within the box. This raises the possibility of a dangerous short to ground through the operator's body. Pendant controls take much abuse and need to be of durable construction.

Not related to electrical shock but on the subject of pendant control boxes is the requirement that boxes be clearly marked for identification of functions. Some older model or homemade cranes might have pendant control boxes without function markings. Without a great deal of trouble or expense, the safety and health manager can check the cranes in-house for compliance and get the control functions marked on the pendant controls.

FIGURE 15.4

Hand-held pendant control for overhead crane.

One hazard to think about with overhead cranes is what would happen if a temporary power failure occurred. Suppose that the crane were in the process of lifting a heavy load by means of its hoist mechanism. Obviously, no one would want the crane to drop its load to the floor upon power failure, but the hazard does not end here. Suppose that the crane bridge is traveling in a horizontal direction, whether loaded or unloaded. Upon power failure, the bridge would stop, which might not be dangerous. But when power is *restored*, dangerous lurching action might occur. In fact, upon a power failure, the crane operator might even leave the crane cab!

Several design alternatives can protect against these hazards. One solution is to equip the control console with spring-return controllers. Pendant boxes can be constructed with spring push buttons instead of toggle switches. A disconnect device can neutralize all motors and not permit a reconnect until some sort of positive "reset" action is taken. Even if the power remains on, it could be a hazard to inadvertently switch on a lever at the wrong time. Notches, latches, or detents in the "off" position can prevent such inadvertent actions.

Brakes are of obvious importance to the safe operation of a crane, yet a large number of crane operators do not use brakes, but instead rely on a practice the industry calls "plugging." The operator merely reverses the control and applies power in the opposite direction, thereby stopping the load. Although no OSHA standard prohibits the practice of *plugging*, it should be pointed out that plugging is not as effective as applying a brake under extreme conditions, such as stopping a large, fast-moving load. Under no circumstances should a crane operator depend entirely on plugging due to the brake being inoperative. In fact, plugging would be completely useless in the event of crane motor failure.

A crane has many moving parts, many of which are located far from the operator's console in the cab or from a floor operator holding a pendant. Moving machine parts are hazardous, and the remoteness characteristic amplifies the hazard. Moving parts are hazardous not only to personnel; they can be hazardous to the crane itself, which in turn can be indirectly hazardous to personnel. Hoisting ropes, for instance, can possibly run too close to other parts in some crane configurations and in some positions of the bridge and trolley. The result can be chafing or fouling of the hoist rope. If the configuration of the equipment will permit this situation to develop, guards must be installed to prevent chafing or fouling. Such moving parts as gears, setscrews, projecting keys, chains, chain sprockets, and reciprocating components need to be checked to determine whether they present a hazard; if so, they must be guarded.

As with conveyors and other material-handling equipment, overhead cranes are often large and widely distributed items of equipment. Electrical power is distributed over long distances, sometimes by means of open runway conductors. Portions may be so far away as to be obscured from view from the location of the power supply switch. Picture the insecurity of the maintenance worker who is compelled to repair a crane and is in direct contact with an exposed 600-volt (but deenergized) runway conductor, but the power supply switch is so far away that it is out of sight! Therefore, such switches should be so arranged as to be *locked* in the open or "off" position. This is an example of a *lockout/tagout* requirement that was in place before the general lockout/tagout standard was promulgated by OSHA in 1989.

Ropes and Sheaves

Safety standards for wire rope strength state that "rated load divided by the number of parts of rope shall not exceed 20% of the nominal breaking strength of the rope." The term *rated* implies that a safety factor has been applied, which is numerically equivalent to 5, as can be derived from the standard as follows:

$$\frac{\text{Rated load (including load block)}}{\text{Number of parts of rope}} \leq 20\% \times (\text{nominal breaking strength}) \quad (15.1)$$

It will later be explained that the "number of parts of rope" is a multiplying factor that enables a multiple-sheaved block-and-tackle assembly to be loaded much higher than the wire rope load. Thus,

$$\text{Wire rope load} = \frac{\text{rated load (including load block)}}{\text{number of parts of rope}} \quad (15.2)$$

From equations (14.1) and (14.2)

$$\text{Wire rope load} \leq 20\% \times (\text{nominal breaking strength}) \quad (15.3)$$

Multiplying each side of the inequality by 5, we have

$$5 \times (\text{wire rope load}) \leq 100\% \times (\text{nominal breaking strength}) \quad (15.4)$$

Rearranging to create a ratio yields

$$\frac{\text{Nominal breaking strength}}{\text{Wire rope load}} \geq 5 \quad (15.5)$$

Since the ratio of the strength to the load is at least 5, the *safety factor is 5*.

The term *parts of rope* refers to the mechanical advantage provided by the block-and-tackle assembly. *Parts of rope* is computed by counting the number of lines supporting the load block. Of course, all the lines make up one continuous line that is reeved through several sheaves to achieve mechanical advantage. The concept is best explained by a picture; Figure 15.5 shows five different reeving combinations. Note that the mechanical advantage is numerically equivalent to the number of parts of line.

One additional caution is in order when determining the appropriate maximum load to be applied to a given reeving setup. The weight of the load-carrying sheave must be added to the weight of the load to be picked up to arrive at the total load of the line. The weight of the load block cannot be ignored, as is emphasized by the massive load block displayed in Figure 15.6. Case Study 15.1 will now be used to illustrate calculations used to determine the safety of a wire rope reeving application.

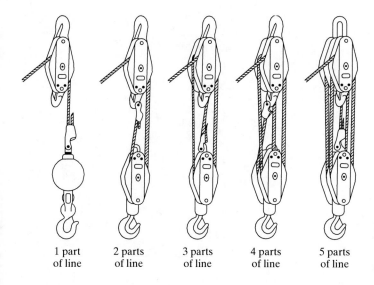

FIGURE 15.5

Five different reeving combinations. The mechanical advantage is equal to the number of "parts of line" supporting the load block.

| 1 part of line | 2 parts of line | 3 parts of line | 4 parts of line | 5 parts of line |

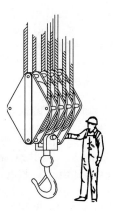

FIGURE 15.6

Massive load block. The load block becomes part of the total load on the line.

CASE STUDY 15.1

BLOCK-AND-TACKLE SAFETY FACTOR

The lower block of a block-and-tackle assembly has three sheaves and is thus supported by six parts of line as the wire rope is wrapped around the sheaves, plus a seventh part as the wire rope is tied off on the lower block. The wire rope has a nominal breaking strength of 4000 pounds. The lower block (the load block) itself weighs 80 pounds. Calculate what maximum payload this block-and-tackle assembly can pick up safely.

Solution:

$$\frac{\text{Rated load (including load block)}}{\text{Number of parts of rope}} < 20\% \times \text{(nominal breaking strength)}$$

$$\frac{\text{Rated load (including load block)}}{7} < 20\% \times 4000\,\text{lb}$$

$$\text{Rated load (including load block)} < 7 \times 20\% \times 4000\,\text{lb}$$

$$< 5600\,\text{lb}$$

$$\text{Maximum payload} = \text{rated load} - \text{weight of the load block}$$

$$= 5600\,\text{lb} - 80\,\text{lb} = 5520\,\text{lb}$$

One way to prevent overloading the wire rope and the crane itself is to provide a hoist motor that can develop insufficient torque to overload the wire rope. The combination of such a hoist motor and correct reeving for the crane design will result in no overloading. Under this arrangement, the crane simply will be unable to lift any load that would damage the crane or exceed its safety factor. Most overhead cranes today are designed this way. How fortunate it would be if the human back had this design feature.

Any time a rope is wound on a drum, the rope-end anchor clamp bears very little of the load when several wraps are on the drum. The friction of the rope on the drum holds the load. But if the drum is unwound to less than two wraps, dangerous loading of the anchor clamp may result in failure—the wire rope will break free from the drum. Usually, the overhead crane is set up so that, even if the load block is lying on the floor, several wraps remain on the hoist drum. The floor may not be the extreme low position for the crane, however. The safety and health manager should look around for pits or floor openings into which the overhead crane might operate, resulting in dangerous unwinding of the hoisting drum.

"Don't saddle a dead horse" is a familiar safety slogan that refers to the improper mounting of wire rope clips employing U bolts. Such a clip assembly bears a resemblance to a saddle, and the U bolt represents the cinch strap. The U bolt places more stress on the wire rope and has less holding power than the clip. Therefore, it should not be placed on the live portion of the rope when a loop is formed. The "dead" end of the rope gets the U bolt, and the "live horse" gets the clip. Right and wrong methods are illustrated in Figure 15.7. Unfortunately, some workers in the field, unsure of the correct method, place the clips *both ways* in alternating fashion, thinking they are "playing it safe." Such an arrangement may be even more unsafe than "saddling dead horses" with every clip.

Before leaving the subject of wire rope, the hazard of rope whip action should be emphasized. Wire rope "cable" seems so heavy and inflexible that it seems unnatural

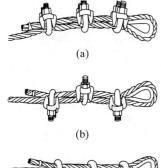

(a)

(b)

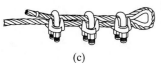

(c)

FIGURE 15.7

"Don't saddle a dead horse." Right and wrong ways to secure wire rope loops using U-bolt clips. (a) Incorrect—"saddle" is on dead end of rope; (b) incorrect—clips are staggered both ways; (c) correct—all clips are placed with the saddle assembly on the live portion of the rope and the U bolt on the dead end.

that it could crack like a whip or any fiber rope. It is difficult for anyone to visualize the tremendous tension forces on a wire rope during use in material-handling operation, until that wire rope breaks. Most workers have never seen what happens when a wire rope breaks; perhaps this explains why so many workers stand too close while the rope is drawn taut by the load. The hazard is very serious, and an injury accident is very likely to be a fatality.

Crane Inspections

Almost everyone is aware of the long, perhaps tedious checklists for inspection of an aircraft every time it flies. An aircraft must not fail in any catastrophic way during operation, and this makes frequent inspections worthwhile, even if they are repetitious and rarely uncover any defects. In some ways, a crane is like an aircraft; it, too, must not fail.

With regard to crane inspections, the standards use the terms *frequent* or *periodic* to specify when various items on the crane should be checked. Such usage is an attempt to avoid being overly specific in telling the employer *what* to do and *how often* to do it. Some broad guidelines describing the meaning of these terms are illustrated in Figure 15.8. Note that there is some overlap, as monthly inspections can be considered either frequent or periodic.

The crane manufacturer is a good source for detailed guidance in what to look for in the frequent inspections. This type of inspection is performed by the crane operator, just as a pilot inspects his or her aircraft before a flight. This analogy between aircraft and cranes might be a starting point for a safety theme in a training program for crane operators.

The frequent-inspection routine should include a daily visual inspection of hoist chains, plus a monthly inspection with a signed report. In the field, the term *hoist chains* has been widely misinterpreted to include chain *slings* for handling the load. A separate standard exists for slings. Figure 15.9 identifies which chain is hoist and which is sling.

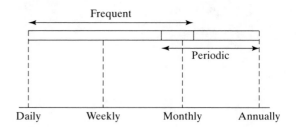

FIGURE 15.8

Inspection intervals for overhead cranes.

Crane hooks take a great deal of abuse and are critical to the safe operation of the crane. Although they usually contain considerable overdesign, damage or wear can reduce the margin of safety. Telltale signs of an abused and dangerous hook are illustrated in Figure 15.10.

A more thorough inspection of crane components is needed for "periodic" intervals. Whereas daily inspection of crane hooks is merely visual, the periodic inspection calls for a more scientific approach, such as using magnetic-particle techniques for detecting cracks. More extensive checks for wear are appropriate also, such as the use of gauges on wire rope sheaves and chain sprockets.

For most kinds of plant equipment, safety testing is customarily done by an independent testing laboratory such as Underwriters' or Factory Mutual. But the safety of an overhead crane is in part a function of the installation method and proper adjustments at the site. Therefore, an actual rated-load test is needed prior to initial use to

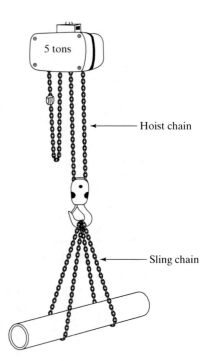

FIGURE 15.9

Hoist with sling. Hoist chain is not to be confused with the sling chain.

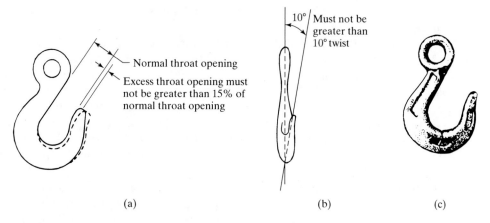

FIGURE 15.10

Defective crane hooks: (a) bent hook; (b) twisted hook; (c) cracked hook.

confirm the load rating of the crane. This is a bit tricky, because if the crane is subjected to too heavy a load, the crane may fail; but if it is not tested with a heavy enough load, why conduct the test? Standards specify that the maximum load during the test should go 25% higher than the crane's load rating. This will provide some assurance that the crane will withstand its rated load. During use, however, the crane should not be loaded with more than its rated load. Any extensive repair or alteration of the crane may subject it to a retest.

Wire Rope Wear

The two principal moving parts of an overhead crane are the wire rope and the drum and sheaves on which they travel. In addition, the wheels for the bridge and trolley move, as do a few other items on the crane. Whenever parts move and contact other parts, they are subjected to wear. Wear on the bridge and trolley wheels may eventually lead to problems, but is not likely to cause crane failure. Wear on the drum and sheaves is more dangerous because of the harm this can bring to the wire rope. But worn sheaves and drum *alone* are generally not the *direct* cause of crane failure. The wire rope remains as the most critical moving part. With continued use, every wire rope will eventually wear out and fail, a hazard that generally is not tolerable. Some way has to be devised to predict the failure of wire rope and withdraw it from use before a catastrophe.

It is not a simple matter to determine when a wire rope needs replacing. A wire rope has many individual wires, and it is easy to cut or break away any one of these small wires. Almost everyone has seen broken wires in an old wire rope (or "cable," as laypersons often say), which raises the question, "Is such a wire rope dangerous?" Safety and health managers do not survive long in their companies if they go around ordering wire rope replaced every time they find a broken wire. And if they did survive, their companies would not survive. Before delving into this issue, some basics about wire rope need to be examined.

A wire rope should really be considered a machine because the individual wires move on each other while the rope flexes, resulting in friction and wear. Furthermore, unless the individual strands are able to move properly during flexure, tremendous tensile stresses may be placed on some of the wires, causing them to break. Rust, kinks, and other types of abuse can interfere with the movement of the wires and lead to the stresses that cause wire breakage. As some wires break, the tensile stresses on other wires increase, leading to their breakage as well. Eventually, the force of the crane load will be sufficient to overcome the tensile strength of all remaining wires combined, and the wire rope will fail.

Even a well-maintained wire rope will be subject to wear on the individual wires, especially the outside wires. As the wear causes the diameter of the wire to become smaller, the tensile force increases the tensile stress on that single wire due to its reduced cross-sectional area. Thus, the worn wire, too, may break due to stress concentration, even if there are no kinks or rust, and even if the wires move properly to distribute the load among all wires.

For obvious purposes, a wire rope is overdesigned and will withstand more than its rated load. Equally obvious is that all wire rope will eventually develop broken wires with continued use. Broken wires are permissible to an extent, but beyond a certain point, the rope becomes dangerous. A means of evaluating the *degree* of wire rope deterioration is awkward and difficult, but nevertheless *necessary*, to prevent catastrophic failure.

The ANSI standard recommends[1] a procedure for counting the broken wires. Figure 15.11 diagrams the components of wire rope, defining the terms *strand* and *lay*. If there are more than 12 randomly distributed broken wires in a single strand in a single lay, there should be cause for questioning the continued use of the rope. A good place to look for broken wires is around end connections. Sometimes an expert can evaluate the remaining strength in a deteriorated rope after inspection. This possibility is acknowledged by the ANSI standard, which advocates the use of good judgment.

Another measure of rope condition is the amount of reduction of rope diameter below nominal. Figure 15.12 shows that when gauging a wire rope, the caliper can be placed on a small diameter or a larger diameter. The convention for wire rope terminology is to use the larger diameter for designation as the nominal diameter of the rope. Most people pay little attention to wire rope, but wire rope is no small matter considering that a quarter million tons of wire rope is sold annually.

Operations

The actual handling and moving of the load by the crane is a function of the skill, knowledge, and performance of the crane operator and the workers who attach and secure the sling or lifting device. As is the case with motor vehicles, the *operator* of the crane is probably the most important factor in preventing accidents.

---

[1]ANSI B30.2–2.4.2.

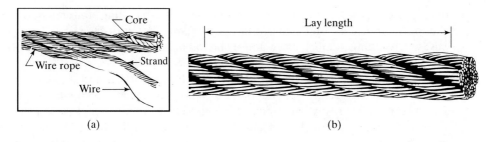

FIGURE 15.11

Wire rope components. (a) This wire rope has six strands plus an inner core. Do not confuse *strands* with *wires*. (b) Wire rope lay. *Lay* is one complete wrap of a single strand around the rope. Since this rope has six strands, lay is the length from the first hump to the seventh hump, as shown in the diagram (*Source:* courtesy of the Construction Safety Association of Ontario, ref. Rigging).

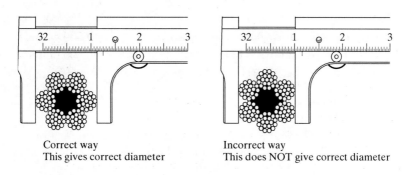

FIGURE 15.12

Gauging wire rope (rotate rope to select largest diameter) (*Source:* Courtesy of the Construction Safety Association of Ontario).

A good deal of skill is required to attach the load safely, especially if a sling is used. Slings will be discussed in the next section. The hoist rope is not intended for wrapping around the load, as this kind of abuse may damage the rope and at the same time be an inadequate support for the load. Misplacing the attachment off the line of the center of gravity can cause dangerous swings when the load is lifted. After the load is lowered, the tendency is to consider the hazards removed. But disengaging the load attachment can also result in dangerous shifts in material that can injure the inexperienced or unwary worker on the floor.

SLINGS

Slings are used to attach the load to the crane, helicopter, or other lifting device. Slings come in a great many varieties and are very important in the safety of material-handling operations. Components of the sling assembly are often subjected to much larger forces during lifting than is the hoist rope or other material-handling equipment. Because the skill of the user is so important in the proper application of the sling, slings are often misused, resulting in much more abuse and damage to slings than to the components of the crane.

The most important point to remember for the safe use of all slings is that the stress on a sling is greatly dependent on the way it is attached to the load. Figure 15.13 shows two different ways of applying a sling to pick up identical loads. If the angle of the supporting legs of a sling is sharp, as in Figure 15.13b, the advantage of multiple legs can be lost. Using too short a sling is the most common cause for this condition. The "rated capacity" of a sling is the working load limit under *ideal* conditions; if the sling is applied at leg angles other than those specified in the rated capacity table, the capacity can be drastically reduced due to the physics of the applied forces. Therefore, *rated capacity* is an incomplete term without the accompanying leg angle.

Note the following progression in capacities of 1/2-inch alloy steel chain as the number of legs increases:

Single (at vertical)	11,250 pounds
Double (at 60° from horizontal)	19,500 pounds
Triple (at 60° from horizontal)	29,000 pounds
Quadruple (at 60° from horizontal)	29,000 pounds

It might be assumed that the capacity of the sling increases as the number of legs or supporting members is increased. But note that no increase in capacity is shown in going from three to four legs. The reason for this is that, as in a four-legged chair, three legs will actually carry the load. At times, the weight distribution might be equal among legs of the sling, but usually the balance is not so perfect. As the load shifts around, it is

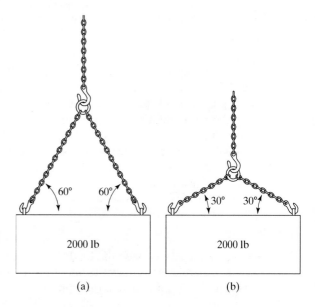

FIGURE 15.13

Comparison of sling tensile forces for two different methods of lifting identical loads: (a) tensile force on the sling is approximately 1150 pounds; (b) tensile force on this sling is approximately 2000 pounds.

entirely possible for one of the four legs to become slack and for the other three to bear the entire load.

Alloy steel chain, besides being very strong, is very durable and capable of withstanding the physical abuse that industrial slings routinely receive. The ordinary carbon steel chain commonly found in hardware stores should not be used for slings. Wire rope slings can be just as strong as steel chain slings, but wire rope is more subject to wear. Individual wires in the wire rope are more easily broken, with eventual incapacitation of the sling.

Wire rope slings also have a specification for the permitted number of broken wires; the rule is no more than ten randomly distributed broken wires in one rope lay, or five broken wires in one strand in one rope lay. Note from our earlier discussion that this is a bit more strict than the requirement for wire rope for overhead cranes.

Selection of the proper sling for a given application can consider several factors besides rated load. The nature of the item to be lifted, its surface finish, temperature, sling cost, and environmental factors must be considered. The safety and health manager is usually not the person who makes this decision, but there is increasing reason for the safety and health manager to have a voice in what is done in this area. Many factory superintendents, supervisors, and material-handling workers are not aware of the many federal standards confronting the criteria for selection of slings. In fact, many of these personnel do not even have a clear understanding of the inherent hazard mechanisms surrounding industrial slings. Therefore, it is recommended that the safety and health manager provide consultation and advice in the selection and use of industrial slings in the interest of worker safety.

For some criteria, such as load markings, repair procedures, proof testing, and operating temperatures, the requirements for various types of slings are not identical, and even vary in curious ways. Some of this is due to the physical differences in sling types, and some is due to the various origins and rationales for the requirements for various slings. Table 15.3 is intended to summarize some of the more curious differences between requirements for various types of slings, but it is by no means exhaustive. For instance, nylon web slings are not permitted in the presence of acid or phenolic vapors. In the case of caustic vapors, polyester and polypropylene web slings and web slings with aluminum fittings are not permitted. The safety and health manager can use Table 15.3 as a first check in an in-house inspection or purchase decision; then further details should be checked out in the standards.

It must be reemphasized, however, that the skill and training of the worker who uses the sling to attach the load is more important than all of the detailed specifications and sling standards combined. This is a good place for the reader to reflect on the fatality described in Case Study 15.2.

CASE STUDY 15.2

Two inexperienced workers had the assignment of hoisting a 40-foot-bundle of channel steel. The question was where to attach the hoist hooks to the load. The solution they selected was based on their experience in lifting loads with which

TABLE 15.3 Comparison of Certain Requirements for Slings

Type of sling	Rated capacity markings required?	Repairs permitted?	Employer required to maintain records of periodic inspection?	Employer required to maintain a certificate of proof test?	Safe operating temperature (°F)		Proof test of sling required?	Repair records required?[a]
					Maximum	Minimum		
Alloy steel chain	Yes	Yes	Yes	Yes	1000[b]	None specified	Yes	No, except for welding or heat treating
Wire rope								
With fiber core	No	Yes	No	Yes, for welded end attachments	200	None specified	Yes, for welded end attachments	No
With nonfiber core	No	Yes	No		400[c]	−60[c]		No
Metal mesh	Yes	Yes	No	No	550[d]	20[d]	Yes	Yes
Natural fiber rope	No	No	No	No	180	20	No	N/A
Nylon fiber rope	No	No	No	No	180	20	No	N/A
Polyester fiber rope	No	No	No	No	180	20	No	N/A
Polypropylene fiber rope	No	No	No	No	180	20	No	N/A
Nylon web	Yes	Yes	No	Yes, for repaired slings	180	None specified	Yes, for repaired slings	Yes
Polyester web	Yes	Yes	No	Yes, for repaired slings	180	None specified	Yes, for repaired slings	Yes
Polypropylene web	Yes	Yes	No	Yes, for repaired slings	200	None specified	Yes, for repaired slings	Yes

[a]N/A, not applicable.
[b]If alloy steel chains are working in temperatures exceeding 600°F, load limits are reduced.
[c]Seek manufacturer's recommendations for use outside the temperature range.
[d]Impregnated metal mesh slings have more restricted temperature requirements.

they were familiar—hand-held loads. To these workers, the heavy, steel straps used to secure the bundle seemed to be a natural attachment point. But these straps were not intended to be used as a substitute for a sling. Their strength was insufficient, and the angle of attachment was severe. The angle of attachment will always be severe when bundle straps are used in this way, because to do their job, the straps must be tight. When the load was lifted one of the straps gave way and one of the workers was killed.

CONVEYORS

Hazards with conveyors can be quite serious, and workers seem to sense these hazards more than with some other types of machines. It seems that all of us have implanted somewhere in our imaginations the vision of being tied to the conveyor in a sawmill about to be sawed in half. The truth is that sometimes workers *are* caught in industrial conveyors and not only killed, but dismembered or even pulverized beyond recognition. The horror of this truth instills a healthy respect on the part of most workers around industrial conveyors.

By contrast, some of the worst conveyor hazards are very innocent in appearance. In-running nip points that themselves might not even seriously injure a hand or arm can start an irreversible process once the employee is caught, resulting in an employee's entire body being drawn into a machine. Loose clothing in particular can get caught, and the employee, even before being injured in the slightest way, can become doomed.

Belt Conveyors

On a belt conveyor, in-running nip points are seemingly everywhere. Pulleys are required to drive the belt, change direction of the belt, support the belt, and tighten the belt. One side of every pulley is always an in-running nip point. Defense against this hazard generally consists of one of three means: isolating the nip points, installing guards, and installing emergency tripping devices.

The best method of protection is to isolate the in-running nip point so that an employee would not or could not come into the danger area. If isolation is impractical, a guard can sometimes be installed to keep out the worker's body or extremities. The design of the guard must vary with the application, and sometimes it is difficult to make the guard practical because it may interfere with the operation of the conveyor. Because of body geometry, distance from the danger zone is a design factor in building the guard.

If both isolation and guarding are impossible or infeasible for the application, the workers can be protected by some type of emergency tripping mechanism. A wire or rope can be run along the length of the conveyor so that a worker falling into the conveyor can grab the trip wire and stop the machine. Unfortunately, this method of protection requires the overt action of an alert worker or coworker.

Overhead Conveyors

Large appliance parts or vehicle assemblies are often handled by overhead conveyors. Hooks attached to a moving chain support each item as it is moved. This type of conveyor is particularly suited for products that have delicate or finished surfaces because so little of the conveyor actually contacts the product. For the same reason, overhead conveyors are very useful for paint spray or finishing operations.

Overhead conveyors avoid many of the risks of belt conveyors by eliminating many of the in-running nip points and by removing the moving parts from worker access. But overhead conveyors have hazards of their own, such as dropping conveyored materials to the plant floor or onto workstations. Screens or guards can protect against this hazard, but not entirely, because the moving parts must be accessible to workstations for processing. A good rule is to place screens or shields under the conveyor whenever it passes over an aisle or other area where personnel are likely to gather. Another good place for screens is where the conveyor chain moves up or down an incline. Such movements cause the loads to shift on their hangers and increase the possibility of a falling load.

Figure 15.14 shows three different orientations for the hangers or hooks that support the work held by an overhead conveyor. Note how much safer is the orientation in which the work is held in front of the hook. If the work encounters an obstruction, it is more likely to catch and stop the conveyor if the work is in front of the hook. If the work trails the hook, an obstruction may lift and knock off the load.

Screw Conveyors

Screw conveyors can be very dangerous. The very principle of their operation is an ingoing nip point at the intake. Complicating the hazard is the fact that in order to operate at full capacity, the intake must be completely submerged in the material to be transported. *Submerged* usually also means hidden, so an unseen serious hazard exists at the intake. Finally, there may be a need for the worker to be fairly close to the screw conveyor for many applications in order to shovel or distribute material into the intake.

A simple and often effective way to protect workers from the hazards of the screw intake is to box the intake area in a small screen enclosure that allows passage of the

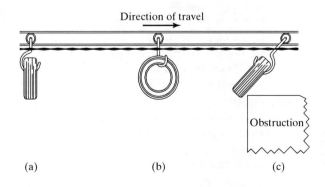

FIGURE 15.14

Three different orientations for conveyor hooks:
(a) hook trails the load; (b) side orientation;
(c) load trails the hook (dangerous).

(a)   (b)   (c)

material, but keeps out fingers, hands, and feet. If even a coarse screen mesh is too fine to permit passage of the material, an enclosure with larger openings may be necessary, perhaps with openings large enough to admit a finger or hand. This type of enclosure can be made safe, too, by making the box large enough that the worker's *reach* will not permit entry of hands or fingers into the danger zone. This follows principles of machine guarding.

LIFTING

Before closing this chapter on materials handling, we return to the subject of lifting. It was stated earlier that back injury, mostly from lifting, is one of the biggest compensable injury categories of all. Lifting injuries are very complex and very difficult to control. Naturally, the amount of weight lifted is important, but many other factors determine whether an injury occurs. Even a lightweight lift of 5 to 10 pounds can cause serious back injuries if conditions are just right (rather, wrong). The physical condition of the person doing the lifting is also important.

Much emphasis has been placed on technique, with the most frequently heard saying being "Lift with your legs, not with your back." Unfortunately, the rule is rather difficult to follow because almost everyone is able to lift a heavier weight with the back than with the legs. Lifting with the legs requires squatting down and then lifting both the load and the lifter's body. This requires a great deal of leg strength for heavy lifts and is especially difficult when the worker is unaccustomed to lifting with the legs. Training and exercise with light loads can help in developing the technique, but there are other disadvantages of lifting with the legs. Chaffin and Park (ref. Chaffin) have shown that if the shape of the load is such that it must be brought out in front of the knees, lifting with the legs *increases* the compression force on the lower back! Also overlooked by the often-quoted rule is the fact that lifting with the legs takes as much as 50% more energy as lifting with the back, especially when the load is light and the frequency of lifting higher.

The capacity to lift varies greatly with the horizontal position of the load, which is determined largely by the shape of the object being lifted. Various independent studies of this relationship have been analyzed by NIOSH, resulting in a proposed specification for maximum weight lifted versus the horizontal distance of the load from the center of gravity of the body. This specification is summarized in Figure 15.15, but it must be remembered that the graph represents merely a NIOSH recommendation, not an established standard.

SUMMARY

This chapter has brought recognition to the fact that the handling of material in a manufacturing plant can be as hazardous as the industrial process itself. The basic nature of material-handling hazards were examined; then hazards of specific machines and equipment were discussed.

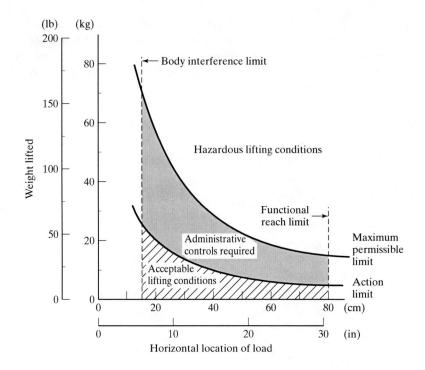

FIGURE 15.15

NIOSH-recommended specification for maximum lift weights at various horizontal distances for infrequent lifts from floor to knuckle height (*Source:* NIOSH).

The safety and health manager needs to be aware not only of the proper safety features to seek in new equipment, but also of the inspection, service, and maintenance of equipment in-house. However, for industrial trucks, cranes, slings, and perhaps *all* material-handling equipment, the operator's skill, attitude, and awareness of hazards are probably more important to the safety of the worker than are the safety features of the equipment itself.

EXERCISES AND STUDY QUESTIONS

15.1 Why are four-legged slings rated no higher than three-legged slings?

15.2 An often-heard safety slogan is "Don't saddle a dead horse!" What does this slogan mean?

15.3 What *safety* design feature do most modern overhead cranes have that is unfortunately not characteristic of the human back?

15.4 Name a part of the plant to which the safety and health manager should give special attention when production and sales are booming.

15.5 In the diagrams, which orientation of the 4000-pound load will place less stress on the sling that handles it? Explain.

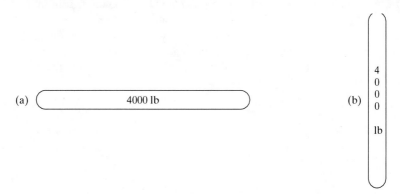

(a)   4000 lb

(b)   4 0 0 0 lb

15.6 Suppose that a company was able to save some money by trading in its type LPS forklift truck for a type DY. Would this introduce some safety problems? What if the trade were from DY to LPS?

15.7 Why might spring push buttons be a better crane control than toggle switches?

15.8 In Figure 15.16, what is the mechanical advantage? If the nominal breaking strength of the rope is 5000 pounds and the load block weighs 200 pounds, calculate the maximum rated payload of the hoist (not including the load block).

FIGURE 15.16

Blocks and pulleys for Exercise 15.8.

15.9 What is a rail sweep, and why is it needed?

15.10 Name in order of preference three methods of protection for in-running nip-point hazards on conveyor belts.

15.11 Why are overhead crane access ladders specified to be of the fixed type?

15.12 Because of rising gasoline costs, a company desires to convert existing gasoline-powered forklifts to LPG powered. What implications would such a decision have?

15.13 Identify a performance standard in the standards for materials handling. Explain why it is a performance-type standard.

15.14 Explain the following terms as applied to industrial cranes: *bridge, trolley, pendant, pulpit, gantry*, and *cantilever gantry*.

15.15 Name at least four characteristics of forklift trucks that require more skill for safe operation than is required for operation of an automobile.

15.16 At least four general characteristics of materials handling contribute to its intrinsic hazard potential. Name and explain four such characteristics.

15.17 A 2000-pound payload is supported by the crane block-and-tackle assembly shown in Figure 15.17. In addition to the payload, the load-carrying sheave weighs 100 pounds. Calculate the approximate load on the wire rope. How many parts of rope are used in the reeving, as shown in Figure 15.17?

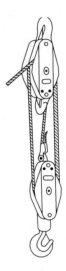

FIGURE 15.17

Blocks and pulleys for Exercise 15.17

15.18 What minimum nominal breaking strength is specified by safety standards to be suitable for the application described in Exercise 15.17?

15.19 Suppose the wire rope in use in the reeving shown in Figure 15.16 is rated at 2000 pounds and the load-carrying block weighs 150 pounds. The objective is to lift a load weighing 3000 pounds. Does the assembly as described meet safety standards?

15.20 What maximum payload rating would you assign to the block-and-tackle assembly described in Exercise 15.19? What is the nominal breaking strength of the wire rope?

15.21 A sling with three legs is used to pick up a 1000-pound load. The load is distributed equally among the three legs. When the load is picked up, each leg forms an angle of 30° with the horizontal. Calculate the tensile force on each leg.

15.22 A three-legged sling distributes its load equally among its three legs. When the load is picked up, each leg forms an angle of 60° with the horizontal. The rated load of the chain used in the sling is 6 tons. Calculate the maximum total load this sling is rated to pick up?

15.23 From a safety standards aspect, what is the significance of whether a crane trolley rides on top of the rail or hangs from the lower flange?

15.24 Explain the term *plugging* as it applies to the operation of an overhead bridge crane. Do the OSHA standards prohibit plugging?

15.25 Explain the difference between a sling and a hoist.

15.26 Explain the relationship of leg angle to the stress that is placed on a sling.

15.27 What is the principal hazard of using a sling that is too short?

15.28 Explain why it is often hazardous to pick up a load by its binding straps.

15.29 Explain two complicating factors that heighten the hazard of the in-running nip point at a screw conveyor intake.

15.30 Explain how to design out the risk created by the hazards of the in-running nip point at a screw conveyor intake.

15.31 Explain why there is a concern for pits in the floor of a factory served by an overhead crane.

15.32 Give probable reasons for the fact that there is no OSHA standard for lifting.

15.33 Describe the general relationship between maximum lifting capability and horizontal distance between the load and the person performing the lift.

15.34 Explain why lifting with the legs requires more energy than does lifting with the back.

15.35 **Design Case Study.** The objective is to design a trolley hoist for an overhead bridge crane that will meet OSHA standards. The hoist must be rated at 10 tons. The hoist will be reeved with wire rope that has a nominal breaking strength of 30,000 pounds. Specify the reeving arrangement, including the number of sheaves on the load block and on the upper block. Include a reasonable estimate of the weight of the load block. Sketch the reeving arrangement showing the relationship between the blocks and the number of parts of rope.

15.36 **Design Case Study.** Specify the lighting in the aisles of a warehouse with a ceiling height of 20 feet. The objective is to specify the minimum lighting required for forklift trucks to operate without the requirement for headlamps. Specify the lumen output per overhead lamp and the spacing of the lamps.

15.37 **Design Case Study.** You are on the design team for building an overhead bridge crane for use in-house within the company. The design team is considering a proposal to place a switch box on the wall with toggle on/off switches for control of the bridge, trolley, and hoist, respectively. What would be your design input to this committee? Explain the rationale behind your recommendations.

RESEARCH QUESTION

15.38 Search for currently available simulation tools to enable a designer to use virtual reality to test various workplace designs to determine whether the human operator at a proposed workstation will exceed NIOSH recommended lifting limits.

CHAPTER 16

Machine Guarding

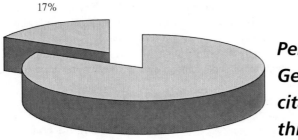

17%

Percentage of OSHA General Industry citations addressing this subject

Most people think of a machine guard when industrial safety is mentioned, and for good reason. More efforts and resources have been expended to guard machines than for any other industrial safety and health endeavor. To modify or guard a single machine is generally not a major project when compared with installing a ventilation system or a noise-abatement system. But although each machine guarding modification is usually small, the aggregate becomes a major undertaking involving plant maintenance, operations, purchasing, scheduling, and, of course, the safety and health manager. The safety and health manager should take a leadership role in the implementation of machine guards—enumerating problem areas, setting priorities, selecting safeguarding alternatives, and ensuring compliance with standards.

GENERAL MACHINE GUARDING

If safety and health managers are to be able to "enumerate problem areas" and "set priorities" as just suggested, they need to be knowledgeable about what makes a machine dangerous. Despite wide differences between machines, some mechanical hazards seem to be shared by machines in general, and these mechanical hazards will be discussed first.

Mechanical Hazards

The following are general machine mechanical hazards listed in approximate order of importance:

1. Point of operation
2. Power transmission
3. In-running nip points
4. Rotating or reciprocating machine parts
5. Flying chips, sparks, or parts

In addition to the mechanical hazards listed are others, such as electrical, noise, and burn hazards. These hazards are usually controlled by other methods, however, and are covered elsewhere in this book. It is predominantly the mechanical hazards that are controlled by machine guards, the subject of this chapter.

Although the sequence of priority in the foregoing list is only approximate, there is no question about which hazard should be at the top of the list. By far the largest number of injuries from machines occur at the point of operation, where the tool engages the work. This machine hazard is so important that it is discussed later in a separate section detailing various strategies and guarding devices in controlling the hazard.

The power transmission apparatus of the machine, typically belts and pulleys, is the second most important general machine hazard. Belts and pulleys are usually easier to guard than is the point of operation. Access to the belts and pulleys is usually necessary only for machine maintenance, whereas the point of operation must be accessible, at least to the workpiece, every time the machine is used. Although belts and pulleys are easier to guard, they also are easily overlooked by the safety and health manager. A later section is devoted to belts and pulleys, due to their overall importance to safety.

Machines that feed themselves from continuous stock generate a hazard where the moving material passes adjacent to or in contact with machine parts. This hazard is called an *in-running nip point* or an *ingoing nip point*. Even on machines not equipped with automatic feed, in-running nip points occur where belts contact pulleys and gears mesh. Figure 16.1 shows examples of in-running nip points. In-running nip points are not only direct hazards, but can cause injury indirectly by catching loose clothing and drawing the worker into the machine.

Rotating or reciprocating moving parts can present hazards similar to those of belts and pulleys and in-running nip points—in truth, there is overlap between these categories. But rotating or reciprocating moving parts bring to mind other parts of the machine that might need guarding. Particularly dangerous is a part of the machine that moves *intermittently*. During the motionless part of the cycle workers might forget that the machine will later move. Material-handling apparatus, clamps, and positioners are in this category, as are robots and computer-controlled machinery. The most intermittent motion of all is *accidental* motion. It pays to consider what would happen in the event of a hydraulic failure, broken cotter pin, loosened nut, or some other accidental occurrence. Would the guard on the machine protect workers in these circumstances? Is the risk of occurrence of enough significance to warrant installing a guard?

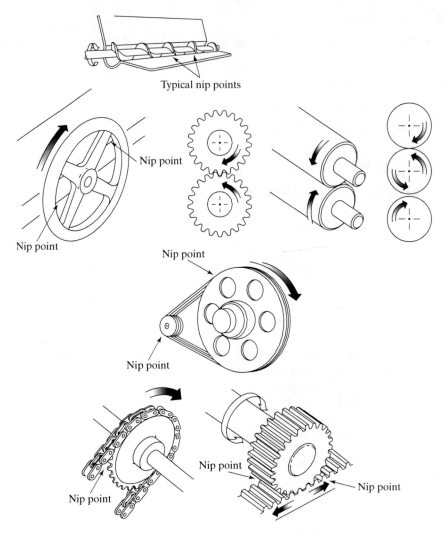

FIGURE 16.1

In-running nip points.

The fifth item listed earlier, flying chips, sparks, or parts, is not necessarily the least significant; it merely stands alone as a somewhat different category. Many machines obviously throw off chips or sparks from the area of the point of operation. Flying objects should also be included because sometimes the product being manufactured actually breaks, and pieces may be hurled at the operator. It is also possible for parts of the machine to break and fall on or be thrown at the operator. One means of protecting workers from flying chips and sparks is with personal protective equipment. But this is not nearly as effective as using machine guards to protect the operator and other workers in the vicinity. Often, the term *shield* or *shield guard* is used to describe guards that protect the operator from flying chips, sparks, or parts.

Guarding by Location or Distance

The easiest and cleverest way to guard a machine is not to use any physical guard at all, but rather to design the machine or operation so as to position the dangerous parts where no one will be exposed to the danger. This is usually in the realm of machine design, and more and more attention is being given to safety in modern machine designs. But even without altering a machine, the machine can be turned and backed into a corner so that its belts, pulleys, and drive motor are impossible to reach during normal operation. A good example would be a portable concrete mixer. Admittedly, this strategy makes the motor and drive difficult to reach for maintenance, but on the other hand, so do ordinary bolt-on guards.

Guarding "by distance" refers to the protection of the operator from the danger zone by setting up the operation sequence such that the operator does not need to be close to the danger. For some difficult-to-guard machines, such as press brakes, the distance method of guarding the point of operation (see Figure 16.2) is expressly permissible. Press brakes are used to bend sheet metal, and their long beds make it difficult to guard their points of operation. When the workpiece is a large piece of sheet metal, the operator stands well back from the point of operation out of necessity and is thus safeguarded by "distance." Although guarding by distance is recognized as an acceptable method of guarding certain difficult-to-guard machines, the safety and health manager is cautioned against generalizing the concept to other types of machines. Guarding by distance is not a positive control to keep the operator or other personnel out of the danger zone at all times.

Tagouts and Lockouts

A surprising number of industrial machine accidents occur not when the machine is in operation, but when it is down for repair or cleaning. A worker simply turns a machine back on, not realizing that it is down for repair and that a maintenance worker is still close to or inside the machine!

FIGURE 16.2

Press brake guarding "by distance."

Such accidents seem like freak occurrences, but that is because most of us are more accustomed to small machines around the home, where only a few persons, usually family members, may be in the area. But factory machines may be large, and their repair status may not be obvious. Large numbers of personnel may have access to the machine, and a miscommunication between operating supervisors and maintenance crews can easily occur. Case Studies 16.1 and 16.2 will illustrate what can happen when multiple workers are working independently on the same piece of equipment. Human beings have been literally mangled and digested by large industrial machines.

CASE STUDY 16.1

FLOUR BATCH MIXER

A flour batch mixer is sometimes so large as to occupy several floors of a building. In this case, a trainee employee was on the third floor, reaching in to clean a flour mixer when it suddenly turned on, pulling him into the rapidly rotating blades. The start switch for the mixer was situated on the fourth floor of the building, and it was positioned next to a similar-looking switch that controlled the flow of flour from a storage bin to a scale. At the same time that the victim was cleaning the mixer on the third floor, another employee was on the fourth floor weighing out batches of flour. When the fourth-floor employee reached for the switch to weigh a batch of flour, he accidentally pushed the mixer start switch instead, fatally injuring the employee on the third floor. There was an unwritten company procedure for locking out during all maintenance. The procedure was not followed (ref. Preamble).

Two simple safety procedures for preventing accidents of this type are the tagout system and the lockout system. In the tagout system, the maintenance worker places a tag on the on/off switch or control box, so that anyone who might have occasion to turn the machine back on will be warned by the tag to leave it alone. The lockout system (see Figure 16.3) provides positive protection to the maintenance worker because he or she is the only person who has the key to the lockout. Note in Figure 16.3 that the lockout has several positions for separate padlocks for each maintenance worker exposed. Each maintenance worker therefore has an element of personal responsibility and control for his or her safety while working on the machine.

The tagout system is simpler, but the lockout system is required when feasible. It would seem that a lock would not be necessary, because, after all, who would turn on a machine when a maintenance worker's tag warned not to do so? But factories are operated by humans, and various mistakes can lead to a tagout accident. For instance, the maintenance worker can forget to remove the tag after the repair work is complete. Operating personnel may think that the maintenance personnel have forgotten to remove the tag and ignore it. The reader can no doubt think of other scenarios that would lead to an accident with tagouts, but that would have been prevented with the lockout. When the maintenance worker has the only key to the lock, there is no way for an operator to turn the machine back on—that is, with the assumption that the maintenance worker was careful enough to actually use the lock.

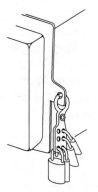

FIGURE 16.3

Lockout system for protection of maintenance workers while the machine is being repaired.

CASE STUDY 16.2

SHEAR HAZARD

An employee was cleaning scrap from beneath a large shear when a fellow employee hit the control button activating the blade. The blade came down and decapitated the employee cleaning scrap (ref. Preamble).

Some types of switches are good for normal starting and stopping of a machine, but they are inadequate for assuring that the machine cannot be turned on accidentally. Push-button switches and selector switches, for instance, do not qualify as *energy isolation devices*, since they cannot safely be locked off. To qualify for lockout, a disconnect switch or circuit breaker should be locked off to nullify the effect of a normal push-button or selector start switch.

Federal standards for lockout/tagout are among the most frequently cited standards in the nation. Not adopted in the beginning as a National Consensus Standard, the OSHA lockout/tagout standard was promulgated in 1989 and quickly rose to near the top of the frequently cited standards list in the early 1990s. Today it remains a high priority for enforcement. Perhaps even more significant is the seriousness of the citations. Nearly 80% of the alleged violations in a single year have been classified as "serious." Proposed OSHA penalties for violation have totaled millions of dollars per year. A majority of the OSHA citations for lockout/tagout have been for lack of proper training and documentation. Thus with the lockout/tagout standard, it is seen once again that the primary problem in complying with many OSHA standards is not the physical control of the hazards, but the failure to provide employee training and documentation of compliance.

Zero Mechanical State

One of the more insidious hazards of machines is that they can quietly hold dangerous energy even when they are turned off. Various forms of energy can be stored, such as pneumatic or hydraulic pressure, electrically charged capacitors, spring tension or compression, or kinetic energy from flywheel rotation. Flywheels are massive wheels that rotate continuously to deliver a uniform source of energy to a machine while running. Flywheels continue to rotate by their own momentum after the power is turned off until the energy of rotation gradually dissipates due to friction. This momentum is sometimes available to operate the machine partially, even after the power is turned off! The great mass of the flywheel often makes it impractical to brake the wheel to bring it to an abrupt stop. However, the stored energy in the rotating flywheel still represents a hazard to maintenance workers. Case Study 16.3 demonstrates what the tremendous energy of an unleashed rotating flywheel can do.

CASE STUDY 16.3

FLYWHEEL ACCIDENT

Two employees were repairing a press brake. The power had been shut off for *10 minutes!* They positioned a metal bar in a notch on the outer flywheel casing so that the flywheel could be turned manually. The flywheel *had not stopped completely.* The men lost control of the bar, which flew across the workplace and struck and killed another employee who was observing the operation from a ladder (ref. Preamble).

The hazards of stored energy in machines, even when they have been turned off, have led to a safety concept known as *zero mechanical state*. To reduce a machine to zero mechanical state, the residual sources of energy still in the machine after it is turned off must be relieved or restrained in such a way as to render them harmless. Pressure must be relieved, springs released, counterweights lowered or locked, and fly-wheels stopped so that they cannot continue to power the moving parts of the machine. Zero mechanical state thus goes beyond lockout or tagout of the power switch.

At this point, the reader should recognize that the concept of zero mechanical state relates to the general fail-safe principle. The fact that some machines can retain dangerous energy in various forms after being turned off or after accidentally losing power is a hazard to be considered in the design of the machine.

Interlocks

Contrasted with the lockout is a safety device called an *interlock*. Modern clothes dryers stop rotation as soon as the door is opened, and thus comply with industry safety standards for revolving drums, barrels, and containers. Even if the drum itself is closed, its rotation can present a hazard unless it is guarded by an enclosure. An interlock between the enclosure and the drive mechanism is specified to prevent rotation whenever the guard enclosure is not in place.

A tumbling machine is a popular industrial machine that uses a revolving drum to rotate metal parts in the presence of an abrasive tumbling medium to improve their surface characteristics. Many tumbling machines found in industry do not have interlocked enclosure guards, and safety and health managers should check for such deficiencies.

Trip Bars

Large machinery layouts are often difficult to guard, but can be provided with trip bars that stop the machine if the operator falls into or trespasses into the danger zone. The

Triprod

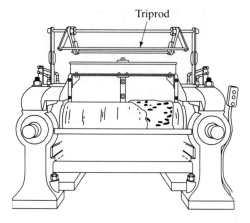

FIGURE 16.4

Pressure-sensitive body bar on a rubber mill.

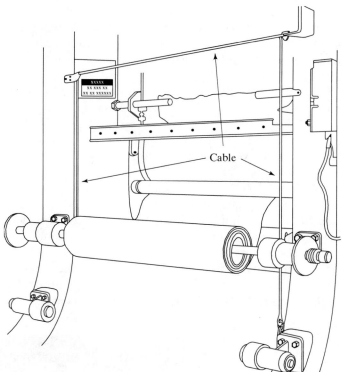

Cable

FIGURE 16.5

Safety triprods and tripwires.

operator's hand or body deflects the bar that trips a switch. Figure 16.4 illustrates an emergency trip bar on a rubber mill, a very dangerous machine.

It is sometimes impractical to place the trip bar such that any time the worker falls into the danger zone the bar will trip automatically. An alternative in these situations is to provide a triprod or tripwire for the worker to grab to switch off the machine. Examples are shown in Figure 16.5. Such devices deserve some careful study and experimentation to be sure that workers are able to reach the triprod or tripwire if they get into trouble.

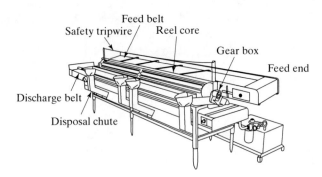

Feed belt
Safety tripwire / Reel core
Gear box
Feed end
Discharge belt
Disposal chute

FIGURE 16.5   (*Continued*)

Fan Blade Guards

A very prominent safety standard is the one that requires fan blades to have guards whose openings do not exceed 1/2 inch. Literally millions of ventilation fans are distributed throughout industries all over the country, and many of them have guards with openings larger than 1/2 inch. New fan designs are generally built according to the latest standard, but a principal problem is the retrofit of old fans to meet the 1/2-inch-opening-size standard.

An enterprising safety equipment manufacturer got the clever idea of marketing a nylon mesh that could be wrapped around the existing noncomplying guard and then be drawn up tightly with a drawstring in the rear. (See Figure 16.6.) The nylon mesh was 1/2-inch gauge, and if it was drawn tight, it kept workers free from danger. Before rushing out to purchase these inexpensive nylon mesh guards, the safety and health manager should realize that they are not a panacea. First of all, the nylon mesh, or any guard for that matter, cuts the efficiency of the fan. Furthermore, any fan will gradually accumulate oil and lint on its blade surfaces and on the guard. The nylon mesh seems even more susceptible to oil and lint buildup than does the metal guard, generating a nuisance to maintenance in keeping the guard clean or else resulting in a gradual deterioration in the effectiveness of the fan.

To deal with the fan blade guard dilemma, many innovative guard and fan blade designs are beginning to appear on the market. Some of the new guards are removable for easy washing, and some small plastic-bladed fans have no guards at all. A very

FIGURE 16.6

Nylon mesh guard for ventilation fan blades.

light-weight fan with plastic blades, powered by a small motor, presents no hazard to personnel. With no guard at all, the increased efficiency can go a long way toward making up for the low-power motor on such an unguarded fan.

Anchoring Machines

Another troublesome machine guarding standard is the rule for anchoring fixed machinery to the floor to keep it from "walking," or moving. Such anchoring is required for all machines *designed for a fixed location*. Machines that have reciprocating motions, such as presses, have a tendency to "walk" unless securely anchored. Drill presses and grinding machines can also be hazardous unless anchored.

One interpretation of the phrase "designed for a fixed location" is any machine that has mounting holes in the feet or bases of the legs. It is true that these holes are for the purpose of anchoring machines, but the mere presence of the holes is not proof that the machine must be anchored. The mounting holes might simply be a convenience feature for ease in shipping or to permit the machine to be mounted at the discretion of the user for whatever reason, such as security purposes instead of safety.

SAFEGUARDING THE POINT OF OPERATION

Injury statistics bear witness to the fact that the point of operation is the most dangerous part of machines in general. On some machines, the point of operation is so dangerous that some type of safeguarding is required for every setup; mechanical power presses are one example. Taking guidance from the specific rules for mechanical power presses, the safety and health manager can extend the principles to other machines because most of the safeguarding methods specified will work also for other machines.

A general classification of methods of safeguarding the point of operation is into guards and devices as follows:

1. Guards

    (a) Die enclosures
    (b) Fixed barriers
    (c) Interlocked barriers
    (d) Adjustable barriers

2. Devices

    (a) Gates
    (b) Presence-sensing devices
    (c) Pull-outs
    (d) Sweeps (no longer accepted for mechanical power presses)
    (e) Hold-outs
    (f) Two-hand controls
    (g) Two-hand trips

The reader will note that nowhere in this list do hand-feeding tools such as tongs appear. Hand-feeding tools (see Figure 16.7) are helpful in eliminating the *need* for

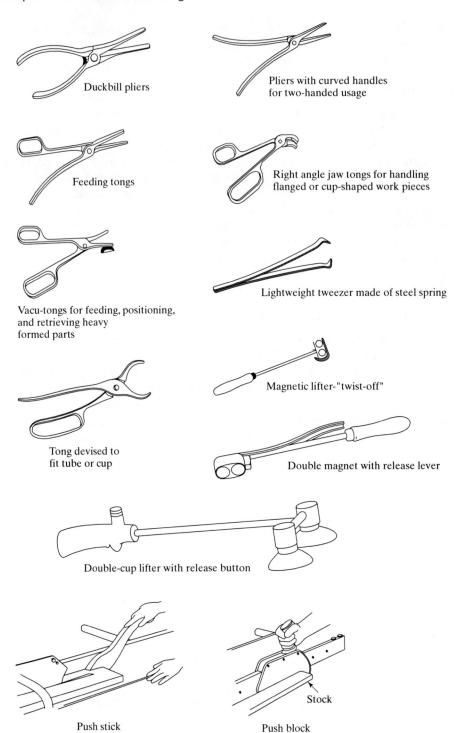

Duckbill pliers

Pliers with curved handles
for two-handed usage

Feeding tongs

Right angle jaw tongs for handling
flanged or cup-shaped work pieces

Vacu-tongs for feeding, positioning,
and retrieving heavy
formed parts

Lightweight tweezer made of steel spring

Tong devised to
fit tube or cup

Magnetic lifter-"twist-off"

Double magnet with release lever

Double-cup lifter with release button

Push stick

Push block

Stock

FIGURE 16.7

Hand-feeding tools help with, but do not replace, the function of a point-of-operation guard.

operators to place their hands in the danger zone, but it must be emphasized that these tools do *not* qualify as guards or devices for safeguarding the point of operation.

Guards

The function of a guard is obviously to keep the worker out of the danger area, but many guards do not succeed in this function. Some guards merely screen part of the danger area around the point of operation, but this can be hazardous. Too many workers will defeat the purpose of the guard by reaching through, over, under, or around it, exposing themselves to perhaps a greater hazard than if the guard were not present. Of course, every guard has to be removable between jobs for maintenance or setup purposes, but even this must be kept inconvenient, or operators will take it upon themselves to unfasten the guard to get it out of their way. Wing nuts or quick-release devices should not be used to secure guards. Nuts and bolts are better, but even better than ordinary nuts and bolts are recessed head fasteners, such as Allen screws.

Most guards are metal, and popular design uses expanded metal, sheet metal, perforated metal, or wire mesh as filler material. A secure frame is needed to maintain the structural integrity of the guard. When a guard panel becomes larger than 12 square feet, the rigidity of the guard is in jeopardy, and additional frame components are needed. Many types of ordinary wire mesh are unsuitable because the wires are not secure at the cross points. Ordinary window screen would be in this category. Galvanized screen is better as are some types that are welded or soldered at the cross points.

One principle of machine guarding borrowed from the power press standard is the maximum permissible opening size. A contemplation of human anatomy results in the conclusion that the farther away from the danger zone, the larger can be the openings in the guard without creating a hazard. If the guard is at arm's length from the danger zone, an opening of several inches still might not be dangerous. But if the guard is immediately adjacent to the danger zone, no opening should be large enough to permit a finger to reach through. Standard guard opening sizes are specified in Table 16.1. The

TABLE 16.1   OSHA's Specification for Maximum Permissible Guard Opening Size versus Distance from the Point of Operation

Distance of opening from point of operation hazard (in.)	Maximum width of opening (in.)
$\frac{1}{2}-1\frac{1}{2}$	$\frac{1}{4}$
$1\frac{1}{2}-2\frac{1}{2}$	$\frac{3}{8}$
$2\frac{1}{2}-3\frac{1}{2}$	$\frac{1}{2}$
$3\frac{1}{2}-5\frac{1}{2}$	$\frac{5}{8}$
$5\frac{1}{2}-6\frac{1}{2}$	$\frac{3}{4}$
$6\frac{1}{2}-7\frac{1}{2}$	$\frac{7}{8}$
$7\frac{1}{2}-12\frac{1}{2}$	$1\frac{1}{4}$
$12\frac{1}{2}-15\frac{1}{2}$	$1\frac{1}{2}$
$15\frac{1}{2}-17\frac{1}{2}$	$1\frac{7}{8}$
$17\frac{1}{2}-31\frac{1}{2}$	$2\frac{1}{8}$

Source: OSHA Standard 1910.217, Table O–10.

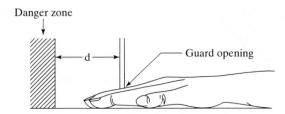

FIGURE 16.8

Maximum permissible guard opening should
depend on distance to the danger zone.

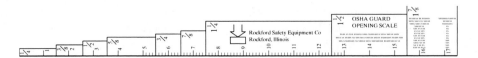

FIGURE 16.9

Guard opening size gauge.

principle behind the standard openings is illustrated in Figure 16.8. Some companies
have made available a simple go/no-go guard gauge (see Figure 16.9): Insert the point
of the gauge through the guard. If the gauge reaches the danger zone, the guard opening is too large.

Visibility through the guard is a problem with some guards. An old practice was
to paint all guards orange. But the bright orange color makes it difficult to see through
the guard to the point of operation of the machine; black is by far the superior color for
point-of-operation guards. Even better than the color black would be a transparent
material.

Die Enclosures

Punch presses and similar machines have mating dies that close on each other to act as
the point of operation. The space between the upper and lower dies is the danger area,
and the die enclosure guard is designed to enclose only this small area. The advantage
over other guard types is that the die enclosure guard is small, but still it is not the most
popular guard. Since dies vary widely in size and shape, the die enclosure guard must
be essentially custom-made to fit the die or at least the die "shoe" that acts as a base to
hold the die. Another disadvantage is that the die enclosure guard is essentially right at
the point of operation, which permits no latitude for the guard mesh size or grillwork
spacing. The maximum permissible opening size at this point is 1/4 inch, and this may
limit visibility. Figure 16.10 illustrates a die enclosure guard.

Fixed Barriers

Fixed barrier guard is a general term for a wide variety of guards that can be attached
to the frame of the machine. Figure 16.11 shows one example of a fixed-barrier guard,
but remember that there is no set style or shape for such guards. Even the mesh or
spacing of the bars is variable, depending on the distance of the guard to the point of
operation. (Refer back to Table 16.1.) Large fixed-barrier guards can permit large distances between the guard and the point of operation and a coarser mesh for the guard
material.

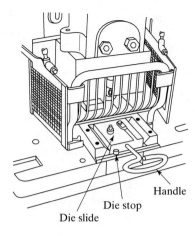

Handle

Die stop

Die slide

FIGURE 16.10

Die enclosure guard used with sliding die for feeding.

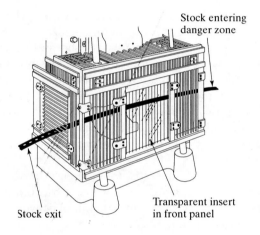

Stock entering
danger zone

Transparent insert
in front panel

Stock exit

FIGURE 16.11

Fixed-barrier guard.

Interlocked Barriers

More sophisticated is the interlocked-barrier guard shown in Figure 16.12. An interlock, typically electrical, disables the actuating mechanism whenever the guard is opened. But the interlock is not required to stop the machine if it has already been tripped, and thus it usually affords inadequate protection to an operator who is attempting to hand

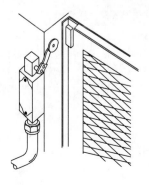

FIGURE 16.12

Interlocked-barrier guard.

feed the machine. If the barrier is so easy to open and close that the operator can open it and reach in while the machine is still moving, the interlocked barrier is not doing its job. Instead of a guard, such an arrangement would be more properly labeled a gate, a device that will be discussed later.

Adjustable Barriers

Guard manufacturers have devised some clever ways for guards to be adjusted to individual applications during the setup. Unlike the fixed-barrier guard, the adjustment is temporary, and the same guard can be reshaped later for a different setup. The trick with adjustable barriers is to make them easy enough to adjust to be practical, but not so easy as to tempt an unauthorized person to tamper with them or gain access to the danger zone. Figure 16.13 shows one type of adjustable-barrier guard.

Awareness Barriers

Some people confuse the term *adjustable-barrier guard* with the term *awareness barrier*. An awareness barrier (see Figure 16.14) is not recognized as a guard and does not meet the guarding criteria of keeping the operator's hands or fingers out of the danger zone. Although the awareness barrier is not a guard, it does provide a reminder that the hands are in danger. In the style pictured in the figure, metal rings or cylinders lie on the table and are lifted by the operator's fingers when the fingers are too close to danger. The operator at that point could go on to reach further into the machine, which could result in injury, but training and good judgment should inhibit him or her from taking this action. Contact with the awareness barrier should be a learned cue to immediately withdraw the hands. The effectiveness of awareness barriers remains in doubt, as some feel that a mere deterrent is not enough to protect the operator. An added complication is that the awareness barrier may obscure the real danger from view. Many operators believe that it is not only a matter of convenience, but also one of safety to be able to see the actual point of operation.

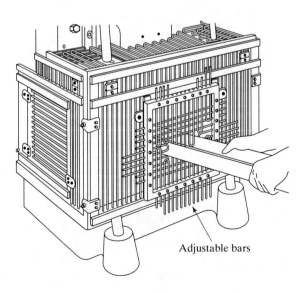

FIGURE 16.13

Adjustable-barrier guard.

Adjustable bars

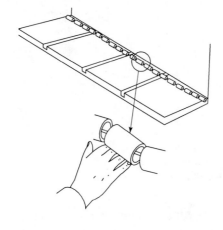

FIGURE 16.14

Awareness barrier installed on a shear.

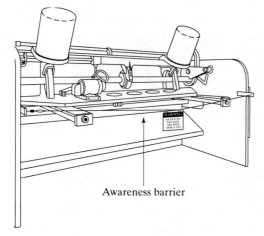

Awareness barrier

FIGURE 16.15

Rear view of power-squaring shear.

Sometimes the term *awareness barrier* is also used to describe a simple rope or chain suspended in front of a danger area with perhaps a sign hanging on it to warn personnel to keep out. An example is the back side of a metal shear, as shown in Figure 16.15. The chain will not ensure that personnel will stay out of the point of operation or danger zone, but it will warn employees of the danger.

Jig Guards

The design of a jig guard is integral to the engineering of the manufacturing operation. The guard has the function of both protecting the operator and facilitating the operation to increase productivity. There is nothing standard about a jig guard because it is designed to fit the individual workpiece and hold it in place while the machine performs the cut or other operation. Jig guards usually move with the work while the operation is performed. The jig guard depicted in Figure 16.16 is being used to notch cross members in the manufacture of four-way pallets. This clever guard keeps the circular table saw blade covered at all times, either by the jig guard between cuts or by the workpiece itself during the cut.

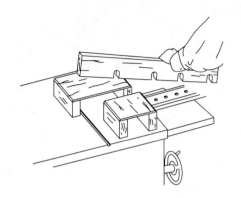

FIGURE 16.16

Jig guard for notching cross members of a four-way shipping pallet.
(Idea credited to the Occupational Center of Central Kansas, Inc.)

Point-of-operation guards are excellent when the machine can be fed effectively by automatic means or through a guard window without the operator's having to reach into the danger zone. But the only feasible way to feed some machines is manually, and some of these machines are very dangerous. This class of machine is typified by the mechanical power press, to be discussed next. The only way to assure protection of the operator while hand feeding these very dangerous machines is to use some kind of *device* that keeps the operator's hands out of the danger zone while the machine cycles and does its work. Some ingenious devices have been developed for this purpose, as will be seen in the next section.

POWER PRESSES

Punch presses are at the same time one of the most inherently dangerous and most useful production machines in industry. The epitome of mass-production machines, the press excels when huge volumes of identical products are required. Mass production depends on interchangeable manufacture, which in turn requires machines that successively produce parts that are essentially identical. The power press is superbly qualified for this task.

Figure 16.17 illustrates two popular model power presses. The term *power press* is really a general one that encompasses hydraulic-powered models and forging presses in addition to the popular mechanical punch press. The outstanding feature of a power press is the set of mating dies that close on each other to cut, shape, or assemble material, or to do combinations of these operations in one or more strokes. The more subtle features of presses, such as methods of power transmission and control of the stroke, are important determinants of permissible safeguarding. It is at the mechanical models, powered by flywheels, that the most restrictive press standards are aimed.

Press Hazards

There are, of course, reasons that so much importance is attached to safeguarding the point of operation of mechanical power presses. The injury record for power presses is not a good one. An estimate by Ryan in 1987 indicates that there are about 2000 press-operator work-related amputations each year in the United States (ref. Ryan). When feeding the press by hand, the operator is close to danger every time the dies close, and this happens thousands upon thousands of times in a press operator's career. One slip

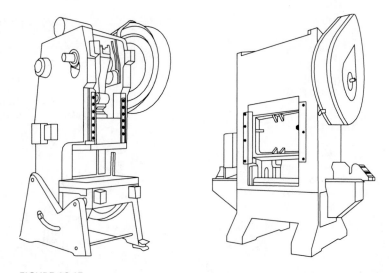

FIGURE 16.17

Typical power presses: (a) open-back inclinable (OBI) model; (b) straight-sided model.

and in a fraction of a second a finger or a hand is amputated. Such accidents were commonplace in the first half of the 20th century. Shortly before World War II, there developed an awareness that even the careful operator could become a victim of the power press, and efforts were initiated to eliminate the hazard.

To understand the nature and significance of the power press hazard, it is necessary to study the interaction between human being and machine. In a hand-feed setup, the press and the operator are alternating actions in a rhythm that cycles every few seconds, and some bench press operations may cycle in a fraction of a second. Figure 16.18 depicts the sequence of actions in a typical press cycle employing hand feeding without safeguarding. Production incentives motivate the operator to higher and higher speeds as skill develops. The operator learns to develop rhythm with the press motion. The sound of the press-tripping mechanism, the closing dies, and other press motions can become cues to the operator to make a hand or foot motion. The process involves eye–hand–foot coordination every cycle. It is easy to visualize the hazards involved in hundreds of thousands of repetitive cycles.

One of the biggest causes of accidents with power presses is an attempt on the part of the operator to readjust a misaligned workpiece in the die. The motivation is a very powerful one to reach back in to correct the error even after the ram has been tripped. If the operator lets the error go, the misaligned workpiece can wreak havoc when the dies close. At the very least, the workpiece will be ruined. More likely is that the expensive dies will be broken or ruined, and it is very possible that the press frame itself will be damaged or broken. One misaligned workpiece can result in many thousands of dollars damage to the dies and the press itself. But even worse, the misaligned workpiece or the dies can be fragmented when the dies close, subjecting the operator to injuries from flying metal pieces. It is no wonder, then, that the operator has a powerful urge to reach back in to correct a misaligned workpiece. The operator's eye will

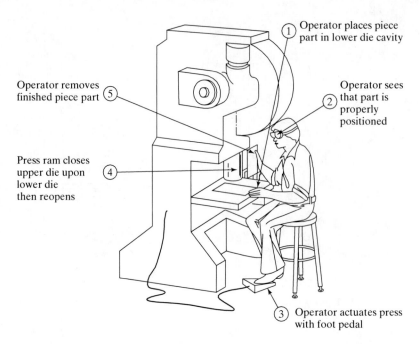

Operator places piece
part in lower die cavity

Operator removes
finished piece part

Operator sees
that part is
properly
positioned

Press ram closes
upper die upon
lower die
then reopens

Operator actuates press
with foot pedal

FIGURE 16.18

Press-cycle operation sequence (no safeguarding).

see the error, and the hand will reach in—even though the foot may have already depressed the pedal to actuate the press.

The somewhat insidious nature of power press hazards motivated the standards
writers to initiate a policy of "no hands in the dies." The theory was that tongs or other
tools and devices could be used to feed workpieces, eliminating the need for the worker to put his or her hands into the danger zone. In addition to the tongs or other feeding tools, press guards or safety devices would prevent operators from placing their
hands or fingers into the danger zone, even if they tried, while the dies were closing.

The theory worked for most jobs, but some applications presented awkward
feeding problems that defied solution with the no-hands-in-the-dies approach. It became clear that the metal-stamping industry would not be able to comply with a rigid
no-hands-in-the-dies rule in all situations, and support for the theory began to crumble.
In its place, new rules were established for assuring the reliability of safeguarding devices for protecting operators at the point of operation.

Press Designs

To understand the somewhat complicated rules for safeguarding a power press, it is
necessary to examine the basics of how presses work. Most presses are mechanically
powered, although there are a large number of hydraulically powered models, generally recognizable by the presence of a large hydraulic cylinder above the ram. The cylinder usually resembles the large cylinder in an automobile service station lift. Hydraulic

power presses are explicitly excluded from coverage by standards for mechanical power presses, as are pneumatic presses, fastener applicators, and presses working with hot metal, *even if they are mechanically powered*. Also excluded is the press brake, a power press with a long bed (refer back to Figure 16.2) that is used to bend sheet metal. Shears, because they employ blades instead of dies, are not considered within the definition of mechanical power presses.

The easiest way to distinguish a mechanical power press from other types is by the presence of a large heavy flywheel that, by its rotation, carries energy that is imparted to the ram when the press is tripped. The flywheel is *usually* mounted on one side of the press near the top, as was shown in the typical presses in Figure 16.17.

One of the most important features is whether the press is a *full-revolution* or a *part-revolution* type. This refers to the method of engaging and disengaging the flywheel to deliver power to the ram. Full-revolution types make a positive engagement that cannot be broken until the crankshaft and flywheel make one complete revolution together. During this revolution, the press ram goes down, the dies close and then reopen, and the ram returns to its full-up position to await another cycle. At the end of the revolution, the flywheel is disengaged and rotates freely under the power of the motor.

The part-revolution machine typically has a friction clutch that can be disengaged at any time during the press cycle. Compressed air is used to engage or disengage the clutch instantly at the discretion of the operator. Upon disengagement of the clutch, a brake is applied that immediately or almost immediately stops the ram. It is easy to see the advantage of being able to interrupt a press stroke at any point in the cycle, but the part-revolution advantage does not stop there. The instantaneous engagement is also valuable in causing the press to cycle quickly once engaged, giving less time for the operator to get into trouble by making an afterthought reach into the point of operation.

The safety and health manager must know which presses are full revolution and which are part revolution in order to know how to equip the press with the proper safety equipment. Thousands of dollars have been foolishly spent by purchasing the wrong safety equipment for a power press. One way to get a rough idea whether the press is full revolution is by the age of the press. Most presses, and invariably the older presses, are full revolution, unless they have gone through a renovation process. Not incidentally, the average age of mechanical power presses in the United States is steadily increasing. Statistics suggest that about half of all presses in the United States are more than 20 years old!

Since part-revolution presses employ a friction clutch, the housing on the flywheel often has a bulge to accommodate the clutch, as shown in Figure 16.19. The clutch is actuated pneumatically, and this generally means that an extra line can be seen on the outside of the flywheel cover running to the center of the clutch, as shown in the figure. Full-revolution clutch machines may also have a small line running outside the flywheel housing, but this is an oil line for lubricating purposes. None of these criteria for distinguishing machines is 100% reliable, so they should be used only as a means of preliminary screening for possible troublespots. Press engineers or the equipment manufacturer's representative can be consulted for an authoritative determination.

Point-of-Operation Safeguarding

Once having determined whether a press is a full- or a part-revolution unit, the safety and health manager or engineer can proceed to a determination of the most effective

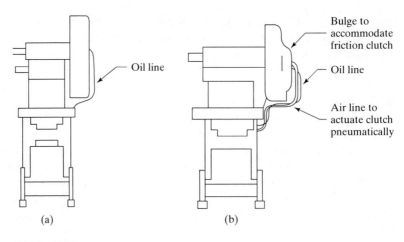

FIGURE 16.19

Full-revolution and part-revolution machines: (a) full revolution; (b) part revolution.

means of safeguarding its most dangerous zone, the point of operation. There are at least ten recognized methods of power press safeguarding, but acceptability of each depends on the press configuration and method of feeding. The various safeguarding methods can be divided into the following four categories, ranked according to degree of security:

1. Methods that prohibit the operator from reaching into the danger zone altogether
2. Methods that prohibit the operator from reaching into the danger zone any time the ram is in motion
3. Methods that prohibit the operator from reaching into the danger zone only while the dies are closing
4. Methods that do not prohibit the operator from reaching into the danger zone, but that stop the ram before the operator can reach in

Only categories 1 and 2 are to be trusted for a full-revolution press. Some category 3 methods are permissible for full-revolution presses, but with category 3, there is exposure to the hazard that the press will "repeat." So far, no antirepeat mechanism has been found to ensure absolutely that a full-revolution press will not repeat with an extra unwanted stroke. These repeat strokes are a terrifying possibility, but fortunately that possibility has been significantly reduced in recent years. Recalling that it is likely that about half of all presses are more than 20 years old, the threat of repeats is still something to consider.

Category 4 methods of safeguarding are permitted by OSHA only for part-revolution presses, and this is where many safety and health managers go wrong. It should be obvious that any method that depends on stopping the ram to protect the operator must be installed only on part-revolution presses. Full-revolution presses, by definition, cannot be stopped. It is surprising, though, how many category 4 devices are seen in industry installed on full-revolution presses. It is true that these devices can afford some protection on full-revolution presses by locking out the tripping mechanism while the operator is in the danger zone. Once the press is tripped, however, these devices are powerless to stop the ram.

Press Guards

The earlier section on guarding described types of guards for use on machines in general. Four of these types—die enclosure, fixed barriers, interlocked barriers, and adjustable barriers—are acceptable on mechanical power presses. Indeed, the die enclosure guard is used almost exclusively on mechanical power presses, although it is not as popular as some of the other types. The fixed-barrier guard is a very popular method of guarding power presses that employ automatic feeding of coils of strip stock and automatic ejection of the finished parts. The interlocked press barrier guard is not permitted for hand feeding, but a gate *device* (not a guard) can be used. Indeed, *none* of the four types of guards is permitted for hand feeding the press (putting the hands in the dies) because by definition of a press guard, "it shall prevent the entry of hands or fingers into the point of operation by reaching through, over, under, or around the guard."

With only one exception, a guard or some type of point-of-operation safeguarding device must be installed on *every* mechanical power press. That one exception is where the full-open position of the ram results in a gap between the mating dies of less than 1/4 inch, too small to permit entry of the fingers (see Table 16.1), and thus too small to be a hazard. But for all other mechanical power presses, even the automatic-feed models or the robot-fed setups, point-of-operation safeguarding is required. An accident can occur even with automatic feeding if a worker tending the automatic setup attempts to adjust a workpiece during operation.

We have already established that guards cannot be used where the operator feeds the press by putting his or her hand in the die. We have also stated that virtually every mechanical power press is required to have point-of-operation safeguarding. Does this make hand feeding illegal? The answer is no, and the key is the difference between the terms *guarding* and *safeguarding*. *Safeguarding* is a more general term and encompasses a variety of mechanical or electromechanical devices that protect the operator even when hand feeding is used. The standards are specific about which devices can be used with which types of machines and appropriate setups. Each of these configurations for mechanical power press devices will now be considered.

Gates

Gates look somewhat like a guard (see Figure 16.20), but are different in that they open and close with every machine cycle. In contrast to interlocked barrier guards, gates *can* be used for manual feeding. Gates are used almost exclusively with mechanical power presses.

There are two types of gates: type A and type B. The *type A gate* is the safer of the two because it closes before the press stroke is initiated, and it *stays closed* until all motion of the ram has ceased. *Type B gates* are the same except that they remain closed only long enough to prevent the operator from reaching in during the more dangerous downward stroke. Although the upward stroke is less dangerous, there is still the hazard of repeats when an operator reaches in on the upward stroke. Type B gates are not

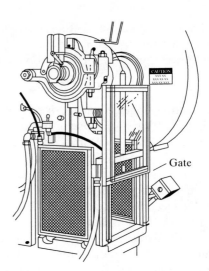

FIGURE 16.20

Gate devices.

forbidden for full-revolution clutch machines, but the occasional tendency of these machines to repeat is a sobering thought, and type B gates are not recommended for
presses with full-revolution clutches.

In defense of the type B gate, however, is its efficiency over the type A gate. A
substantial percentage of the press cycle time can be saved if the operator can start
reaching in as soon as the ram starts back upward. The savings may be only a fraction
of a second per cycle, but over hundreds of thousands of cycles, the difference can be
significant. The labor and overhead cost associated with the operator's time is saved,
and also conserved are productive capacity of the press and the plant floorspace in
which it is housed. It is possible for these combined costs to exceed $50 an hour. This
represents an incentive to modernize the power press equipment so that it qualifies for
the most efficient safeguarding systems.

Presence-Sensing Devices

Modern electronic detection devices have made their way into the machine-guarding
industry, and there are several devices of this type available for protection of the point
of operation. One type uses a bank of photoelectric cells to set up a light screen, the
penetration of which will immediately stop the ram. Figure 16.21 illustrates this type of
device.

It becomes a game for workers to defeat these devices intended for their protection. It is obvious that if a worker can reach over or around the light screen, the machine will not stop. Alternate points of entry not covered by the sensing device should
be guarded so that the operator cannot reach into the point of operation without tripping the device.

Another way to defeat a photoelectric device is to use ambient light to maintain
the sensors in an energized condition at all times even if the worker's hand has broken
the field. To compensate for the ambient-light problem, most presence-sensing devices
function in the infrared frequencies rather than in the visible-light spectrum. This
makes the "light screen" invisible, and this feature may have some advantages, too.

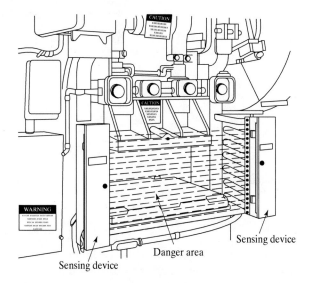

FIGURE 16.21

Photoelectric presence-sensing screen.

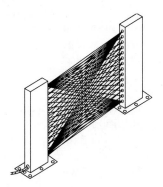

FIGURE 16.22

Programmed crisscross scan for sensing plane.

Another way to trick a light screen is to somehow squeeze between the beams. If the sources and sensors are tightly spaced, squeezing between the beams becomes impossible for the parts of the human body. The concept can be demonstrated, however, by carefully slipping a paper or cardboard edgewise between adjacent beams. Many commercially available screens have a sophisticated programmed scan that crisscrosses the field in such a complicated fashion as to prevent defeating the device. Such crisscrossing may reduce the number of sensors required to protect a given area. The concept is illustrated in Figure 16.22.

Another type of presence-sensing device uses a conductor to set up an electromagnetic field in its vicinity. Many variables affect the tripping threshold of these devices, sometimes called *radio-frequency sensors*, and this has damaged their reputation. For instance, one person's body, due to its mass or conductivity characteristics, might trip the mechanism from a distance of 2 feet from the point of operation. Another person might not trip the device until he or she has actually entered the danger zone. If this type of device is used, it should be "tuned" to have the proper sensitivity for a given operator and setup. Figure 16.23 illustrates the electromagnetic field type of

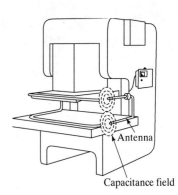

Antenna

Capacitance field

FIGURE 16.23

Electromagnetic field type of presence-sensing device.

presence-sensing device. Late-model versions of this device have been found to be very effective.

Presence-sensing devices are quite practical for hand feeding in conjunction with a foot switch. Thus, if the operator's rhythm is off and the foot switch is depressed too soon (while the operator's hand is still in the sensing field), the machine will not operate. Even more important, if the operator sees a misaligned workpiece and attempts to reach in after the ram has started its downward motion, the sensing field will detect this action and stop the ram. Thus, the device not only prevents operator injury, but it also arrests a costly smash-up of the dies and possible damage to the press itself.

From what the reader has already learned, it should be obvious that this advantage of the presence-sensing device is feasible only for part-revolution presses. Indeed, the use of presence-sensing devices for safeguarding the point of operation on full-revolution mechanical power presses is prohibited.

Although the presence-sensing device is designed to stop the ram before the operator can reach the danger zone, the worker should not tempt the machine. The author knows of a case in which a new machine[1] equipped with a presence-sensing device was being demonstrated by a proud worker to his family during an open house. The worker repeatedly thrust his hand into the machine to prove that the photoelectric cell was quicker than his hand. Finally, he succeeded in beating the machine and lost the ends of his fingers. This "accident" actually happened.

Presence-sensing devices are like gates in that they are subject to the issue of when to return access to the point of operation to the operator. Since presence-sensing devices are permitted only for part-revolution presses, it seems sensible to afford them the same production efficiencies permitted the type B gate. Therefore, it is permissible to deactivate the sensing field on the upstroke. This process of bypassing the protective system is called *muting*. As soon as the ram reaches its home position, the system is reset to its protective mode. Muting permits the same production efficiencies that the type B gate holds over the type A gate.

While we are discussing efficiency, why not go one step further and eliminate the foot switch? It would be feasible for the press to be restrained by the control system for as long as the operator's hand or arm breaks the sensing field during hand feeding.

---

[1]A printing press, not a punch press, in this instance.

Then, as soon as the operator withdraws his or her hand from the danger zone, the press would *automatically* cycle without a signal from the operator! Feasible? Yes. Legal? No. The presence-sensing device is prohibited as a press-tripping mechanism, although many European factories do employ this highly productive mode of operation for power presses.

There is a way that a presence-sensing device *can* be used to trip the press—when the presence-sensing device is used in conjunction with another safeguarding device, such as a gate. Thus, the gate represents the safety device, and the presence-sensing field acts as a tripping device. This would be a complicated and expensive system and should be considered rare.

Presence-sensing devices must be designed to adhere to the general fail-safe principle. Thus, if the presence-sensing device itself fails, the system must remain in a protective mode. A failure in the device must prevent the press from operating additional cycles until the failure is corrected. But such a failure must not deactivate the clutch and brake mechanisms, which are essential in stopping the press. If a failure in the device causes an interruption of the main power supply to the machine, the clutch must automatically disengage. Of course, the clutch and brake system should have this characteristic, regardless of the choice of safeguarding devices; the clutch and brake are simply additional examples of systems that should be designed in accordance with the general fail-safe principle.

One final note about failures in the presence-sensing system should be mentioned. It is not enough that the failure inhibits the operation of the press; the system must also indicate that a failure has occurred. This is usually done with a trouble light on the panel.

Pullbacks

A very popular method of safeguarding a power press is by means of cables mechanically linked to the travel of the ram. These cables are attached to wristlets which pull the operator's hands out of the danger area as the ram makes its downward stroke. Figure 16.24 shows one example setup of *pullbacks*, or *pull-outs* as they are sometimes called.

One reason for the popularity of pullbacks is their versatility. They can be used with virtually any power press, regardless of power source or type of clutch. However, pullbacks do have their disadvantages.

Proper adjustment is very important to the effectiveness of pullbacks, especially with respect to close work done on bench model machines. Even the method of attachment to the wrists is important because ordinary wristlets permit too much variation in reach. Figure 16.25 is a close-up of a wristlet assembly that minimizes variations in an operator's restricted reach. Even with properly designed wristlets, proper adjustment is critical. Differences in operators' hand sizes can be a factor, but much more important are variations in die setups. A large die set will of course have a danger zone that extends closer to the operator, requiring an adjustment in the pullback limit of reach.

Recognizing the hazard of improper adjustment of pullbacks, safety standards require an inspection for proper adjustment at the start of each operator shift, following a new die setup, and when operators are changed. This inspection requirement, and especially the *frequency* of the inspections, decidedly cools the interest of employers in the use of pullback devices. Were it not for this problem and the fact that many workers dislike wearing pullbacks, these devices would be extremely popular. These drawbacks

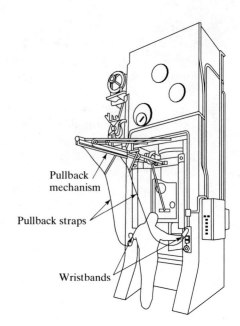

FIGURE 16.24

Pullback devices for safeguarding the point of operation.

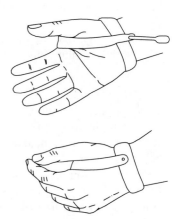

FIGURE 16.25

Close-ups of wristlet assembly for pullback device.

notwithstanding, the pullback device remains one of the most popular press-safeguarding devices.

It is usually the diesetter or operating supervisor who makes the actual check of the pullbacks for proper adjustment. The concern of the safety and health manager should be that the job is done effectively and that a record is made of the inspections. Simplicity is the key to the inspection record system for pullback devices. Simplicity will help to ensure that the job gets done and will also minimize the impact on production efficiency. One convenient method is to use a tag attached to the pullback device itself, with blank lines for indicating "date inspected" and "initials" by the responsible party. In multiple-shift operations, in new die setups, or in operator changes, more than one line would be initialed in one day on the tag, but the tag still could be easily designed to accommodate multiple entries on the same day.

Sweeps

Very popular in the past, and still seen on some power presses, are devices that sweep away the operator's hands or arms as the dies close. These devices, illustrated in Figure 16.26, have fallen into disfavor as a means of protecting the operator. Operators even fear injury from the sweep device itself as it comes swinging down in front of the machine. The design dilemma of these devices is that they must be powerful enough to inflict injury themselves in order to be effective in positively removing the operator's hands from the point of operation. But the overriding reason for their disfavor is that the design and construction of sweeps are inherently inadequate as a press-safeguarding device. Sweeps are no longer recognized as adequate point-of-operation safeguarding devices on mechanical power presses.

Hold-Outs

A simplification of pullbacks is the *hold-out* (sometimes called *restraint*) device, which is feasible only for setups in which it is unnecessary for the operator to reach into the danger area. Figure 16.27 shows that hold-outs look almost exactly like pullbacks, the

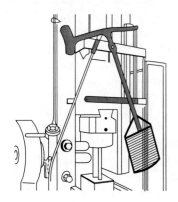

FIGURE 16.26

Sweep device. This device no longer qualifies as an acceptable safeguard for mechanical power presses.

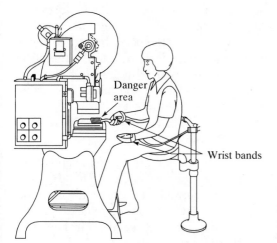

Danger area

Wrist bands

FIGURE 16.27

Hold-outs or restraints for restraining the operator's hands from reaching into the danger zone at *all* times (compare with pullbacks).

difference being that the hold-out reach is fixed and does not permit the operator to reach in at all, even between strokes of the machine. If tongs, suction cups, or other gripping devices can be used to feed a machine manually, it is feasible to use hold-outs instead of pull-outs to protect the operator. Even without these gripping devices, long workpieces can be hand fed into the machine without actually placing the hands in danger. For these applications, hold-outs are appropriate. If the operator's hands must enter the zone between the dies, however, hold-outs are infeasible as safeguarding devices.

It would seem that protection for the operator would be unnecessary for applications in which tongs or other feeding devices are used instead of the hand to feed a machine. However, this idea does not recognize the strong tendency for the worker to reach in when something goes wrong. Therefore, although hand-feeding tools are somewhat useful in promoting safety, they are not recognized as point-of-operation safeguarding devices. Another means must be used to *ensure* safety, and hold-outs are a good method when hand tools are used.

Two-Hand Controls

Since people have only two hands, neither hand will be injured by the point of operation if the machine can require both of them to operate the controls, or so the theory goes. The theory is a good one, but some sophistication is necessary to ensure that the device achieves its goal. Workers take pride in "beating the system" or in tricking the machine to make it operate without their using the controls. One trick is to use a board or rope to tie down one control so that the operator can operate the machine with one hand and feed it with the other. Another trick is for workers to use their heads, noses, or even toes to depress one of the controls. Workers have been known to try almost anything to defeat the safety features of a machine in order to achieve a production breakthrough and receive a higher production incentive payment. This points to the power of money over personal safety in motivating workers. It may also reveal some inefficiencies in safety devices as currently designed—inefficiencies that unduly compromise productivity in the name of safety. Industry workers and managers will tolerate some slowdown of an operation for the cause of safety, but not much.

Figure 16.28 illustrates a two-hand control device and some of the features that attempt to prevent the worker from defeating the device. Note the smooth, rounded surface of the palm button, which makes it convenient for the palm, but not for tying down. Also note the cups around the button, which are intended to foul attempts at tying down the button. Control circuitry can also be used to detect foul play and stop the machine if the buttons are not depressed concurrently and released between cycles.

Controls versus Trips

The term *control* implies a more sophisticated device than a mere *trip* to actuate the machine. Within the context of safeguarding the point of operation, a two-hand control means a device that not only requires both hands concurrently to actuate the machine, but also stops the machine by interrupting its cycle if the controls are released prematurely. The nature of some machines does not permit such a degree of control over the machine cycle. Two-hand controls are infeasible for these machines.

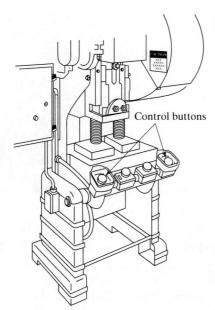

Control buttons

FIGURE 16.28
Two-hand control.

For full-revolution presses and other machines that cannot be stopped once their cycle has begun, two-hand trips are used instead of two-hand controls. Two-hand trips require both hands to start the machine cycle, but once started there is no protection for the operator. If the machine cycle is fast, and if the operator is far enough away to stay out of danger, two-hand trips effectively protect the operator. But if the machine is slow or the trip station is close enough, the operator can reach into the machine *after* it has been tripped. This gets into the subject of safety distances, covered in the next section. After studying the section on safety distances, it will be easy to see that controls are superior to trips.

Safety Distances

In reviewing the safeguarding devices for protection of operators from the points of operation of machines, we see that most of them protect the operator by making it impossible to reach into the danger zone after the machine cycle has begun. However, two of these devices—the presence-sensing device and the two-hand control—rely on a capability of interrupting a machine in *midcycle*. Every mechanical machine has inertia, so some time must elapse between the signal to stop and the complete cessation of motion of the machine in the point-of-operation area. If the inertia is great, an operator might be able to reach quickly into the danger zone before the protective device is able to completely stop the machine. Therefore, the operator station must be moved back from the point of operation a sufficient distance so that a reach into the danger zone before the machine stops is impossible.

In addition to the presence-sensing device and two-hand control, the two-hand trip device must also be located at a sufficient distance, as was mentioned earlier. Although the two-hand trip is not capable of stopping the machine, protection is possible if the distance to the danger zone is great enough to prevent the operator from reaching in after releasing the palm buttons.

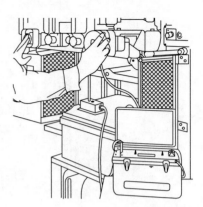

FIGURE 16.29

Brake-stop-time measurement device.

To compute a *safe distance* for a presence-sensing device or a two-hand control, it is necessary first to compute the stopping time of the machine. Figure 16.29 shows one model of a stop-time measurement system that connects one sensor to a palm button and the other to the machine motion. Upon a signal that the palm button has been depressed, the system starts counting in fractions of a second until motion of the machine ceases. Keep in mind that we are speaking here of the motion of the machine's ram, die, cutter, or other part *at the point of operation* that could cause injury. Flywheel motion or motor rotation may continue and indeed due to their inertia would usually be impossible to stop in time to be of any benefit. The resulting stopping time is generally displayed by the portable instrument. The reader should take care not to confuse the brake stop-time measurement device in Figure 16.29 with a *brake monitor* to be discussed later.

Once the stopping time has been determined, this time must be multiplied by the maximum speed the hand can move toward the point of operation, as in the following formula:

$$\text{Safety distance} = (\text{stopping time}) \times (\text{hand speed constant}) \qquad (16.1)$$

OSHA relies on a maximum hand movement speed of 63 inches per second, sometimes referred to as the hand speed constant; this constant is credited to L. Lobl of Sweden. Consider the next example.

Example 16.1

A power press is protected by an infrared-beam-type presence-sensing device. A stop-time measurement system is used to compute the time between breaking of the infrared beam and stoppage of the press ram. This stop time is found to be 0.294 second. The safety distance then is computed to be

$$\text{Safety distance} = 0.294 \text{ second} \times 63 \text{ inches/second}$$

$$= 18.5 \text{ inches}$$

Thus, all points in the plane of the infrared sensing field must be at least $18\frac{1}{2}$ inches away from the point of operation for this power press.

The calculation would have been identical if the device in the example had been a two-hand control (but not a two-hand trip!). The palm buttons of the two-hand control would have to be placed $18\frac{1}{2}$ inches away from the point of operation.

The safety distance calculation for the two-hand *trip* uses an entirely different logic from that used for the two-hand *control*. True, the same hand-speed constant of 63 inches per second is used. But with two-hand trips, the idea is for the machine to complete the dangerous part of its cycle before the operator can reach in after releasing the palm buttons. Thus, the *slower* the machine, the more dangerous it is when using trips. It is paradoxical that the *faster* the machine, the harder it is to stop and the greater must be the safety distance for two-hand *controls*, whereas for *trips*, it is just the opposite: the *slower* the machine, the greater must be the safety distance.

With many machines, hydraulic presses, for example, the commencement of the cycle is virtually instantaneous with the depressing of the palm buttons. But with machines that commence the cycle with the mechanical engagement of a flywheel, there is an inevitable delay as the engagement mechanism waits for its mating engagement point on the flywheel. The delay can be considerable for a slow-rpm machine, especially if it has only one place on the flywheel suitable for making the mechanical engagement. The process is best explained by a diagram, as in Figure 16.30. Part (a) of the figure shows a very unlucky happenstance in the position of the flywheel with its engaging point just past the tripping mechanism at the moment of actuation. This follows the principle that the *worst state* of the machine should be used to determine how to make the operation safe. Since the position of the flywheel at the moment the machine is tripped is purely a matter of chance, it is equally likely that the flywheel will be in the lucky position indicated in Figure 16.30(b). But since this position cannot be counted on, the safety distance is computed assuming the flywheel is in the position indicated in Figure 16.30(a).

One complete rotation of the flywheel completes the machine cycle for most machines. One-half of this rotation of the flywheel is the dangerous portion of the stroke, the closure motion of the machine. Thus, adding a complete revolution for engagement plus one-half revolution for closure motion, the resultant danger period is one and one-half revolutions of the flywheel for a machine whose flywheel has only one engagement point. For machines that have several engagement points evenly spaced around the flywheel, the danger period is shorter, depending on how many engagement points exist. To see this, consider an example of a machine with four engagement points. In the worst case, the farthest the engagement point could be from the tripping mechanism at the moment of tripping would be 90° or one-quarter revolution. Add this

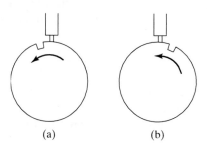

(a)   (b)

FIGURE 16.30

Two possible positions of the flywheel when a machine is tripped: (a) unlucky position—the engagement point has just passed the tripping mechanism; (b) lucky position—the engagement point is approaching and is very near the tripping mechanism.

to the one-half revolution during machine closure, and the total danger period becomes three-quarters revolution.

Summarizing the calculation of safety distances for two-hand *trip* devices is the following formula:

$$\text{Safety distance} = \frac{60}{\text{rpm}}\left(\frac{1}{2} + \frac{1}{N}\right) \times 63, \tag{16.2}$$

where rpm represents the flywheel speed in revolutions per minute while engaged, and N is the number of engaging points on the flywheel.

In Equation (16.2), the factor 60/rpm is used to determine the time in seconds required for the flywheel to complete one revolution. The computation in parentheses is the worst-case number of flywheel rotations until closure, and the factor 63 is the hand-speed constant in inches per second. The computed safety distance is in inches.

It is important to remember that Equation (16.2) is to be used for two-hand *trips*, not two-hand controls. It is easy to determine that two-hand controls are superior to two-hand trips. From a production efficiency standpoint, two-hand controls can be normally placed much closer to the machine, which facilitates hand feeding. Two-hand trips can be more dangerous unless moved to a greater safety distance, which in turn impairs productivity.

Figure 16.28 was captioned "two-hand control," but the figure could also represent a two-hand trip. The device in Figure 16.28 could have been mounted on a pedestal so that it could be moved closer or farther from the point of operation, dependent on calculation of the formula for the given setup. Two-hand devices can also be mounted directly on the machine if the safety distance is short enough to permit this.

Neither Equation (16.1) nor (16.2) is constant for a given machine; both are dependent on a given setup because of variations in die dimensions and die weight, which in turn affect flywheel speed, stopping time, and dimension of the danger zone on the machine. The pedestal is movable, but only a supervisor or safety engineer should be capable of moving it. This can be accomplished by locking the pedestal in position with a key or by bolting it to the floor and forbidding operators to unbolt it, or some other means of fixing the position. Failure to fix the position results in a temptation to the operator to move the pedestal closer to the machine to speed up production.

Because of the superiority of two-hand controls over two-hand trips, both in terms of safety and productivity, many industrial plants are converting their older machines equipped with trips to the more modern two-hand controls. Such a conversion is not a mere change in the two-hand device, but also generally represents a major modification to the machine itself and its power transmission apparatus, so that the machine can be classified as part revolution instead of full revolution. Brake monitoring and control reliability features are also required on part-revolution presses and will be explained next.

Brake Monitoring

It can be seen from the preceding discussion that the stopping time is very important in computation of permissible safety distance for part-revolution machines. But stopping time is dependent on the brake, and unfortunately brakes are subject to wear. Stopping time is also dependent on die setup, which can change from production lot to lot. Therefore, it is naive to apply the principle of safety distances and then to walk away and trust the press to always respond in the same way as it did the day it was tested for safety distances. So for every part-revolution press whose safeguarding device depends on the brake, a brake-monitoring system is needed to monitor the brake *every stroke*. Note how different this is from the brake stop-time measurement system of Figure 16.29, which would be set up only occasionally to check or set safety distances. In contrast, the brake monitor is a permanent installation on the press, monitoring the overtravel of the ram past the top stop every stroke.

Since the system is mechanical, there will be some overtravel, and a tolerance must be set that permits this overtravel. Employers can set this tolerance as high as they desire, but it will not be to their advantage to set the tolerance very high because a larger overtravel means a longer stopping time, which means a greater safety distance, which means reduced efficiency. There is no safety distance for type B gates, but the employer is still allowed to reasonably establish a "normal limit" for ram overtravel.

The brake monitor can be engineered to measure either stopping time or overtravel distance. The most popular style is electromechanical, with a pair of limit switches triggered by a cam linked to the press crankshaft. This type is commonly known as a *top-stop* monitor. (See Figure 16.31.) The first switch signals the application of the brake, and the second signals overrun. The cam must not trigger the overrun switch until a new cycle is initiated. Sooner or later, the brake will deteriorate, and the overrun switch will be tripped, which means that brake-stopping-time tolerance has been exceeded. At that point, the monitor system must provide an indication to that effect.

In addition to the brake monitor, a control system is required to ensure that the press will cease to operate after a failure in the point of operation safety system occurs, *but* the brake system will *not* be shut down due to the system failure. This requirement is a direct application of the general fail-safe principle.

The reader should be reminded that brake system monitoring and control reliability are not required on all power presses. The logic is that on many press setups, the brake monitor and control system would have marginal benefit, whereas on others, they would be of critical importance due to the selection of safeguarding methods, the mode of operation, and the construction of the press itself. Table 16.2 summarizes the

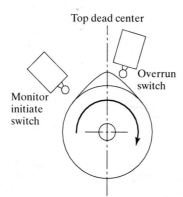

FIGURE 16.31

Top-stop brake monitor.

TABLE 16.2   Power Press Safeguarding Summary[a]

Guard type or device	Full revolution		Part revolution	
	Hands in	Hands out	Hands in	Hands out
Guards Barrier guards (fixed, adjustable or die enclosure)	Illegal	Inspect weekly	Illegal	Inspect weekly or Brake monitor and control system
Interlocked barrier guards	Illegal	Inspect weekly	Illegal	Inspect weekly or Brake monitor and control system
Type A gate	Inspect weekly	Inspect weekly	Inspect weekly or Brake monitor and control system	Inspect weekly or Brake monitor and control system
Type B gate	Inspect weekly	Inspect weekly	Brake monitor and control system must detect top-stop overrun beyond limits	Inspect weekly or Brake monitor and control system
Presence sensing devices	Illegal	Illegal	Safety distance and Brake monitor and control system	Safety distance and Inspect weekly or Brake monitor and control system
Pullbacks	Inspect: each shift, each die setup, each operator	Inspect: each shift, each die setup, each operator	Inspect: each shift, each die setup, each operator	Inspect: each shift, each die setup, each operator
Sweeps	Does not qualify as safeguard	Does not qualify as safeguard	Does not qualify as safeguard	Does not qualify as safeguard
Hold-outs (restraint)	Illegal	Inspect weekly	Illegal	Inspect weekly or Brake monitor and control system
Two-hand controls	*See* Two-hand trips	*See* Two-hand trips	Safety distance and Fixed control position and Brake monitor and control system	Safety distance and Fixed control position
Two-hand trips	Safety distance and Fixed trip position and Inspect weekly	Safety distance and Fixed trip position and Inspect weekly	Inspect weekly or Brake monitor and control system	Inspect weekly or Brake monitor and control system

[a] This summary compares inspections requirements, brake monitoring and control system requirements, safety distances, and legal and illegal arrangements. The summary does not include detailed specifications, requirements for multiple operators, and other details too numerous to include in this summary. For details, see OSHA Standard 1910.217.

various options for guarding or safeguarding presses, the need for brake monitors and control systems, and alternate permissible configurations.

GRINDING MACHINES

Grinding machines are in almost every manufacturing plant—on the production line, or in a toolroom, or maintenance shop.

There are two or three items that create the most trouble as follows (shown in Figure 16.32).

- Failure to keep the workrest in close adjustment (within $\frac{1}{8}$ inch) to the wheel on off-hand grinding machines
- Failure to keep the tongue guard adjusted to within $\frac{1}{4}$ inch
- Failure to guard the wheel sufficiently

These rules may seem "nitpicking," but there is a grave hazard with grinding machines that most people do not know about—the breakup of the wheel while rotating at high speed. It does not happen very often, but when it does, the injuries to the operator can be fatal. It is against this hazard that all three of the items just listed are aimed, even the workrest adjustment requirement.

Severe stress can be placed on the grinding wheel if the workpiece becomes wedged between the workrest and the wheel. A large gap invites the workpiece to become pinched and then drawn down by the wheel, resulting in a severe wedging action, as illustrated in Figure 16.33. The forces of this wedging action threaten the integrity of the bonded abrasive wheel, possibly causing it to break up and hurl stone fragments at the operator at near-tangential velocities. The only protection to the operator from these flying stone fragments are a good wheel guard, a properly adjusted tongue guard, and any personal protective clothing the operator might be wearing.

It is a simple matter for anyone to check the gap adjustment on the grinding machine workrest—easy to check, but not so easy to *keep* in adjustment. Since the wear of

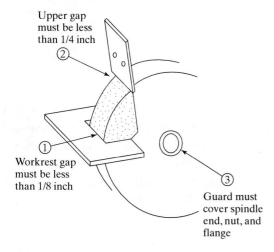

Upper gap must be less than 1/4 inch
②

①
Workrest gap must be less than 1/8 inch

③
Guard must cover spindle end, nut, and flange

FIGURE 16.32

The three biggest troublespots on ordinary grinding machines.

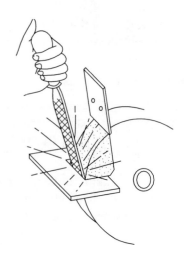

FIGURE 16.33

Severe wedging action due to a large gap between workrest and wheel.

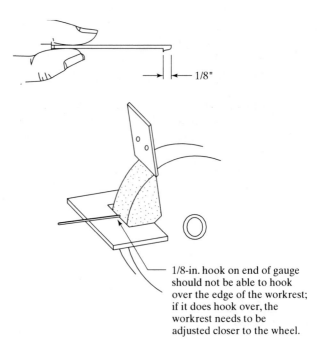

1/8"

1/8-in. hook on end of gauge should not be able to hook over the edge of the workrest; if it does hook over, the workrest needs to be adjusted closer to the wheel.

FIGURE 16.34

Grinding machine workrest gauge.

the grinding wheel causes the gap to gradually widen, constant surveillance is needed to assure that the gap is maintained less than $\frac{1}{8}$ inch. There is little tolerance for over-compensating for the wear because $\frac{1}{8}$ inch leaves little margin for setting the workrest closer than required. Since there is no way to avoid frequent adjustment, some convenient means should be initiated to make adjustments quickly and efficiently. To this end, a workrest gauge is recommended, as illustrated in Figure 16.34. The go/no-go character of this gauge aids in a quick and sure decision as to whether to adjust the workrest every time it is checked.

Another easy check is the maximum spindle speed; it should not exceed the maximum speed marked directly on the wheel. Operation of an abrasive wheel above its design speed subjects the wheel to dangerous centrifugal forces that also could lead to wheel breakup.

Sometimes an abrasive wheel has manufacturing imperfections or transportation damage that makes it dangerous. Before the wheel is mounted, it should be visually inspected for such damage or imperfections. Invisible imperfections can sometimes be detected by tapping the wheel gently with a nonmetallic implement such as the plastic handle of a screwdriver or a wooden mallet. A good wheel typically produces a ringing sound, whereas a cracked wheel will sound dead. The reason nonmetallic objects are used to make the *ring test* is that metallic objects might themselves ring, giving the impression that a defective wheel is good.

SAWS

Saws have some obvious hazards and some not-so-obvious ones. Almost everyone respects the danger of a power saw, but serious injuries continue to occur, and acceptable means of guarding both obvious and subtle hazards from saws need to be considered.

Radial Saws

If the safety and health manager learns about no other saw, he or she should become familiar with this one. Radial saws or radial arm saws can be quite dangerous, and in addition they are difficult to guard. Figure 16.35 depicts a typical radial arm saw, but although the blade can be seen to be partially guarded on the top half, the lower portion of the blade is exposed. Figure 16.36 illustrates one type of lower blade guard for radial arm saws. The guards are very unpopular and are often removed by employees.

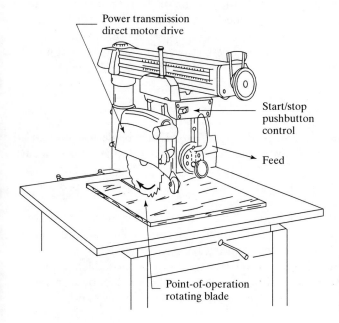

Power transmission direct motor drive

Start/stop pushbutton control

Feed

Point-of-operation rotating blade

FIGURE 16.35

Typical radial saw, not properly guarded and in violation of OSHA standard (*Source:* NIOSH, ref. Machine).

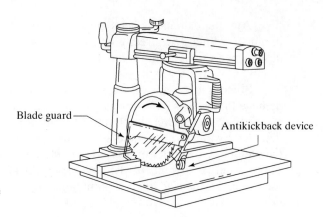

Blade guard

Antikickback device

FIGURE 16.36

Radial arm saw equipped with lower blade guard.

Another problem with radial saws is the return-to-home position. The saw should be mounted such that "the front end of the unit will be slightly higher than the rear, so as to cause the cutting head to return gently to the starting position when released by the operator." A radial saw that creeps out while running is an obvious hazard, but one that is adjusted too much at an angle will "bounce" on the home position stop—another hazard. A radial saw also will have a stop that prevents the operator from pulling the saw off the radial arm or beyond the edge of the saw table. This stop should be adjustable for limiting travel of the saw head only as far as necessary.

A radial saw is usually used as a cutoff saw and is mounted as shown in Figure 16.35. It is possible, though, to reorient the cutting head 90° so that the blade is parallel to the table and thus to convert the saw to a ripsaw for long pieces of stock. In this mode of operation, the saw head is locked into position, and the material is pushed into the saw. There is a hazard, though, if the material is fed into the saw in the wrong direction. To be safe, the material must be fed *against* the rotation of the blade. If the material is fed *with* the rotation of the blade, especially if the feed rate is fast, the saw teeth are likely to grab the workpiece and pull it into the machine at high speeds, possibly pulling the operator's hands into the blade with the material being sawed. It is not uncommon that a radial saw fed incorrectly in this manner will hurl the workpiece through the machine and toss it across the room.

Table Saws

Table saw is an everyday term for a hand-fed saw with a circular blade mounted in a table. Unlike the radial saw, the table saw head always remains stationary during a cut while the work is fed into it. With table saws, the three biggest problem areas are hood guards, spreaders, and nonkickback fingers (see Figure 16.37). Antikickback protection is more important for ripsaws than for crosscut saws.

The hood guards present the most problems because the obstructed view makes the saw operator's job more difficult and awkward. Although most of the hood guards in the field are metal, most new machines come with transparent plastic guards. But the rapidly rotating saw blade can cause a static charge to develop on the nonconducting plastic guard, causing it to become covered with sawdust so that the blade cannot be seen. Also, the plastic guard is easily scratched, further reducing visibility through the guard.

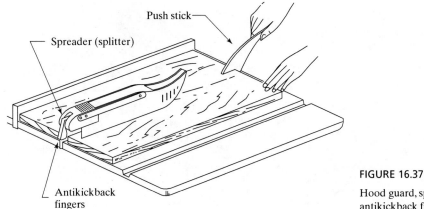

Push stick

Spreader (splitter)

Antikickback
fingers

FIGURE 16.37

Hood guard, spreader, and
antikickback fingers on a table saw.

It is true that hood guards will not absolutely prohibit contact of the operator's hands with the saw blade. The hood guard, with its spring action, acts more as an *awareness barrier*, as was discussed earlier in the section on safeguarding the point of operation on general machines. But there is another reason for using a hood guard: to protect the operator from flying objects. The saw blade rotates at 3000 rpm, and this produces large centrifugal forces and high tangential velocities. Consider the following calculation for a popular make of a table saw:

Blade speed	3450 rpm
Blade diameter	10 inches

$$\text{Tangential velocity} = (\text{rpm}) \times (\text{blade perimeter})$$
$$= 3450 \text{ rpm} \times 10 \text{ in.} \times \pi$$
$$= 108{,}385 \text{ in./min}$$
$$= 102.63 \text{ miles per hour}$$

This means that if a tooth breaks off the saw or if a small chip or block of wood breaks off and is carried on the blade for nearly a full revolution, as in Figure 16.38, it will be propelled at the face of the operator at a velocity of over 100 miles per hour. It is little wonder that eye protection is considered necessary for operating a table saw.

Kickback

Kickback is the word used to describe the situation in which the entire workpiece is picked up and thrown back at the saw operator. The energy for the kickback comes from the sawblade itself. The rotation of the blade is toward the operator. At the front of the blade where the saw first meets the work, the direction of blade motion is toward the operator and *down*. But at the back of the blade, the direction of motion is toward the operator and *up*. Because the saw teeth are slightly wider than the blade thickness, a correctly aligned workpiece will contact the blade only at the point at

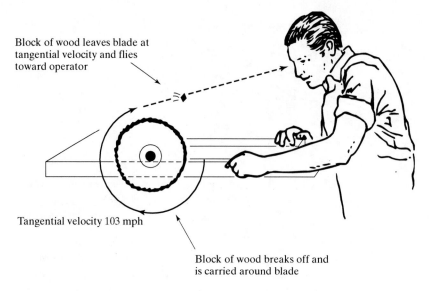

Block of wood leaves blade at tangential velocity and flies toward operator

Tangential velocity 103 mph

Block of wood breaks off and is carried around blade

FIGURE 16.38

Broken saw tooth or chips of wood are a hazard to the saw operator.

which the cut is taking place. But if the workpiece should shift slightly, the exiting portion of the cut at the back of the blade will become misaligned, causing the edge of the material adjacent to the cut to contact the blade as it emerges from the table. This contact can result in a sudden and powerful upward thrust which causes the material to break contact with the table surface. Further misalignment becomes almost inevitable at this point, and the workpiece is grabbed firmly by the blade. If the workpiece is extremely thin or fragile, it will break up at this point, with thin portions or chips continuing with the blade down under the table. But a much more likely result is that the rigid material cannot follow the blade, and it is hurled at tangential velocity directly at the operator.

Both the spreader and the nonkickback fingers are intended to help prevent kickback. The spreader keeps the saw kerf open or spread apart in the completed portion of the cut so that the material will not contact the blade. The nonkickback fingers, or "dogs," are designed to arrest the kickback motion should it start to occur. The shape of the dog permits easy motion in the direction of the feed. A backward motion, however, causes the dog to grip the material and prevent a kickback.

Band Saws

It is essentially impossible to guard the point of operation in most band saw operations. However, the unused portion of the blade can feasibly be guarded. A sliding guard is used for this and is moved up or down to accommodate larger or smaller workpieces, respectively. This sliding guard, together with the wheel guards, permits the entire blade except for the working portion to be guarded.

Hand-Held Saws

Hand-held circular saws are subjected to a variation of the hazard of kickback, except that it is the *saw* that is kicked back instead of the material! Proper training and operator respect for the saw are important, as are a clean, sharp blade, a "dead-man" control, and a retractable guard for the lower portion of the blade. A dead-man control is simply a spring-loaded switch (button or trigger) that will immediately cut off power to the saw if the operator releases the switch.

The retractable guard for the lower portion of the blade on a hand-held circular saw is perhaps analogous to the lower blade guard on a radial saw and the hood guard on a table saw. However, on a hand-held circular saw, the retractable guard is much more important. If the operator locks the retractable guard open with a small wedge, as operators will sometimes do, the saw becomes very hazardous both before and after the cut. The blade is exposed, and direct damage or injury can result if the saw is dropped or set down on a surface.

Cutting aluminum with a hand-held circular saw can be a real problem. Hand-held circular saws are widely used to cut aluminum extrusions to length to manufacture windows, storm doors, shutters, and other architectural aluminum extrusion products. The problem is that the saw blade gets very hot, reaching the melting point of aluminum at around 1200°F; drops of molten aluminum start flying off the blade onto the guard, causing quite a mess. The aluminum later solidifies, causing the guard to stick and malfunction.

One prominent manufacturer of architectural aluminum extrusions wrestled with this problem for five years before turning to alternate means of protecting the operator. Reverse polarity brakes were installed on the saws, which caused the blade to come to an immediate halt as soon as the operator released the trigger. This removed most of the hazard, because it is while the blade coasts to a stop after use that the lower blade guard is most important. For added protection, the workers were provided with protective gloves and pads for the hands and wrists.

Chain Saws

Without doubt, the most hazardous hand-held saw of all is the chain saw. Binding of the blade can cause the saw to kickback and cause severe, perhaps fatal, injury to the operator. A dull or poorly lubricated chain can overheat and break, resulting in severe injury to the operator or to the other workers in the area. The Consumer Product Safety Commission is leading the effort to improve hand guards and minimize kickback.

Power Hacksaws

Power hacksaws are difficult to guard, more so than their cousins, the horizontal band saws. The band saw can be feasibly guarded with an adjustable guard along all portions of the blade except the portion actually performing the cut. Because of the reciprocating action of the power hacksaw, however, a much more complicated guard would be required to adjust back and forth *during* the cut every stroke. Guards, guardrails, or guarding by location would be appropriate for this hazard. Some modern power hacksaws are equipped with enclosures that contain the entire stroke of the reciprocating blade.

BELTS AND PULLEYS

Almost every industry has a wide variety of belts and pulleys and other driving systems for transmitting power from motors to machines. The hazards are well understood, and the technology is simple. Belts and pulleys represent a good target area for the safety and health manager to institute a low-cost program of in-house safety improvement.

It should be recognized that not all belts and pulleys are hazardous, and the standards acknowledge this fact by excluding certain small, slow-moving belts. The exclusions are intricate and are best represented by a decision diagram, as in Figure 16.39. A height of less than 7 feet off the floor or working platform is generally considered a working zone where personnel need protection from belts and other machine hazards.

Related to belts and pulleys are shaft couplings, such as are typically found between a pump and the motor that drives it. The preferred method of eliminating hazards with these couplings is to design them such that any bolts, nuts, and setscrews are used *parallel* to the shafting and are countersunk, as shown in Figure 16.40. If these fasteners do not extend beyond the edge of the flange as shown in the figure, it is unlikely that they will cause injury. The greatest hazard with exposed setscrew heads is that they will catch parts of loose clothing and then draw the worker into the machine. The setscrews and other projections are typically invisible on the rapidly spinning shaft or flange, adding to the hazard. The installation of U-type guards, wherever needed throughout the plant, is an objective that needs to be set by the safety and health manager. Once they are aware of the hazard, maintenance personnel can go about systematically taking measurements, having U-type guards fabricated in the sheet metal shop, and then installing these guards.

The possibility of safeguarding belts and pulleys by *location* should not be overlooked. Some belts and pulleys are located in a part of the machine that is protected from worker exposure. Some people believe that location is the answer to safeguarding the belt and pulley on motor-driven air compressors that operate intermittently. But because this equipment starts automatically, safeguarding by location may not be sufficient to eliminate the hazard.

One approach to guarding large air compressors is to place them in a room by themselves. The door should be kept locked. It is best that the room be kept small if heat dissipation methods permit so that it will not be used for storage or other purposes that will result in worker exposure. The safety of maintenance personnel who must enter the room to service the compressor should not be overlooked. Administrative procedures and training can be used to reduce hazards to these personnel.

It is important to call attention to the hazards of compressed air hoses used for cleaning. Compressed air hoses with nozzles are often used to spray chips away from machine areas. Safety standards specify that the air pressure used for such purposes must not exceed 30 psi. Most industrial compressed air systems operate at working pressures greater than 30 psi. Therefore, a reducer at the nozzle or a reducing nozzle is used to bring the air pressure within the specified maximum of 30 psi. Figure 16.41b shows one type of nozzle for this purpose.

Excessive air pressure from these nozzles can make flying chips hazardous. Even with proper air pressure, chip guarding and personal protective equipment are needed to protect the worker. If alternate means can be used to remove chips, it is usually in the

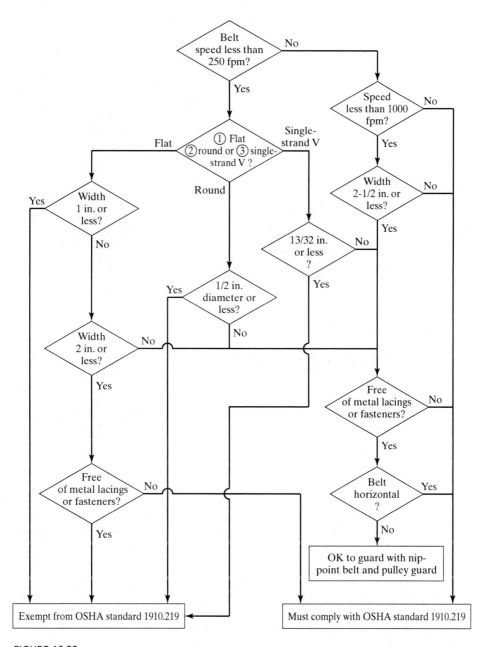

FIGURE 16.39

Decision diagram for OSHA belt guarding standard.

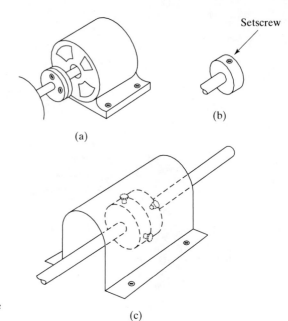

FIGURE 16.40

Safety with shaft couplings: (a) Screws or bolts are mounted parallel to the shafting and are countersunk; (b) setscrew is mounted in the periphery of the flange, but is countersunk and does not extend beyond the flange; (c) exposed setscrews present no hazard because the shaft coupling is covered by a U-shaped guard.

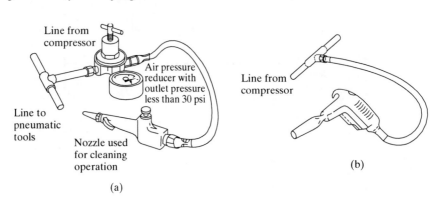

FIGURE 16.41

Two ways to comply with OSHA's requirement to reduce compressed air for cleaning to pressures less than 30 psi (a) pressure reducer in line; (b) special ventilating nozzle reduces pressure to less than 30 psi.

interest of safety to discontinue the use of air nozzles. Unfortunately, metal chips are very sharp and hazardous to handle, making the cleaning process somewhat of a problem.

The hazard of flying chips is fairly obvious, but most people do not realize that compressed air hoses used for cleaning can even present hazards of *fatalities*. There have been a few recorded cases of fatalities where horseplay has failed to consider the hazards of compressed air. There is no way that the human body can contain without serious damage internal overpressures of even 30 psi. Unfortunately, workers have rarely been trained to respect the lethal pressures presented by the ordinary and seemingly harmless compressed air nozzle used for cleaning.

Jacks

A frequent weekend accident is the familiar fatality when a "shade tree mechanic" is killed under an automobile that has fallen from the jack supporting it. A jack is essential for lifting, but the supported load is usually much more stable if transferred to secure blocks, removing the load from the jack. What is unsafe for the shade tree mechanic is also unsafe for the industrial worker as far as jacks are concerned.

As with a crane or a hoist chain, the temptation is to use a jack until failure, but the result of this policy will eventually be a catastrophic failure, an unacceptable alternative for the end of life for a jack. Therefore, the only other alternative is to inspect the jack at intervals throughout its life to watch for signs that the jack either needs repair or is worn to the danger point.

SUMMARY

Machine guarding is a term almost synonymous with industrial safety and is a high-priority item for safety and health managers. Although passed off by some health and safety professionals as old fashioned and nontechnical, machine guarding is actually a challenging task with new guarding technologies pressing the state of the art.

The most dangerous part of most machines is the point of operation, where the tool meets the workpiece. Unfortunately, it is also the most difficult part of the machine to guard in most cases. When guarding becomes impractical or infeasible, electromechanical devices have been devised for protecting the operator from the point of operation. Not to be overlooked are the indirect hazards at the point of operation such as flying chips or sparks.

Next in importance to the point of operation are belts, pulleys, and other power transmission apparatus. Usually more easily guarded than the point of operation, belts, pulleys, gears, shafts, and chains should receive plantwide attention. Guards often can be fabricated in-house with supervision of the safety and health manager. Remember to consider the possibility of guarding by location. Not to be confused with guarding by location is guarding by *distance*. Guarding by distance is intended for point of operation guarding for machines, such as press brakes, that fabricate large workpieces.

One of the most important and dangerous of production machines is the mechanical power press. Safety requirements for guarding the point of operation of presses can be quite technical and complicated. Many of the guarding methods specified for presses can be used as principles for guarding machines in general.

The hazards of radial saws are exemplary of those of other types of saws. Kickback is a hazard with most saws, and various mechanical devices in addition to training workers in the mechanism of kickback are viable remedies.

OSHA's abrasive wheel machinery standard is quite complicated, but the principal problems are short and simple—guarding the wheel, nut, and flange; adjustment of the workrests on grinding machines; and adjustment of the tongue guards. The safety and health manager should also give attention to such miscellaneous equipment as hand-held power tools, compressed-air equipment, and jacks. Significant among these is the requirement to reduce air pressure to 30 psi or less when the air is used for cleaning.

EXERCISES AND STUDY QUESTIONS

16.1 Explain the term *point of operation*.

16.2 Name several types of mechanical hazards on machines in general. Which is the most important from a safety standpoint?

16.3 Identify several examples of in-running nip points.

16.4 Name two ways of safeguarding a machine that require no physical guard or device at all. What is the difference between these two methods of safeguarding?

16.5 What is a lockout? How does it differ from an interlock?

16.6 What are the disadvantages of nylon mesh guards for fans?

16.7 The stopping time of the ram on a certain part-revolution press has been measured to be 0.333 second. At what minimum safety distance should a presence-sensing device be placed?

16.8 A popular mechanical power press has a full-revolution clutch and 14 engagement points on the flywheel, which rotates at 90 rpm. At what minimum distance from the point of operation on this press should a two-hand trip device be placed?

16.9 Name some reasons why a machine might have bolt holes in its feet.

16.10 Name several types of safeguarding devices for the point of operation.

16.11 What is the difference between an interlocked-barrier guard and a gate?

16.12 What is the difference between two-hand controls and two-hand trips?

16.13 What is the difference between type A and B gates?

16.14 What is the advantage of Allen-head screws over wing nuts for machine guards?

16.15 A guard has a maximum opening size of 3/4 inch. The guard openings are 6 inches from the danger zone. Does the opening size meet requirements?

16.16 What is an awareness barrier? What is a jig guard?

16.17 Explain the terms *full revolution* and *part revolution* as applied to press clutches. Which is safer?

16.18 What is muting of safeguarding devices, and when is it permitted?

16.19 What is the principal reason that galvanized wire mesh is a better material for constructing machine guards than is ordinary screen mesh? (*Hint*: The answer is not rust prevention.)

16.20 What is the biggest disadvantage of pullbacks?

16.21 What is the difference between pullbacks and restraints?

16.22 A part-revolution clutch press has a brake stop time of 0.37 second. At what minimum distance should two-hand controls be placed?

16.23 Where should a presence-sensing device be placed on the press of Exercise 16.22?

16.24 If the press of Exercise 16.22 had been a full-revolution press operating at 60 rpm and having four engagement points, at what distance should a two-hand trip device be placed?

16.25 Would a two-hand control offer any improvement in the press of Exercise 16.24? What about a presence-sensing device?

16.26 What are the three biggest problems with grinding machines? Why are they so important from a safety standpoint?

16.27 What single characteristic of the point of operation can exempt a mechanical power press from the requirement for guarding or safeguarding?

16.28 Compare hazards for table saws that are used as ripsaws versus those used as crosscut saws.

16.29 What is the ring test?

16.30 How can compressed air used for cleaning be dangerous? Under what circumstances is it permitted?

16.31 When do shaft couplings need no guards?

16.32 The expanded metal mesh in a machine guard has a maximum opening size of 3/8 inch. What minimum distance from the point of operation can this guard be legally placed?

16.33 Describe the nature of frequent OSHA citations involving lockout/tagout.

16.34 Explain how a machine designed to be started and stopped with push-button on/off switches can be modified to qualify for lockout.

16.35 What is the meaning of guarding by location? How does guarding by location differ from guarding by distance?

16.36 Explain the term *zero mechanical state*.

16.37 Explain the term *energy isolation device*.

16.38 The term *shield guard* applies to which type of machine hazard?

16.39 Which of the fail-safe principles applies to the term *zero mechanical state*?

16.40 What is generally the best color for a point-of-operation guard? Explain why.

16.41 Comment on the suitability of hand-feeding tools or tongs for safeguarding the point of operation.

16.42 Name the types of machine guards that are inappropriate for hand feeding the point of operation.

16.43 Discuss the comparative advantages of die enclosure guards versus fixed-barrier guards.

16.44 Explain likely outcomes when punch press dies close on a misaligned workpiece.

16.45 One recognized method of safeguarding the point of operation can be made safe for hand feeding if facilitated with hand tools or tongs. Name this method of safeguarding.

16.46 Is it legal to use a type B gate on a full-revolution press? Is it advisable? What is the potential hazard in using a type B gate on a full-revolution press?

16.47 Discuss at least two advantages of a friction clutch drive on a punch press versus a positive mechanical drive engagement.

16.48 List and describe all mechanical press setups for which a brake monitor and control system are required by standards.

16.49 List and describe all mechanical press setups for which it is legal to use hand feeding.

16.50 List and describe all mechanical press setups for which a brake monitor and control system are required by standards.

16.51 What optional feature of presence-sensing devices is permissible to give the presence-sensing device the same production advantage that the type B gate has over the type A gate? Explain the advantage.

16.52 Describe two disadvantages of awareness barriers.

16.53 Relate at least two advantages of using infrared instead of visible light as the medium for presence sensing devices.

16.54 Explain the difference between the terms "brake monitor" and "brake-stop-time measurement device."

16.55 The top-stop overtravel limit switch on a brake monitor for a mechanical power press is adjustable. What is the advantage of adjusting the overtravel high? What is the advantage of adjusting the overtravel low?

16.56 What happens when the top-stop overtravel limit switch is tripped at the end of a press cycle?

16.57 Describe two required features on a table saw that are intended to prevent kickback. Which one prevents kickback from starting and which one arrests the kickback motion if it does start?

16.58 What characteristic of a hand-held circular saw makes the retractable blade guard even more important than it is on table saws or radial saws?

16.59 What is the difference between a power hacksaw and a band saw? Which is more difficult to guard? Why?

16.60 Explain why large fixed-barrier guards can permit large distances between the guard and the point of operation and a coarser mesh for the guard material.

16.61 Describe the disadvantages of awareness barriers in lieu of machine guards.

16.62 Explain the benefits of using a footswitch to trip a press in which the point of operation is protected by an infrared light screen.

16.63 Describe two advantages of using infrared light instead of visible light as the medium for a presence-sensing device.

16.64 What design features of a presence-sensing system are permitted to improve system efficiency in the same way that type B gates improve workstation efficiency over type A gates?

16.65 Comment on the relationship between the speed of a punch press and its safety. When is a slower machine usually better and when is a fast one better?

16.66 Why should control pedestals, if used for punch presses, be rigidly fixed to the floor?

16.67 **Design Case Study.** A workstation is being redesigned to increase its production rate to make it more competitive in an industry that competes in the global marketplace. The old workstation is a punch press operation, utilizing a full-revolution flywheel press employing a type A gate. By utilizing robot feeding, the production standard for this workstation is 600 units per hour. Describe three alternative designs for this workstation and explain why they should be capable of substantially increasing the production rate without violating safety standards. Qualify each alternative with a description of the disadvantages of each approach.

16.68 **Design Case Study.** A full-revolution press with two engagement points on the flywheel has two-hand palm buttons installed at a distance of 16 inches from the point of operation. Calculate the minimum flywheel speed that will permit this press to be in compliance with standards. Explain why a slower flywheel speed would be more dangerous.

16.69 **Design Case Study.** A full-revolution press has 100 rpm flywheel rotation. The press is equipped with two-hand palm buttons mounted on the machine at a distance of 20 inches from the point of operation. How many engagement points on the flywheel would be necessary to make this machine safe?

16.70 **Design Case Study.** In the press design of Exercise 16.69, suppose that the maximum available number of flywheel engagement points is 14. What modification of the mechanical drive would be needed to make the press setup described in Exercise 16.69 safe?

STANDARDS RESEARCH QUESTIONS

16.69 Review OSHA enforcement statistics to determine the frequency of citation for "general point-of-operation guarding." How does the OSHA standard for general point-of-operation guarding rank among all OSHA standards in terms of frequency of citation?

16.70 Review OSHA enforcement statistics to determine the frequency of citation for "point-of-operation guarding" on mechanical power presses.

16.71 Review OSHA enforcement statistics to determine the top three most frequently cited standards in the abrasive wheel machinery standard.

CHAPTER 17

Environmental Control and Noise

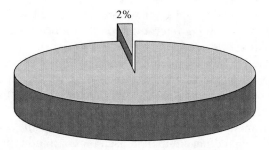

2%

***Percentage of OSHA
General Industry citations
addressing this subject***

We explored the important task of measuring and evaluating air contaminants to determine the degree of exposure to health hazards. Once having found that an air contaminant does exist, there are a variety of strategies available for dealing with it. It was stated that from the profession, there has emerged a definite hierarchy of strategies that have come to be known as the "three lines of defense." These strategies are engineering controls, work-practice controls, and personal protective equipment, in that order. In this chapter, we will examine methods to provide engineering solutions to the air-contaminant problem, chiefly through ventilation. Noise hazards will also be examined, along with both engineering and work-practices controls to control these hazards.

VENTILATION

Ventilation may be the most obvious engineering solution to an air-contaminant problem, but before acceding to this solution, it should be recognized that other ways to deal with the problem may be even better. Previously, a series of approaches was enumerated as "engineering design principles." In this chapter, some applications of these engineering principles will be seen.

The most desirable way to deal with an air contaminant is to change the process so that the contaminant is no longer produced. This is so obvious that it is sometimes overlooked. It may be that the process cannot be changed, but if it can, there may be tremendous gains in store, not only in health and safety, but in production cost and efficiency as well. For instance, it may be found that machined parts can be machined dry, avoiding cutting oil exposures to the machinist's skin as well as solvent contamination of the air as the parts are later cleaned. Forging, die casting, or powdered metal technology may eliminate several machining processes, changing the process in beneficial ways. Some of these ideas may generate more disadvantages than advantages in given situations, but each application should be checked for potential benefit. There is no better way for the safety and health manager to win recognition from top management than by generating a clever idea that cuts costs or increases production while it also enhances safety or health.

For more ideas, consider the hazards of toxic air contaminants from welding operations. Sometimes the principal source of the contaminant is the surface coating on the metal to be welded. Perhaps as a process change, this surface coating can be removed prior to the commencement of welding. Better yet, perhaps the material does not require welding at all. Possibly a crimping operation could produce an effective joint, eliminating the need for welding or soldering.

Chemical processes are classified as batch or continuous. The choice between the two usually involves many considerations, including investment cost, length of production run expected, volumes to be produced, and the important factor of air contamination. Continuous processes generally reduce the exposure of materials to the air because open handling is reduced, and batches of materials are not sitting idle awaiting processing. However, the mechanical handling equipment used for continuous processes may increase the contamination levels. Each situation must be studied to determine the best solution, keeping in mind safety and health aspects.

One way a process can be changed is to isolate or enclose it. If a particularly contaminating process is in the plant, perhaps it should be located in a separate building so that it does not contribute to the overall ventilation problem.

A slight variation to changing the process is to change the materials used. Carbon tetrachloride has been found to be a health hazard, so other solvents have been substituted. The chlorinated hydrocarbon solvents substituted, such as trichloroethylene and perchloroethylene, are also being found to be hazardous, but fortunately not as hazardous as carbon tetrachloride. New solvents may be found to reduce hazards even further. Labar (ref. Labar, 1993) classifies many dangerous hydrocarbon solvents as "volatile organic compounds"(VOCs) and suggests substituting water-based solvents for VOCs. An extra benefit of water-based solvents is that sometimes they are not as slippery as VOCs if spilled on the floor. They may be expensive and usually take longer to dry than VOCs. Another problem can be corrosion. Everyone knows that water causes rust, and if water-based solvents are used for wash-downs, stainless steel nozzles may be required. Finally, water-based solvents may themselves be health hazards, such as causing urinary tract infections. Substitution of materials may be a good idea, but all of the pros and cons should be identified and evaluated.

Another possible substitution is in sand blasting. Silica sand is often used for blasting to improve surface characteristics. But airborne silica causes the lung disease called silicosis. Perhaps the silica sand could be replaced by steel shot, removing the silica contamination.

A classic example of changing materials to reduce hazards is the switch from hazardous lead-based paints to substitute materials such as iron oxide pigments. Another classic was the switch from Freon to propane as a propellant for aerosol cans. In this case, the materials switch was intended to protect the environment (the ozone layer), but the solution may be more hazardous to the individual because propane is a flammable gas.

Design Principles

If the process cannot be changed or materials substituted, a well-designed ventilation system may be the best solution to the problem. OSHA has a standard that deals with this subject, but it must be emphasized that ventilation is a very technical subject, and the safety and health manager may want to turn to a professional engineer to design an adequate ventilation solution to an air-contamination problem. Exhaust ventilation is not the same as ordinary heating and air conditioning, and design errors can be made if this difference is not considered. An example is shown in Figure 17.1. Most heating and air-conditioning ducts have right-angle bends, which may be fine for gases, but greatly impair the ability of the ducts to transport particulates.

Another questionable ventilation system is an ordinary household fan used to blow away smoke from a contaminant source. It is true that a fan can dilute the concentration of a contaminant in a given place, and dilution ventilation is a recognized method of reducing concentrations to levels lower than the PEL. But the question is "Where is the fan blowing the contamination *to*?" It is adding to the overall background level of air contamination in the plant and may later have to be dealt with if other processes are also producing contaminations.

A basic objective of exhaust ventilation is to isolate and remove harmful contaminants from the air. The more these contaminants are concentrated into limited plant areas, the easier they are to separate from the air. Dilution ventilation, although expedient in some cases, is counterproductive to the goal of removing the contaminant. Dilution ventilation can be likened to "sweeping the dirt under the rug."

Focus is an important consideration for ventilation systems. Sheer volume or flow velocity is not enough. Ventilation technology is producing some very fine local exhaust systems that focus the intake right on the contaminant, much as a vacuum cleaner

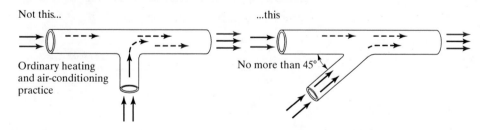

FIGURE 17.1

Avoid sharp angles at duct entry.

is designed to do. Even if sufficient flow could be achieved with a general ventilation system, the flow could be a nuisance because such a wind might blow away papers and other materials, making the job awkward and inefficient.

The earlier mention of a vacuum cleaner might give some safety and health managers the wrong idea. Particle size for fumes or other contaminants will usually be too small to be effectively trapped in the bag of an ordinary vacuum cleaner. If the process does not trap the contaminant, it is merely blowing it around, perhaps increasing exposure.

The best exhaust ventilation systems are the "pull" types, not the "push" types. Even within the exhaust duct, the fan should be placed at the end of the duct if possible, as shown in Figure 17.2. Leaks in the duct then merely draw in more air rather than pump contaminated air back into the plant environment.

Makeup Air

With an exhaust ventilation system or systems, some source of *makeup air* is essential. The traditional way to supply makeup air was simply to open windows and doors. Today, however, it has become increasingly attractive to recirculate the exhaust air after filtration and decontamination. Not only does such a solution save energy, it also reduces external atmospheric pollution, a very important point considering regulations of the Environmental Protection Agency (EPA) and the general environmental concerns of the public.

Figure 17.3 diagrams a recirculating system in which the objective is to remove dust by means of a high-efficiency filter. It is essential to recognize the importance of the condition of the filter to the overall effectiveness of the system. The filter will clog up over time if it is doing its job, and thus it must be serviced, cleaned, or changed. Note the bypass damper, which permits selective proportioning of the system from full recirculating to full exhaust. This bypass can save energy when weather conditions are mild and recirculation is unnecessary. Also note the inclusion of a manometer to detect a pressure differential across the filter as well as an alarm to sound if this differential becomes too great. Both are intended to provide indication or warning to the operator that the filter is in need of service.

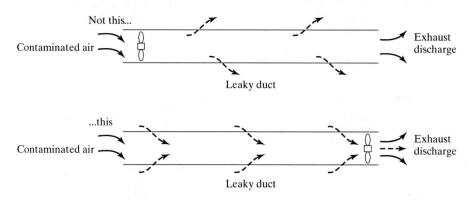

FIGURE 17.2

Fan location—keep negative pressure within the duct.

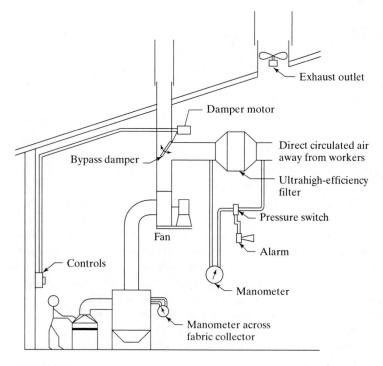

FIGURE 17.3

Example of recirculation from air-cleaning devices (dust) (*Source*: American Conference of Governmental Industrial Hygienists Committee on Industrial Ventilation).

Safety and health managers are warned to monitor recirculation systems closely. Frequently in industry a sophisticated ventilation system is installed for a process, and then it is ignored. Some filter alarms are merely red lights, which operators often ignore. Even audible alarms such as buzzers and horns are sometimes disabled by disconnecting electrical leads. Both operations and maintenance personnel have been found guilty of disabling these devices, which are designed to protect the workers' health.

Besides using recirculating systems, there are some other ways around the problem of energy losses due to the introduction of makeup air into the building. One method is to introduce the makeup air right at the point at which the contamination is taking place. With this strategy, the makeup air may need no air conditioning—no cooling in summer and no heating in winter. The exhaust system will merely suck up the unconditioned makeup air together with the contaminants, and workers will have little exposure to either.

Another solution to the problem is to use a heat exchanger to recapture the energy of the exhaust air and transfer it to the incoming makeup air. It is difficult to make this solution practical, however, because the heat differential between makeup air and exhaust air is usually too low to make the heat exchanger effective. Also, the heat exchanger approach necessitates positioning the makeup air duct close to the exhaust air duct, which introduces the possibility of cross-contamination. Finally, heat exchanger

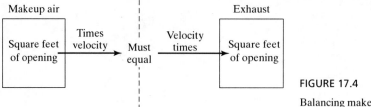

FIGURE 17.4

Balancing makeup and exhaust air.

systems can be expensive, both to install and to maintain effectively—too expensive in many cases to amortize by means of energy cost savings over the life of the system.

Besides the energy problem, another problem with supplying makeup air is the presence of contaminated air from the outside. This is an unusual problem, but it has presented itself on occasion. At one plant, the makeup air inlet was adjacent to a major freeway, which caused carbon monoxide and other automobile exhaust emissions to be drawn into the building. In another poor design, the makeup air inlet was so close to the exhaust system discharge that contaminants were being drawn back in and recirculated around the plant. That way, if workers managed to escape breathing the contaminated air the first time through, they got another chance to become exposed!

A quick check to determine whether there is a sufficient makeup air supply is to check atmospheric pressure both inside and outside the plant. The pressure inside should be only slightly lower than the pressure outside. If the pressure inside is substantially lower, then the makeup air supply is insufficient. The basic relationship between makeup and exhaust is illustrated in Figure 17.4. The cross-sectional area of makeup openings multiplied by the velocity of flow through those openings must equal the cross-sectional area of the exhaust openings multiplied by the velocity of flow through the exhaust.

The provision for adequate makeup air and a sufficient volume of general exhaust ventilation is sometimes the only practical solution to the problem of reducing air-contaminant exposures to specified levels. Case Study 17.1 will illustrate the principle of this solution to the problem.

CASE STUDY 17.1

An industrial process liberates 2 cubic feet of chlorobenzene per hour into a room that measures 20 feet by 40 feet and has a ceiling height of 12 feet. What minimum general exhaust ventilation in cubic feet per minute is necessary to prevent a general health hazard in this room?

Solution

A subtle facet of this problem is that for a continuously operating process, the dimensions of the room are really irrelevant to the solution. It is true that for a short-duration exposure, the size of the room will affect the dilution of the chlorobenzene within the confines of the room. But to deal with a continuous process, one must provide sufficient ventilation to yield an ample supply of makeup air to continuous-ly dilute the chlorobenzene to levels within limits, *regardless of room size.*

The PEL for chlorobenzene is 75 ppm. Let X = the total ventilation necessary to dilute the chlorobenzene. Then,

$$\frac{2}{X} = \frac{75}{1,000,000}$$

$$X = \frac{2 \times 1,000,000}{75} = 26,667 \text{ ft}^3/\text{hr}$$

$$= \frac{26,667 \text{ ft}^3/\text{hr}}{60 \text{ min/hr}}$$

$$= 444 \text{ ft}^3/\text{min}$$

Purification Devices

If the exhaust air is clean enough to meet external standards, no filtration or purification may be necessary once the air gets outside the plant. But often some type of purification device is necessary on the outside as is required indoors for recirculating systems, particularly for the removal of particulates. The paragraphs that follow describe some of the basic types of particulate removal devices.

Centrifugal devices, often called cyclones (see Figure 17.5), take advantage of the mass of the contaminant particles, causing them to collect on the sides of the cyclone in

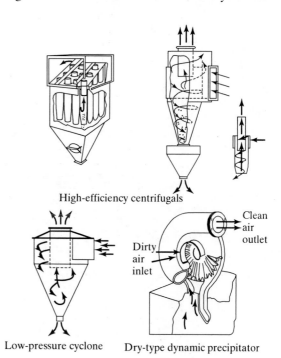

High-efficiency centrifugals

Clean air outlet

Dirty air inlet

Low-pressure cyclone   Dry-type dynamic precipitator

FIGURE 17.5

Cyclone and other dry-type centrifugal collectors for removal of particulates from exhaust air (*Source:* ACGIH Committee on Industrial Ventilation).

the swirling air and then slide to the bottom and settle in the neck of the funnel, where they can be periodically emptied. Another type of centrifugal device causes the dirty air to strike louvers, whereupon particles separate from the air. A typical application for cyclones is grain dust removal for grain elevators and mills. Cyclones are also used for woodworking sawdust, plastic, dusts, and some chemical dry particulates.

Electrostatic precipitators place a very high (e.g., 50,000-volt) electrical charge on the particles, causing them to be attracted to an electrode of opposite electrical charge. The collecting electrode can consist of plates, rods, or wires, all of which can be agitated to shake off the collected dust and cause it to settle in the bottom of the chamber. Figure 17.6 illustrates one type of high-voltage electrostatic precipitator. Electrostatic precipitators are used in the steel, cement, mining, and chemical industries. Electrostatic precipitators are also used in smokestacks to reduce fly ash.

Wet scrubbers include a wide variety of devices that employ water or chemical solution to wash the air of particulates or other contaminants. Some types pass the dirty air through standing water or solution. Another type forces dirty air to rise in a tower packed

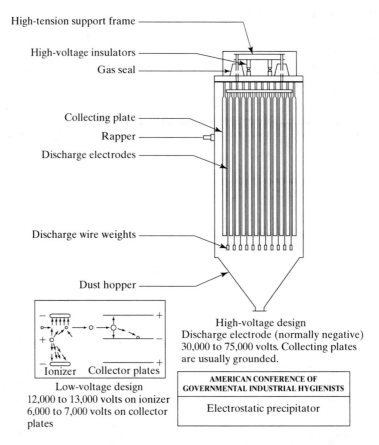

High-tension support frame

High-voltage insulators

Gas seal

Collecting plate

Rapper

Discharge electrodes

Discharge wire weights

Dust hopper

High-voltage design
Discharge electrode (normally negative)
30,000 to 75,000 volts. Collecting plates
are usually grounded.

Ionizer   Collector plates
Low-voltage design
12,000 to 13,000 volts on ionizer
6,000 to 7,000 volts on collector
plates

AMERICAN CONFERENCE OF
GOVERNMENTAL INDUSTRIAL HYGIENISTS

Electrostatic precipitator

FIGURE 17.6

Electrostatic precipitators for removing particulates (*Source*: ACGIH Committee on Industrial Ventilation).

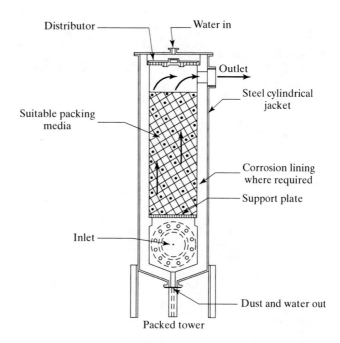

Distributor — Water in

Outlet

Steel cylindrical jacket

Suitable packing media

Corrosion lining where required

Support plate

Inlet

Dust and water out

Packed tower

FIGURE 17.7

Packed tower type of wet scrubber
(*Source*: ACGIH Committee on Industrial Ventilation).

AMERICAN CONFERENCE OF GOVERNMENTAL INDUSTRIAL HYGIENISTS
Wet-type dust collector

with a filler media through which water falls, as shown in Figure 17.7. Note in the figure that the cleanest water is at the top of the tower, where the exiting air is at its cleanest. The bottom of the tower is the dirtiest, where the water vehicle is exiting the packing and is contacting the dirtiest, untreated exhaust air. Wet centrifugal types, like dry centrifugal types, take advantage of the mass of the particles by causing them to impinge on blades, plates, or baffles. Wet scrubbers are seen in the chemical industries, where they are able to remove gases and vapors in addition to particulates. Other industries that use wet scrubbers are the rubber, ceramics, foundries, and metal-cutting industries.

Fabric, or bag-type, filters are essentially like a vacuum cleaner bag. Some are huge and are located in separate buildings called *baghouses.* Figure 17.8 shows three types of fabric filters. Fabric filters are used in the refining of toxic metals such as lead and in the woodworking, metal cutting, rubber, plastics, ceramics, and chemical industries.

INDUSTRIAL NOISE

Noise exposure is another classic health problem because chronic exposures are the ones that typically do the damage. A single acute exposure can do permanent damage, and in this sense, noise is a safety problem, but noise exposures of this type are extremely rare.

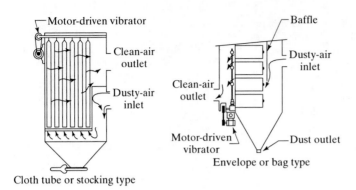

Cloth tube or stocking type

Envelope or bag type

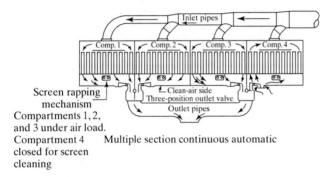

Screen rapping mechanism
Compartments 1, 2, and 3 under air load.
Compartment 4 closed for screen cleaning

Multiple section continuous automatic

AMERICAN CONFERENCE OF GOVERNMENTAL INDUSTRIAL HYGIENISTS
Fabric collectors

FIGURE 17.8

Fabric filters for exhaust air (*Source*: ACGIH Committee on Industrial Ventilation).

As with other health hazards, noise has a threshold limit value, and exposures are measured in terms of time-weighted averages. To understand the units of these measures, some background is needed in the physical characteristics of sound.

Characteristics of Sound Waves

Noise can be defined as unwanted sound. In the industrial sense, noise usually means excessive sound or harmful sound. Sound is generally understood as a pressure wave in the atmosphere. In liquids, sound is also a pressure wave; in rigid solids, sound takes the form of a vibration.

Two basic characteristics of sound waves important to the subject of noise control are

1. the amplitude, or pressure peak intensity, of the wave;
2. the frequency in which the pressure peaks occur.

Our sense of hearing can detect both of these characteristics. Pressure intensity is sensed as loudness, whereas pressure frequency is sensed as pitch. Figure 17.9 illustrates the wave

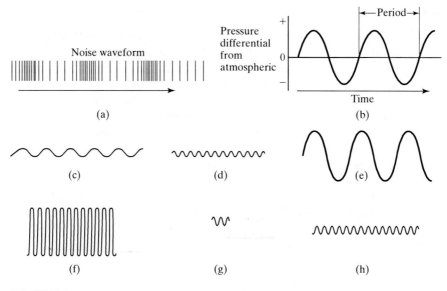

FIGURE 17.9

Characteristics of sound waves—(a) pressure wave is longitudinal (in the direction of travel of the sound); (b) relationship between pressure and time at a given point of sound exposure; (c) low pitch, soft sound; (d) high pitch, soft sound; (e) low pitch, loud sound; (f) high pitch, loud sound; (g) short-duration sound; (h) sustained sound.

form of sound and also graphs the relationship between pressure and time. Note in Figure 17.9(b) that the *period* is the length of time required for the wave to complete its cycle. In the graph, it is measured at the point at which the pressure differential becomes zero and is starting to become negative. However, it could have been measured from peak to peak, valley to valley, or at any other convenient reference point in the cycle. These periods are always short, too short to count their occurrences while listening to the sound. If we could count the occurrences of these wave cycles, the resulting count per unit time would be the *frequency*, usually measured in numbers of cycles per second (*hertz*). A typical sound is at a frequency of 1000 cycles per second—that is, 1000 hertz (Hz). Obviously, we could never count 1000 pulses of pressure in a single second, but our ears have surprising sensitivity to variations in this frequency count. The sensation is known as *pitch*, and skilled musicians have trained their ears to hear very slight variations in sound-wave frequency. Frequency is important in analyzing the sources of occupational noise exposure.

Even more important than pitch in industrial settings is the pressure intensity of the sound wave. High peaks of pressure in the waves can do permanent damage to the delicate mechanisms in the human ear, causing permanent hearing loss. The ear is delicate enough to pick up the tiny pressures of the faintest audible sounds and also is able to withstand an incredibly large range of pressures. The human ear can withstand, *without damage*, a sound pressure 10,000,000 times as great as the faintest sound it can hear! A necessary result of this incredible range of pressures is that the ear is not very sensitive to shades of differences in these pressures, especially as the pressures get into the upper part of the range. In other words, as sounds get fairly loud, the human ear cannot readily detect a large increase in the intensity, even a doubling or tripling of the intensity.

Decibels

It is difficult to talk sensibly about such a large range of audible pressures, and it is especially difficult to set standards. Imagine a noise meter reading in the millions. The situation is further complicated by the lessening of the ability of the human ear to detect pressure differences as sounds get louder. To deal with these problems, a unit of measure called the *decibel* (dB) has been devised to measure sound-pressure intensity. The decibel has a logarithmic relation to the actual pressure intensity, and thus the scale becomes compressed as the sound becomes louder, until in the upper ranges, the decibel is only a gross measure of actual pressure intensity. But this is appropriate because, as was mentioned before, the human ear only hears gross differences anyway when the sound becomes very loud. Figure 17.10 relates the decibel to familiar sound levels.

The logarithmic decibel scale is convenient, but it does give rise to some problems. If a machine in the plant is very loud, putting a second machine just like it right beside it will not make the sound twice as loud. Remember that the range of sound pressures is tremendous and that the human ear hears only a slight increase in loudness, when the

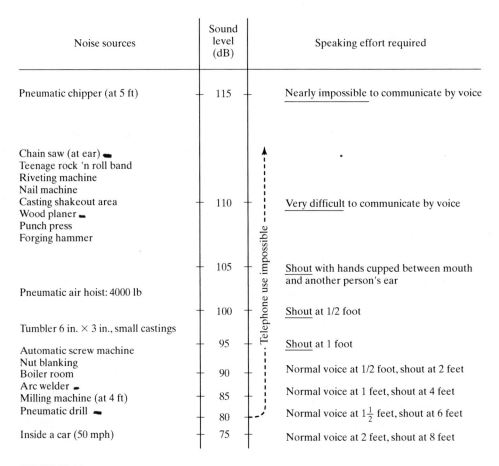

Noise sources	Sound level (dB)		Speaking effort required
Pneumatic chipper (at 5 ft)	115		Nearly impossible to communicate by voice
Chain saw (at ear) ▬ Teenage rock 'n roll band Riveting machine Nail machine Casting shakeout area Wood planer ▬ Punch press Forging hammer	110		Very difficult to communicate by voice
	105		Shout with hands cupped between mouth and another person's ear
Pneumatic air hoist: 4000 lb			
	100	Telephone use impossible	Shout at 1/2 foot
Tumbler 6 in. × 3 in., small castings			
Automatic screw machine	95		Shout at 1 foot
Nut blanking Boiler room	90		Normal voice at 1/2 foot, shout at 2 feet
Arc welder ▬ Milling machine (at 4 ft)	85		Normal voice at 1 feet, shout at 4 feet
Pneumatic drill ▬	80		Normal voice at $1\frac{1}{2}$ feet, shout at 6 feet
Inside a car (50 mph)	75		Normal voice at 2 feet, shout at 8 feet

FIGURE 17.10

Decibel noise levels of familiar sounds (*Source:* NIOSH).

TABLE 17.1   Scale for Combining Decibels

Difference between two decibel levels to be added (dB)	Amount to be added to larger level to obtain decibel sum (dB)
0	3.0
1	2.6
2	2.1
3	1.8
4	1.4
5	1.2
6	1.0
7	0.8
8	0.6
9	0.5
10	0.4
11	0.3
12	0.2

Source: NIOSH (ref. Industrial Noise).

actual sound pressure may have doubled due to the addition of the extra machine. The decibel scale recognizes the addition of the new machine as an increase in noise level of only 3 decibels. Conversely, if the noise level in the plant exceeds allowable standards by very much, shutting off half the machines in the plant—an obviously drastic measure—may have very little effect in bringing down the total noise level on the decibel scale. Table 17.1 provides a scale for combining decibels to arrive at a total noise level from two sources. If there are three or more sources, two sources are combined and then treated as one source to be combined with a third, and so on, until all sources have been combined into a single total. An example is helpful in illustrating the method.

CASE STUDY 17.2

Suppose that noise exposure at a workstation is essentially due to four sources, as follows:

Machine A	86 dB
Machine B (identical to machine A)	86 dB
Machine C	82 dB
Machine D	78 dB

First, the two identical noise sources, Machines A and B, are combined to produce a noise level of 89 dB. Then Machine C is added as follows:

$$dB \text{ difference} = 89 \text{ dB} - 82 \text{ dB} = 7 \text{ dB}.$$

From Table 17.1, a difference of 7 dB between two sources results in the addition of 0.8 dB to the larger source. Therefore, the combined sound of machines A, B, and C is

$$\text{combined sound (A,B,C)} = 89 \text{ dB} + 0.8 \text{ dB} = 89.8 \text{ dB}.$$

Adding Machine D, we have

$$\text{dB difference} = 89.8 \text{ dB} - 78 \text{ dB} = 11.8 \text{ dB} = 12 \text{ dB}.$$

Returning to Table 17.1, a difference of 12 dB between two sources results in the addition of 0.2 dB to the larger source. Therefore, the combined sound of all machines is

$$\text{combined sound (A,B,C,D)} = 89.8 \text{ dB} + 0.2 \text{ dB} = 90.0 \text{ dB}.$$

Figure 17.11 diagrams the computation of Case Study 17.2. It should be noted that the measurement of both the total combined sound and the individual machine contributions toward that total are made from the position of the operator. Otherwise, distance factors would affect the results. The computation of combined noise levels is useful in considering the potential benefits of removing machines, enclosing machines, or changing the process.

We have been emphasizing sound intensity measured in decibels, but frequency (or pitch) also plays a role in noise control. Industrial noise is typically a combination

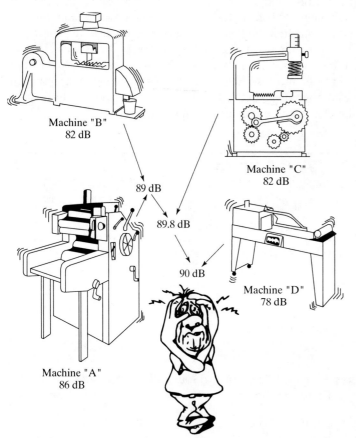

Machine "B"
82 dB

Machine "C"
82 dB

89 dB

89.8 dB

90 dB

Machine "D"
78 dB

Machine "A"
86 dB

FIGURE 17.11

Combining noise from several sources.

of sound frequencies from each of several sources. The total range of sound frequencies audible to the human ear is from about 20 to about 20,000 Hz. The ear is more sensitive to some of these frequencies than others, particularly the upper middle range from about 1000 to about 6000 Hz. Thus, sound-level meters have been devised to bias the decibel reading slightly to emphasize the frequencies from 1000 to 6000 Hz. This biased reading is called the A-weighted scale,[1] and resulting readings are abbreviated dBA instead of simply dB. OSHA recognizes the A-scale, and OSHA PELs are expressed in dBAs.

OSHA Noise Standards

Noise is unusual in that it is a hazard for which OSHA has set both a PEL and an AL. The best known is the PEL, which is set at 90 dBA for an 8-hour TWA. The action level (AL) was established in the early 1980s at 85 dBA for an 8-hour TWA, about 10 years after the 90-dBA PEL was established. It is widely recognized that workers can tolerate short periods of noise higher than the 8-hour TWA without damage, so OSHA specifies a range of decibel exposure levels for various exposure periods. The range of OSHA PELs for noise exposure is given in Table 17.2.

The range of permissible exposures in Table 17.2 makes possible a computation of a time-weighted-average exposure, relating each exposure time to the limit permitted for that sound level. The procedure is very similar to the calculation used earlier when multiple contaminants are present in the atmosphere. The formula used is

$$D = 100 \sum_{i=1}^{n} \frac{C_i}{T_i} = 100\left(\frac{C_1}{T_1} + \frac{C_2}{T_2} + \cdots + \frac{C_n}{T_n}\right) \tag{17.1}$$

where D = total shift noise exposure ("dose") as a percent of PEL

C_i = time of exposure at noise level i

T_i = maximum permissible exposure time at noise level i (from Table 17.2)

n = number of different noise levels observed

An interesting computation is for total shift exposure exactly at the AL of 85 dBA. By using Equation (17.1), the computation is as follows:

$$D = 100 \sum_{i=1}^{n} \frac{C_i}{T_i} = 100\left(\frac{8}{16}\right) = 50\%$$

Thus, the AL is computed to be 50% of the maximum permissible PEL. However, the reader should note from the earlier discussion of sound intensity that 85 dBA represents less than one-half of the absolute sound intensity of noise at 90 dB.

---

[1]There are also a B-scale and C-scale, but these scales are seldom used.

TABLE 17.2 OSHA's Table of PELs for Noise

A-weighted sound level	Reference duration time (hr)	A-weighted sound level	Reference duration time (hr)
80	32	106	0.87
81	27.9	107	0.76
82	24.3	108	0.66
83	21.1	109	0.57
84	18.4	110	0.50
85	16	111	0.44
86	13.9	112	0.38
87	12.1	113	0.33
88	10.6	114	0.29
89	9.2	115	0.25
90	8	116	0.22
91	7.0	117	0.19
92	6.2	118	0.16
93	5.3	119	0.14
94	4.6	120	0.125
95	4	121	0.110
96	3.5	122	0.095
97	3.0	123	0.082
98	2.6	124	0.072
99	2.3	125	0.063
100	2	126	0.054
101	1.7	127	0.047
102	1.5	128	0.041
103	1.4	129	0.036
104	1.3	130	0.031
105	1		

Source: Code of Federal Regulations 29 CFR 1910.95.

CASE STUDY 17.3

Noise-level readings show that a worker exposure to noise in a given plant is as follows:

8:00 A.M. – 10:00 A.M.	90 dBA
10:00 A.M. – 11:00 A.M.	95 dBA
11:00 A.M. – 12:30 P.M.	75 dBA
12:30 P.M. – 1:30 P.M.	85 dBA
1:30 P.M. – 2:00 P.M.	95 dBA
2:00 P.M. – 4:00 P.M.	90 dBA

Adding up the noise durations for each level, we obtain

AT noise level 90 dBA;	$2 + 2 =$	4	hours
AT noise level 95 dBA;	$1 + 1/2 =$	$1\frac{1}{2}$	hours
AT noise level 75 dBA;		$1\frac{1}{2}$	hours (ignore)
AT noise level 85 dBA;		1	hours
Total		8	hours

The reason that the $1\frac{1}{2}$-hour exposure at 75 dBA was ignored is that 75 dBA is below the range of Table 17.2. In other words, workers may be exposed to noise levels of 75 dBA for as long as desired with no adverse effects, at least as far as safety standards are concerned.

Computing the ratios at each level and summing, in accordance with Equation (17.1), yields

$$D = 100 \sum_{i=1}^{n} \frac{C_i}{T_i} = 100 \left(\frac{4}{8} + \frac{1\frac{1}{2}}{4} + \frac{1}{16} \right)$$
$$= 100(0.5 + 0.375 + 0.0625)$$
$$= 93.75\%.$$

Since 93.75% is less than 100%, the PEL is not exceeded. However, since 93.75% is greater than 50%, the AL of 85 dBA (8-hour TWA) is exceeded.

Sometimes noise is percussive or intermittent so that, technically speaking, there are tiny intervals of silence between sharp reports. Some employers have followed the scheme that these tiny intervals of silence can be counted toward the quiet time, reducing the observed duration of noise in excess of 90 dBA, but this interpretation is incorrect. Any variations in noise levels that have maxima less than 1 second apart are to be considered continuous. The slow response scale of modern noise-level meters tends to ignore such tiny interval variations, and thus "slow response" is specified in noise-level metering.

The standards do have a specification for peak impulse or impact noise at 140 dBA, but this, of course, is much higher than the PELs for continuous noise. Thus, the 140-dB OSHA specification can be considered a ceiling, or C, value. The 140-dB ceiling should be considered a limit for acute exposure and is accordingly a safety hazard. However, such exposures are so rare and difficult to measure after the fact that ceiling violations are virtually never cited. Ordinary sound-level meters are not very effective in measuring impact noise. Even for continuous exposures, measurement can be a problem that will now be addressed.

Noise Measurement

As a first check for potential noise problems, the safety and health manager should take a walk through the plant and listen. As a rule of *thumb*, if you can reach out and touch someone with your *thumb* but still cannot hear and understand that person's conversation (without his or her shouting), either your hearing is already damaged or deficient or there is excessive noise in the area. If the noise is continuous throughout the working shift but is no louder than a continuously running vacuum cleaner, there is probably no violation of standards. But if the noise is as loud as a subway passing through a station continuously throughout the full shift, a violation probably exists. If subways are unfamiliar to you, imagine a fast-moving freight train passing within 20 feet; such a noise level would easily constitute a violation if the exposure were continuous for a full 8-hour shift. Some exposures louder than the train might be permissible if they are of short duration, as was obvious in the calculation of average exposures in the preceding section. Anything between the vacuum cleaner and the train in sound level would be a gray area that ought to be measured with accurate meters.

Accurate measurement of sound levels requires instruments such as the sound-level meter (SLM) illustrated in Figure 17.12. The meter registers the sound intensity in decibels. Sound-level meters are delicate instruments and must be handled carefully. Accuracy is a problem, and the safety and health manager should not expect performance better than ±1 dB. Calibration is extremely important, and no sound-level meter is complete without a calibration device (known sound source) nearby. Variations in battery level must be compensated for, and humidity and temperature conditions can cause distortions.

Some skill is required in using the sound-level meter to obtain reliable readings. Naturally, the microphone receiver of the instrument must be held in the vicinity of the subject's ear in order to be representative of the exposure. However, the instrument should not be held too close, as the subject's body may affect the reading. The instrument's microphone receiver should be shielded from wind currents, and the instrument itself should not be subjected to direct vibrations. The safety and health manager may find the sound-level meter most useful in comparing sound levels in various locations in the plant and in comparing different machines and operating modes.

Determining the full-shift, time-weighted average exposure with a sound-level meter is tedious and requires a great number of samples. A convenient substitute is a cumulative device called a *dosimeter*, which is worn on the person of the subject under study. Dosimeters may seem to be a panacea, but they have their drawbacks. The wearer can easily bias the dosimeter by holding it close to a loud mechanism, or by simply rubbing, tapping, or blowing on the microphone. They are useful survey devices, however, and are used to monitor exposures if the firm's noise levels have exceeded the AL of 85 dBA for an 8-hour TWA.

Once it is determined that a problem exists, a more sophisticated measurement of noise level may be necessary to isolate the sources of the undesirable noise. An octave-band analyzer permits decibel readings to be taken at various frequencies over the audible range, as shown in the example in Figure 17.13. Various noise-reduction media have characteristic frequencies at which they are most effective. The octave-band

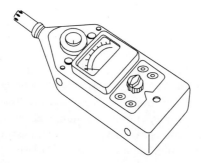

FIGURE 17.12

Example of sound-level meter.

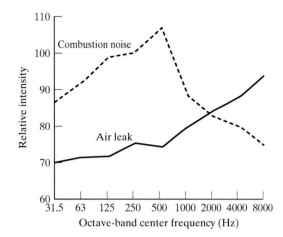

FIGURE 17.13

Example of octave-band analysis (*Source:* NIOSH, ref. Industrial Noise).

analysis will help to delineate the problem frequencies as well as provide evidence to identify the problem sources. Finally, octave-band analysis is useful in determining the frequency characteristics of a particular industry's noise sources so that damage from these sources can be distinguished from damage from noise exposures that have occurred off the job.

Engineering Controls

Once the instruments have proven that a problem exists, the safety and health manager needs physical solutions to the problems. If noise levels exceed the PEL, federal standards require that feasible engineering or administrative controls be used. If these measures fail to reduce noise exposures to within the PEL, personal protective equipment must be provided and used to reduce sound levels to within the PEL. Engineering controls should be considered a more thorough and permanent solution to the problem.

As with the control of toxic substances, the simplest solutions may be so obvious that they are overlooked. Process modification or elimination should always receive consideration. Another very simple solution, if feasible, is merely to move the operator away from the primary source of the noise. This idea has more merit than it would intuitively appear because the noise intensity from a given source goes down as the square of the distance, in the absence of reflective walls and other distorting factors. The reason for this relationship can be seen in Figure 17.14.

It must be remembered that it is absolute sound intensity, not decibels, that varies inversely with the square of the distance from the source. The logarithmic decibel scale results in a 3-dB change whenever the sound intensity is changed by a factor of 2 (doubled or halved). This leads to a rule of thumb for distance. Since sound intensity varies as the square of the distance from the source, a doubling of distance results in a *fourfold* reduction in sound intensity, which in turn reduces the decibel level by 6 dB. The effect is shown in Case Study 17.4.

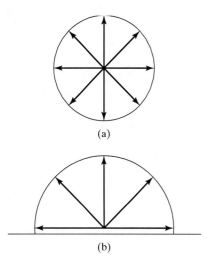

(a)

(b)

FIGURE 17.14

Distribution of sound intensity over the surface of a sphere as it radiates from a single source. (a) Sound emanates from a point source in all directions distributing over the surface of a sphere, the area of which is calculated by the formula $4\pi r^2$. Thus, the sound intensity is reduced as the square of the radial distance from the source. (b) Sound emanates from a point source located on the floor or other surface. The floor either absorbs or reflects the sound, but the resultant sound is still distributed over a hemisphere, the area of which is $2\pi r^2$. The squared-distance relationship still holds approximately.

CASE STUDY 17.4

A worker's machine is located at a distance of 2 feet from the operator and produces a noise exposure of 95 dB to the operator. How much is to be gained by moving the operator to a position 4 feet from the machine? How much reduction could be achieved by a move to 8 feet?

Solution

A move from 2 to 4 feet is a doubling of distance and results in a 6-dB reduction in sound level. The resultant level would be

$$95 \text{ dB} - 6 \text{ dB} = 89 \text{ dB}$$

which would probably be within the 8-hour PEL of 90 dB even after considering reflections and other sources, if these sources are not very significant.

A move to 8 feet would be a second doubling, resulting in a reduction of another 6 dB to a resultant 83 dB, ignoring reflections and other sound sources. This would reduce noise exposures to less than the AL of 85 dBA for an 8-hour TWA.

It is not likely to be feasible to move operators away from their own machines, and even if it is, to move away from one machine may place the operator close to a neighboring machine. Distance factors work best in separating operators from noise arising from adjacent machines or other processes in the area. A general spreading out of the plant layout can be beneficial in this regard.

If spreading out the plant layout is infeasible or too costly, the installation of sound-absorbing barriers between stations can increase their virtual separation as far as noise is concerned. The gain to be achieved by such barriers is variable and complicated

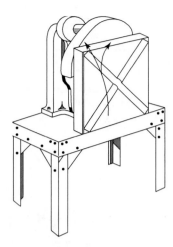

FIGURE 17.15

Application of welded stiffeners to reduce vibrations in a
sheet metal component (*Source:* Arkansas Department of
Labor, ref. Lovett).

to estimate in advance. An acoustics expert is recommended for advice in this area, and
even the expert is likely to experiment with various temporary barriers, measuring the
"before" and "after" sound levels with each. Heavy materials absorb sound vibrations, a
fact that makes curtains or shields containing lead a popular choice.

Sheet metal surfaces on machines are susceptible to mechanical vibrations and may
act as sound-amplifying surfaces. Metal gear contact in the drive mechanism can sometimes be eliminated by substitution of nylon gear wheels for metal gears or by the use of
belt drives instead of gears. Simpler still would be a stepped-up preventive maintenance
schedule to lubricate the gears more often, perhaps reducing noise levels. Useful principles for engineering controls to reduce noise are illustrated in Figures 17.15 to 17.20.

Perhaps more expensive than any of the engineering control approaches discussed
so far would be the isolation of the offending machine by means of an enclosure. The effectiveness depends on the type of material used to construct the enclosure and also depends to a surprising degree on the number and extent of openings or leaks in the

FIGURE 17.16

Enlarge or reduce size of a part to eliminate vibration resonance
(*Source*: Arkansas Department of Labor, ref. Lovett).

FIGURE 17.17

Rubber cushions on both sides of vibrating sheet metal
surfaces where they are joined. (*Source*: Arkansas
Department of Labor, ref. Lovett.)

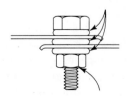

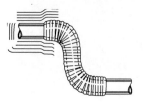

FIGURE 17.18

Flexible section in rigid pipe isolates vibrations (*Source*: Arkansas Department of Labor, ref. Lovett).

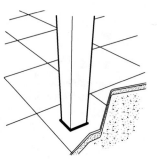

FIGURE 17.19

Resilient floor (*Source*: Arkansas Department of Labor, ref. Lovett).

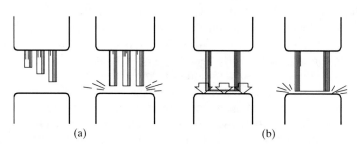

(a)   (b)

FIGURE 17.20

Power press improvements to reduce noise levels: (a) design die to result in a dull, crunching sound instead of a sharp bang; (b) replace the sharp impact action of a mechanical press with the relatively quiet pressure action of a hydraulic press.

enclosure. Figure 17.21 shows the relationship between opening size and loss of effectiveness for an example noise enclosure that has a capability of a 50-dB reduction if there are no leaks. Note that most of the effectiveness of the enclosure is lost if there is a hole in the enclosure wall of less than one-half of 1% of the total area of the enclosure.

Administrative Controls

It was stated earlier that either engineering or administrative controls are specified where feasible for excessive noise levels and that engineering controls are preferable. However, the administrative controls alternative was left unexplained. Administratively, management can schedule production runs so that noise levels are split between shifts and individual workers are not subjected to full-shift exposures. Other tricks are to interrupt production runs with preventive maintenance to give workers quiet time.

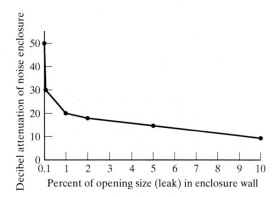

FIGURE 17.21

Loss in effectiveness of a noise enclosure due to leaks. For a sample enclosure that has an ideal (airtight) noise-reduction (attenuation) capability of 50 dB, leaks in the walls reduce the decibel attenuation by remarkable amounts, as shown.

During normal shift breaks, workers can be removed to a quiet rest area. Sometimes workers can share a loud job and a more quiet one by trading jobs at midshift. All of these practices can be used to bring down noise exposure levels to within the PEL for the given time of exposure as determined from Table 17.2. Since the term *administrative control* is somewhat vague, the term *work-practices control* has become preferable to refer to the various methods of shifting employee exposures to comply with Table 17.2.

Hearing Protection and Conservation

Personal protective equipment is required when engineering and administrative controls both fail to reduce noise to legal levels. Specifically, hearing protection is to be provided to all employees exposed to the 85-dBA TWA AL. In addition to providing protection, employers must permit employees to select protectors from a variety of suitable types and must train employees in the proper use and care of the protectors. One aspect of proper use is fit, and employers must ensure proper fit. These actions are mandatory when ALs are exceeded, but the reader may have noted that the actual wearing of the protectors by the workers is not among the mandatory steps to be taken if ALs are exceeded. However, there are conditions under which workers must actually wear the protectors. These are as follows:

1. whenever worker exposures are greater than the PELs (see Table 17.2)
2. whenever worker exposures are greater than the AL of 85 dBA (TWA) *and* the worker has experienced a *permanent significant threshold shift*

When testing shows a threshold shift in a worker's hearing, the implication is that the worker's hearing has been damaged and needs special protection. In these cases, the noise levels are required to be reduced by the protectors to 85 dBA (TWA), not 90 dBA (TWA).

Personal protective equipment should not be considered a final solution, because elimination of the source of the noise provides a more satisfactory work environment. Sometimes workers are lax in the wearing of personal protective equipment, and injurious exposures result.

Whenever the AL of 85 dBA (8-hour TWA) is exceeded, a "continuing, effective hearing conservation program" should be administered, including audiometric testing, noise monitoring, calibration of equipment, training, warning signs for noisy areas, and recordkeeping of audiometric tests and equipment calibration.

Audiometric testing involves a small, perhaps portable, listening station in which a subject listens to recorded sounds and an audiologist measures the subject's hearing acuity at various frequencies. Audiometric testing can be very useful in determining sources of hearing loss, or more particularly in providing data to determine whether hearing loss is due to occupational or off-the-job exposure. If plant noise levels are high, it is foolhardy to hire new employees without first testing their *baseline* hearing acuity. Without any evidence of hearing deficiency at the time of employment, any hearing deficiencies that show up after employment appear strongly to be work related.

When observing the frequency profile of a worker's hearing acuity, the audiologist often looks for a *4000-Hz shift* for evidence of occupational exposure. Experience has shown that much industrial noise occurs in the 4000-Hz frequency range, which causes audiologists to suspect occupational exposure when hearing acuity becomes deficient in this range.

RADIATION

A natural progression from the subject of noise is to the subject of radiation. Noise is, in fact, a form of radiant (wave) energy, but the term *radiation* is generally considered to mean electromagnetic radiation such as X rays and gamma rays, or highspeed particles such as alpha particles, protons, and electrons. Federal standards separate radiation into the categories *ionizing* and *nonionizing*.

Ionizing radiation is the more dangerous of the two types and is the type most associated with atomic energy. By far the most important category of ionizing radiation, from the occupational exposure standpoint, is the X ray. X rays are no longer the exclusive domain of the medical and dental professions. X rays are being widely used in manufacturing operations, especially in inspection systems.

Nonionizing radiation is somewhat of a misnomer, but applies to a more benign type of radiation in the electromagnetic spectrum. Included are radio and microwave frequencies. These phenomena are also increasingly important in industrial applications. Some workers are concerned about radiation exposure from the constant use of computer terminals. Computer terminals are of concern, but their principal hazard is musculoskeletal disorders, not radiation. Musculoskeletal disorders are considered an ergonomics hazard.

SUMMARY

To achieve a safe and healthful workplace and to comply with federal standards, the employer must devise engineering or administrative control solutions to air-contaminant and noise problems, if feasible. For air contaminants, the employer should first seek to eliminate the source of the toxic substances or find more benign substitutes for such process materials. If these attempts fail, ventilation is usually the answer. Ordinary heating and air-conditioning systems are designed for a different purpose and are generally not acceptable for eliminating air contaminants, especially particulates. A basic principle is to attempt to focus the ventilation in the form of local exhaust ventilation. The supply of makeup air also is an important consideration. A variety of filtering or particle removal mechanisms is available for purifying the air and either returning it to the plant atmosphere or exhausting it into the outside environment.

Industrial noise is a phenomenon that requires an understanding of the physics of sound-wave energy, the way in which noise is heard, and how noise affects human hearing. Human hearing is capable of sensing an incredible range of amplitudes (loudness) of wave energy while employing a very fine degree of discrimination among frequencies (pitch). So great is the range of amplitudes that a logarithmic scale is used to measure the absolute sound pressures and describe the levels of sound that humans actually hear. Computations of noise levels can be done by logarithmic manipulations or by using formulas and tables provided by OSHA standards. The basic OSHA noise standard (PEL) is 90 dB as an 8-hour time-weighted average (TWA). The action level is 85 dB, a level that is actually less than half the PEL in absolute sound intensity, due to the logarithmic nature of the decibel scale. A rule of thumb is that a doubling of absolute sound intensity results in an increase of 3 decibels on the decibel scale.

Radiation is another physical phenomenon that has similarities to noise. Two categories of radiation are recognized: ionizing radiation and nonionizing radiation. Ionizing radiation is the more dangerous of the two. The most widely encountered form of ionizing radiation in industry is the X ray.

The subjects of occupational health and environmental control can be quite technical. The safety and health manager probably will find it beneficial to employ experts to take time-weighted averages with appropriate meters and sampling instruments. Subsequent control measures, such as ventilation systems for toxic substances and acoustic panels for noise control, may require the design capabilities of experts in their respective fields. Dealing with these experts demands a degree of understanding of their methods and terminology, but does not require the safety and health manager to duplicate the experts' capability in each field. Such an understanding of methods, terminology, and basic principles of occupational health and environmental control are what these chapters have attempted to provide.

EXERCISES AND STUDY QUESTIONS

17.1 Identify the comparative hazards of batch vs. continuous processes for chemicals.

17.2 Explain the benefits and disadvantages of using an ordinary household fan for ventilation in the presence of toxic substances.

17.3 What are the comparative advantages and disadvantages of using a vacuum cleaner to exhaust toxic air contaminants by placing the hose intake close to the source of the contaminant.

17.4 Why should toxic air contaminant ventilation systems "pull" instead of "push?"

17.5 What is the purpose of a "manometer" in exhaust ventilation systems?

17.6 Explain three solutions to the problem of energy losses in the supply of makeup air for exhaust ventilation systems.

17.7 Identify four different types of devices for the purification of exhaust air before releasing to the outside air.

17.8   What two basic characteristics of sound are easily detected by human hearing? Which of these two is more dangerous?

17.9   Identify the two principal types of hazardous radiation. To which class do X rays belong?

17.10 What is the principal, recognized hazard from working at computer terminals?

17.11 A plant has two identical standby generator units for emergency use. In the area of the generators, the normal noise level registers 81 dBA on the sound-level meter with the generators turned off. When one generator switches on, the SLM needle jumps to 83.6 dBA.

(a) Perform calculations to determine what the dBA reading will be when the second generator also turns on (so that both generators are on).

(b) If both generators are on for a full 8-hour shift, will OSHA's PEL be exceeded? Will the AL be exceeded? Explain.

(c) If one generator is on for half the shift and both are on for the other half, will the PEL be exceeded? Will the AL be exceeded? Explain.

(d) In the absence of any plant background noise, what would be the sound level contributed by a single generator? by both generators? Show calculations to explain.

17.12 Four machines contribute the following noise levels in dB to a worker's exposure:

Machine 1	80 dBA
Machine 2	86 dBA
Machine 3	93 dBA
Machine 4	70 dBA

(a) Calculate the combined noise-level exposure for this worker.

(b) The offending machine is obviously Machine 3. Suppose that Machine 3 was at a distance of 5 feet away from the worker when the 93-dBA noise level was measured. Determine how far away would Machine 3 have to be moved to bring the worker's continuous 8-hour combined exposure from *all* machines down to the OSHA PEL?

17.13 What are some desirable alternatives to industrial ventilation to remove air contaminants?

17.14 What is makeup air?

17.15 Ten machines all contribute equally to the noise exposure of one worker, whose exposure level is 99 dB for a full 8-hour shift. When all the machines are turned off, the noise level is 65 dB. How many of the 10 machines must be turned off to achieve a full-shift noise-exposure level that would meet standards if the worker wears no personal protective equipment?

17.16 A worker stands on a factory floor and a sound-level meter shows a reading of 55 dB at that point. A machine 3 feet away is turned on, and the meter jumps to 90 dB. What will the SLM read if the machine is moved to a point 12 feet away?

17.17 A paper mill uses liquid chlorine, delivered in 90-ton railroad tank cars, as a pulp bleaching agent. One volume of liquid chlorine produces approximately 450 volumes of vapor under normal atmospheric temperature and pressure. The density of liquid chlorine is 103 pounds per cubic foot. In the event of rupture and vapor release of 20% of the tank car contents, how much vapor by volume would be released? If the release were in a closed building with a 30-foot ceiling height without ventilation, how large would the building have to be (in square *miles* of floor space) to contain the thoroughly mixed vapor–air ratio within the OSHA PEL? The logical conclusion to this exercise is that, with or without ventilation, it is more practical to unload chlorine tank cars outdoors.

17.18 A worker exposure to noise in a given plant is measured, resulting in the following readings for various time periods during the 8-hour shift:

8:00 A.M.	–	9:00 A.M.	86 dBA
9:00 A.M.	–	11:00 A.M.	84 dBA
11:00 A.M.	–	12 noon	81 dBA
12 noon	–	1:00 P.M.	101 dBA
1:00 P.M.	–	4:00 P.M.	75 dBA

   (a) Perform computations to determine whether maximum PELs have been exceeded.

   (b) Have ALs been exceeded?

   (c) Given the noise exposure just described, would the employer be required to furnish hearing protectors?

   (d) Would employees be required to use the hearing protectors?

   (e) Suppose that an engineering control could be devised that would cut the noise level (sound pressure level) in half either in the morning or in the afternoon, but not both. Which would you select? Why?

17.19 From the perspective used by the federal enforcement agency, rank the following solutions to a worker noise-exposure problem (from most effective, "1," to least effective, "4"):

   • *Solution A*   Enclose the noise source with a barrier that reduces the noise level by 3 dBA.

   • *Solution B*   Position the operator at a distance twice as far from the source of the noise.

   • *Solution C*   Rotate personnel so that each worker is exposed to the noise source for only one-half shift.

   • *Solution D*   Provide ear protection that cuts the absolute sound pressure in half. Justify your choices with calculations, analysis, and in light of established priorities.

17.20 A certain drying process produces 5 cubic feet of ethanol vapors per hour. If general exhaust ventilation is used, calculate the flow in cubic feet per hour needed to keep the ethanol vapors within OSHA limits. What is another name for ethanol?

17.21 For each of the following materials, suggest substitutes that are feasible for some operations and that prevent certain hazards:

   (a) Silica (for blasting)

   (b) Lead-based paint

   (c) Freon (as a propellant)

   (d) Acetylene (for welding)

17.22 What problem frequently develops with ventilation filter alarms that indicate pressure differential across the filter?

17.23 What is the purpose of using a heat exchanger for makeup air? What is the disadvantage of this approach?

17.24 If the air outside is at substantially higher pressure than the air inside the plant, what ventilation problem probably exists?

17.25 What form of ionizing radiation is most commonly encountered in industrial exposures?

17.26 **Design Case Study**. A glue-making process releases ethylene glycol that becomes generally diluted and interspersed throughout the plant atmosphere. The rate of release is 2.4 cubic feet per hour vapor volume at standard plant temperature and pressure. The plant ventilation system is of the general dilution type, with makeup air being supplied through windows and doors throughout the plant area. The plant area is 12,000 square feet and the average ceiling height is 16 feet. The problem is to specify the capacity of the general ventilation system required to maintain a steady-state condition throughout this process area that protects against both health and safety hazards due to ethylene glycol. For your information in performing calculations, the following data are provided:

ETHYLENE GLYCOL (CH_2OHCH_2OH)
  Molecular weight 62.1
  Boiling point: 197.5° Celsius
  LEL: 3.2%
  Firepoint: −13° Celsius
  Flashpoint: 232° Fahrenheit
  Autoignition temperature: 752° Fahrenheit
  Vapor pressure: 0.05 mm at 20° Celsius
  PEL: 50 ppm (ceiling)

(a) How much exhaust ventilation (in cubic feet per hour, general dilution type) is required to maintain safety hazards below explosive levels?

(b) How much exhaust ventilation (in cubic feet per hour, general dilution type) is required to maintain health hazards below OSHA-specified action levels?

(c) How many plant area room changes per hour would the level of ventilation calculated in part (b) represent?

17.27 **Design Case Study.** A particularly noisy process is operated by a single operator working at a control console. The 8-hour TWA exposure level for this operator is 96 dBA. The company has initiated an engineering project to alleviate the problem and has two plans:

• *Plan A.* Move the operator's control console from its current position 5 feet from the source of the noise to a point 10 feet away.

• *Plan B.* Enclose the noise source in an enclosure that would be effective in reducing the *absolute* sound pressure by 75%.

Evaluate the effectiveness of each of these plans in reducing the noise-exposure level. Suppose that both plans were executed; calculate the combined effect of both plans on the noise-exposure level.

RESEARCH EXERCISES

17.28 An employer is having difficulty meeting the OSHA asbestos standard using engineering controls and is considering using administrative (work-practice) controls. Study current OSHA standards for asbestos and prepare a professional recommendation to this employer, citing appropriate sections of the OSHA standard to justify your position.

17.29 While visiting an industrial site where asbestos is being removed, you observe that air hoses are being used to blow dust off work clothing. Comment on this procedure, citing specific portions of the OSHA standards to justify your position.

17.30 Sometimes industries voluntarily initiate actions to control exposures to levels even lower than those specified by OSHA standards. Examine a noteworthy example of this initiated by the Lead Industries Association, Inc. (LIA). What other industry association joined with LIA in this initiative? Specifically what target improvement became the 5-year goal of this initiative?

STANDARDS RESEARCH QUESTIONS

17.31 This chapter has dealt with noise. Search the General Industry OSHA standard and use the NCM database to determine how seriously OSHA takes the general hazard of noise exposure. Specifically, find the frequency of citation, the percentage of the citations designated as "serious," and the dollar level of proposed penalties for noise citations.

17.32 The effectiveness of exhaust ventilation systems depends on the design of the hood for enclosing the operation to be ventilated. Search the OSHA standards for provisions pertaining to exhaust hoods. Use the NCM database tool to determine whether OSHA ever writes citations for exhaust hoods. If any citations are found, what percentage of the citations are designated as "serious?"

17.33 Examine the OSHA standards for "audiometric testing" and "hearing conservation programs." What is the action level trigger for these programs? Are the standards for these programs frequently cited? How does their citation frequency compare with the frequency of citation for ventilation hazards? How do these standards compare for "seriousness" (percentage of citations that are designated as "serious")?

CHAPTER 18

Construction

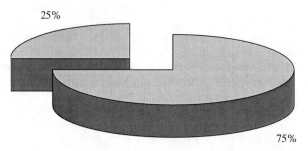

25%

75%

Percentage of OSHA citations addressing this subject

This book would not be complete without a chapter on the construction industry and its relationship to the field of safety and health. Why is this industry singled out, whereas the book has otherwise taken a general approach to the subject? There are two principal reasons. One is that the construction industry has long been recognized as more hazardous than most. Workplace installations are temporary, and economics dictate a different approach to such facilities as guardrails and stairways. The very nature of the work dictates that risks be taken that are not necessary in general industry. This added risk alone would ensure that OSHA would take a special interest in construction, but there is another reason for OSHA's emphasis that is probably more pervasive than the risk factor. The Occupational Safety and Health Act of 1970 was preceded by the Construction Safety Act, Public Law 91–54. The result of this sequence is that federal standards for construction safety were already in place at the time of passage of the more general OSHA law. The OSHA law provided for adoption of "existing federal standards" as national consensus standards, bypassing the lengthy promulgation procedures required for new standards. Thus, a set of rather comprehensive standards for construction (Part 29 CFR 1926) has been maintained separately from the General Industry (Part 29 CFR 1910) standards. The construction standard is a classic example of "vertical" standards, as compared with OSHA's general approach of adopting "horizontal" standards. The safety and health manager for a construction company should look first to the construction vertical standards, but should be aware that if OSHA cannot find a construction standard that covers a given hazard found at a construction site, the compliance officer is free to turn to the general industry standards to write a citattion. This places a new dimension on the problem of bringing a construction industry into compliance with standards.

This chapter is primarily for safety and health managers of construction companies, but even the general industry safety and health manager should find the information herein useful. Almost every industry has occasional remodeling or expansion projects that result in construction. Even if the company contracts out the construction project, what goes on is still important to the company because its own employees can become exposed to hazards created by the contract construction personnel. Such hazards can be both physical and legal.

GENERAL FACILITIES

Lighting

Curiously, there are standards for adequate lighting on construction sites, specifying minimum illumination intensities for various areas, whereas general industry has no such general[1] table of intensities. The reason perhaps has to do with trip hazards and pitfalls (in the literal sense of the word) common to construction sites, hazards that are intensified by poor illumination. The minimum illumination standard of 5 footcandles is really quite low for general construction area lighting, and the standard drops even lower, to 3 footcandles for concrete placement, excavation and waste areas, accessways, active storage areas, loading platforms, and refueling and field maintenance areas. Lighting requirements are higher for most construction shops and indoor areas.

Materials Handling and Storage

The real structural test of most buildings is during their own construction. The heaviest load a floor will probably ever support is the stacked materials used during its own construction. Planning is needed to prevent overloading and possible collapse. All nails should be withdrawn from used lumber before it is stacked.

Rigging equipment for material handling such as chain, rope, and wire rope is, unfortunately, often used until failure. If failure does occur on a construction site, the safety and health manager must be prepared to explain why, because rigging equipment is required to be inspected prior to use on *each shift*.

Disposal of scrap material requires vigilance throughout the construction phase. It is difficult to concentrate on scrap and waste removal when working on a tight project completion schedule, but haphazard scrap accumulation is not only unsafe, it also slows progress. Enclosed chutes are needed for dropping materials from distances of greater than 20 feet. In addition, some scrap material, such as asbestos, may require special protection.

---

[1]Although OSHA does not have a general illumination standard for appropriate levels of lighting, there is a somewhat general table in the standard for Hazardous Waste Operations and Emergency Response.

PERSONAL PROTECTIVE EQUIPMENT

Construction requirements for personal protective equipment are similar to those for general industry, the principal difference being one of emphasis.

Hard Hats

At the top of the list is head protection; indeed, the hard hat is a symbol of the construction industry. So obvious is the absence of a hard hat in a construction work crew that the hard-hat rule can be a source of embarrassment to worker and manager alike. Only general conditions are laid out to describe *when* hard hats are needed. This lays the decision in the safety and health manager's lap, and discretion is advised.

Hearing Protection

It may surprise some readers that hearing protection is a concern for *construction*, but construction work often involves damaging levels of noise. Consider the noise levels and durations of exposures of the compressed-air "jackhammer," for example.

Eye and Face Protection

The greatest concern for construction workers' eyes is for mechanical injury, as from using structural steel riveters, grinders, powder-actuated tools, woodworking tools, concrete nozzles, and other spark- and chip-producing equipment. Surprisingly, construction workers can even be exposed to lasers used as tools for checking steel girder alignment and deflection in bridges and buildings.

Fall Protection

On the bases of both fatalities and injuries, falls are probably the greatest hazard in construction work. Where general industry has a permanent wall, construction may have only a guardrail. Where general industry has a permanent guardrail, construction may have a temporary guardrail or perhaps will have no protective structure at all. Where general industry has a permanent stairway, construction may have a temporary ladder. General industry fixed ladders may have cages or ladder safety devices; construction ladders often have no such safety devices.

Personal protective equipment is the answer to many construction industry fall hazards, simply because protection by other means may be awkward or even impossible. Body harnesses and lanyards tied to lifelines are essential to the safety of construction workers subject to fall hazards.

One mistake made in selecting fall protection equipment is to improvise with ordinary leather belts and ropes. An ordinary leather belt and hardware will not satisfy the specified 4000-pound tensile test for fall protection belt hardware. No one weighs 4000 pounds, but what matters in a fall is the shock load, which can be several times as great as the ordinary dead weight. A falling 200-pound person can therefore result in $\frac{1}{2}$ to 1 ton of force on the fall protection system. Using a safety factor of approximately 4, it is easy to see why the standard specifies a 4000-pound tensile load limit.

The lanyard is that part of the fall protection system that attaches to the body harness on one end and the lifeline or structure on the other. The lanyard must have a nominal breaking strength of 5400 pounds. The applicable standard specifies "$\frac{1}{2}$-inch nylon or equivalent." Beware of substituting materials of equivalent breaking strength to $\frac{1}{2}$-inch nylon. Tensile or breaking strength is not the only consideration in selecting a lanyard. A certain resiliency or elasticity exists with artificial fiber ropes that lessens the shock load when arresting a fall.

An important point with safety lanyards is that they must not be too long. The standard specifies "a maximum length to provide for a fall of no greater than 6 feet." The rationale is that there is no point in breaking a fall with the lanyard if the worker has already fallen so far that the shock of the rope will be lethal. However, the standard is often misunderstood on this point. Note carefully that the wording just quoted does not limit the lanyard length to 6 feet. Figure 18.1 clarifies this point.

One difficulty with limiting the length of lanyards is that they restrict the movement of the worker. Therefore, as with other systems that are designed for protection of the individual, the worker finds a way to get around the system. A common practice in the construction industry is to use "cheater cables," a sort of "extension cord" for a safety lanyard. The worker has a sense of security because he or she is still attached to the lifeline by means of a lanyard plus the cheater. But this sense of security is somewhat misleading, because an accidental fall might be of too great a distance, resulting in a fatal shock load to the worker—even if the worker does not hit the ground or lower platform level.

One difficulty is attempting to attach a lanyard to a vertical lifeline, especially when the lanyard must be adjusted upward or downward on the lifeline, such as in use with a scaffold. It is necessary for the attachment to slide easily when this is intended, but the attachment must lock and hold if the worker falls. There are mechanical devices, but an easy-to-tie knot for this purpose is the triple rolling hitch shown in Figure 18.2.

Fall protection is usually considered from the standpoint of height, but working over or near water presents a different hazard. Even the best of swimmers will have

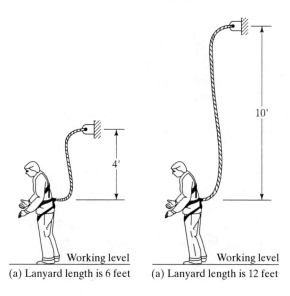

10'

4'

Working level

(a) Lanyard length is 6 feet

Working level

(a) Lanyard length is 12 feet

FIGURE 18.1

Maximum lanyard length must provide for a fall of no greater than 6 feet.

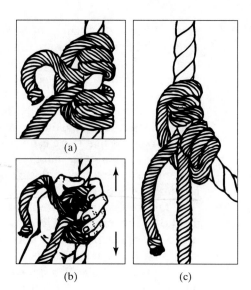

FIGURE 18.2

(a) Triple rolling hitch tied with free end of lanyard; (b) easily raised and lowered slipping on cable or lifeline; (c) when the lanyard is pulled tight, as in a fall, the triple rolling hitch will not slip on the lifeline.

difficulty with a fall into water if he or she is fully dressed and perhaps burdened by tools, equipment, or materials such as rivets or bolts. If the water is rather cold, the danger of hypothermia increases the drowning hazard.

Drowning hazards are taken very seriously in federal standards, which require

1. Life jackets or buoyant work vests *and*
2. Ring buoys every 200 feet *and*
3. A lifesaving skiff

whenever employees work over or near water and a danger of drowning exists.

FIRE PROTECTION

From a property-loss standpoint, fires are more dangerous after a building is completed, but to protect construction workers, fire hazards must also be controlled *during* construction. Construction sites have somewhat more latitude in distributing fire extinguishers than do general industries. Even an ordinary garden hose may be used in place of fire extinguishers on construction sites. But there are so many restrictions on such use of a garden hose that most safety and health managers will regret having considered this alternative.

The biggest problem with fire prevention during construction is the handling of flammable liquids. For ordinary flammable liquids such as gasoline, quantities handled must be no more than 1 gallon unless approved metal safety cans are used. Approved metal safety cans must be used even for quantities up to 1 gallon unless the flammable liquid is used out of its *original* container. Containers should be kept off stairways and away from exits and aisles.

TOOLS

It has been well publicized that mushroomed heads on chisels, wedges, and other impact tools are unsafe. The hazard is that a sliver of metal can break off and cause a severe eye injury, even total loss of sight. Another problem with hand tools is defective handles, in particular loose hammer heads.

Construction sites may employ pneumatic tools, such as jackhammers, staplers, or nailers. Pneumatic tools need to be secured to the hose by some positive means to prevent accidental disconnection. Hoses larger than $\frac{1}{2}$ inch inside diameter need a pressure-reducer device to prevent whip action in case of hose failure. Figure 18.3 is a diagram of a pressure-reducer device for this purpose. It is a simple in-line device, usually placed between the hose and the compressor. Unfortunately, the device reduces the overall capacity of the system. Operating at full capacity, as from several tools operating at once, the pressure downstream from the device becomes so low that the device (a spring-loaded valve) begins to close as if the downstream line had ruptured. This shuts off or nearly shuts off the supply of air to the tools, making the system useless at that capacity. The result is that the worker removes the device from the line, and often as not, it is soon lost. This is a sore point with many construction safety and health managers.

Some construction applications are being found for hydraulically operated tools, especially in the public-utility construction field. Hydraulic tools operate under the same principle as pneumatic tools but use liquids instead of air as the medium. Fluid pressures in these tools can reach 3000 psi gauge, approximately 20 times the maximum pressure achievable with pneumatic tools. Such tremendous pressures give hydraulic tools much greater power than pneumatic tools, but a hazard can exist if operating pressure limits of the equipment are exceeded. Under the criterion of occupational noise, however, hydraulic tools have a safety and health advantage over pneumatic tools. Additional hazards of hydraulic fluids are electrical conductivity and fire. These hazards tend to conflict in that the more fire resistant fluids are electrical conductors. When working in construction and alteration of electric utility transmission and distribution systems, the hazard of electrical conductivity is more serious than the hazard of fire. The hydraulic fluids used for the insulated sections of derrick trucks, aerial lifts, and hydraulic tools that are used on or around energized lines and equipment for power transmission and distribution are required to be of the insulating type. The fluids for hydraulic tools used in other applications are required to be fire resistant.

Powder-actuated tools carry an explosive charge to provide the driving force. The applications of these tools are increasing because they are both fast and effective. Driving fasteners into concrete, masonry, or steel demands large, accurately placed impact forces. Powder-actuated tools are able to provide these forces in a convenient way,

FIGURE 18.3

In-line device for preventing whip action in event of pneumatic hose failure.

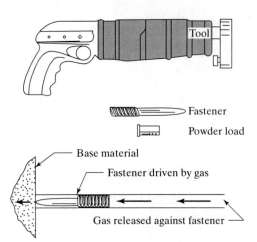

FIGURE 18.4

Powder-actuated fastening tool (*Source*: NIOSH, ref. 121).

speeding up production on construction projects. But together with this speed, force, and convenience come safety hazards.

A powder-actuated tool looks and operates very much like a handgun, as can be seen in Figure 18.4. Even the powder cartridges look like bullets for a gun. In powder-actuated tools, however, the projectile is separate from the cartridge, as shown in Figure 18.4.

In some ways, powder-actuated tools are even more dangerous than handguns. Powder-actuated tools are capable of handling a variety of cartridges with a wide range of power ratings. These cartridges must be selected with care by a knowledgeable person. Insufficient power will fail to do the job, but too much power may drive the fastener completely through the material and kill a coworker in another room. (This has actually happened.) To protect against such hazards and for convenience, cartridges are color coded for easy identification. Metal-cased cartridges are available in a range of 12 different power ratings, as shown in Table 18.1. It may be necessary to back the material with a substance that will prevent the fastener from passing completely through.

TABLE 18.1   Color Identification for Cased Power Loads for Powder-Actuated Tools

Power level	Case color	Load color	
1	Brass	Gray	Lightest
2	Brass	Brown	
3	Brass	Green	
4	Brass	Yellow	
5	Brass	Red	
6	Brass	Purple	
7	Nickel	Gray	
8	Nickel	Brown	
9	Nickel	Green	
10	Nickel	Yellow	
11	Nickel	Red	
12	Nickel	Purple	Heaviest

Knowledge and judgment are also required in avoiding very hard or brittle materials, such as cast iron, glazed tile, surface-hardened steel, glass block, live rock, face brick, or hollow tile. If the material is spalled or cracked by an unsatisfactory previous fastening, the new fastening must be driven elsewhere. Fasteners driven too close to the edge of the material can cause explosive chipping of the material at the edge. Obviously, eye protection is always needed when using powder-actuated tools.

ELECTRICAL

Construction workers are often in close contact with ground and frequently work in wet locations under adverse conditions. Electrocution ranks with falls near the top of the list of causes of fatalities among construction workers.

A principal requirement on construction sites is that all 15- and 20-ampere outlets have either ground-fault circuit-interruptor (GFCI) protection or a program of equipment ground-conductor assurance, including inspection, testing, and recordkeeping. The safety and health manager in a construction company is faced with a decision between the two alternatives, and the paragraphs that follow are intended to assist in making that decision.

The purpose and operating principle of the GFCI were discussed in Chapter 11. The hazards of electrical shock by faults to ground are greater on construction sites than in the general industrial workplace. Because of the increased hazards, the *National Electrical Code*® specified GFCIs for construction, but not for general industry, although they would be of value in any electric circuit serving hand-held appliances or tools. Chapter 11 illustrated how GFCIs work and showed a residential-type receptacle equipped with a GFCI.

It seems that almost every safety device has its drawbacks, and the GFCI is no exception. The GFCI closely monitors any difference in current flow between the ground and neutral conductors, as low as fractions of a milliampere. But there are ways in which these currents can be unbalanced when no hazard exists. Tiny amounts of current leakage to ground occur for quite innocent reasons. Damp or weakened insulation might produce tiny currents in various locations. Even an extension cord that is too long can create a condition of capacitance between the conductor and the ground, resulting in a tiny leak. Although none of these conditions of itself is a significant hazard, the cumulative effect is one that may be great enough to trip the GFCI, shutting down the entire circuit. This is so-called *nuisance tripping* and has made the GFCI a controversial issue in the construction industry.

Chapter 11 mentioned a permissible alternative to the GFCI: the careful maintenance of the grounding conductors of electrical equipment. Such maintenance includes regular inspections and records of these inspections. The idea behind the "assured equipment grounding-conductor program" is that if an electrical tool shorts to the case or handle, the third-wire grounding system will shunt the current to quickly throw the circuit breaker. A good grounding conductor can therefore provide protection similar to the GFCI.

The assured equipment grounding-conductor program is appealing to many construction companies because they can avoid buying the GFCI equipment. They can also avoid the nuisance tripping of the GFCIs discussed earlier. But although the costs are less tangible, they nevertheless exist with the grounding assurance alternative. It takes instruments and time to test the grounding conductors, and the business of recordkeeping always involves intangible costs. An economic impact analysis of the two alternatives has been made that estimated a cost of compliance of $87.5 million for purchase, installation, and first-year maintenance of GFCIs. The study estimated for the alternative assured equipment grounding-conductor program a similar cost of $36 to $43.8 million. Inflation changes absolute annual cost estimates, but the relative difference between the costs of the two alternatives suggests that the assured equipment grounding-conductor program is cheaper.

Temporary lighting is an electrical problem on construction sites more than in general industry. Often seen are ordinary incandescent bulbs suspended from electrical cords. Cords and lights that are suspended in this way must actually be *designed* for this purpose; all electric cords for temporary lighting must be heavy duty, and insulation must be maintained in a safe condition. To prevent accidental contact, bulbs must be guarded, unless the construction of the reflector is such that the bulbs are deeply recessed.

A construction site is a profusion of temporary conditions, and electrical cords or extension cords strung about the area are a common sight. Unfortunately, the area is also visited by heavy-duty vehicles such as excavation equipment, heavily loaded trucks, and very heavy concrete delivery trucks. The situation is too hazardous to permit electrical cords to pass through work areas unless covered or elevated to protect them from hazardous damage. No splices are permitted in flexible cord unless properly molded or vulcanized.

LADDERS AND SCAFFOLDS

The "care and use" provisions for ladders are important for construction ladders, just as they are for ladders used in general industry. Construction ladders have some differences, however, that have caused some problems.

Job-Made Ladders

Construction companies often make their own ladders, and such ladders are not illegal if made properly. The first requirement is to determine how many persons will be needing the ladder. If simultaneous two-way traffic is anticipated, a conventional ladder will not work, and a double-cleat ladder, as shown in Figure 18.5, should be used. In fact, if the ladder is the only means of access or exit from a working area for 25 or more employees, the double-cleat ladder is *mandatory*, unless two ladders are provided.

The biggest mistake made in building job-made or homemade ladders is to fail to inset the cleats into the side rails. (See Figure 18.6.) It is much more trouble to inset the cleats or use filler blocks than to simply nail the cleats in place, but the security and stability of the cleats are increased many times by this additional effort to make the ladder safe.

Scaffolds

The subject of scaffolds can become somewhat technical, and these technical details can be very important. The safety and health manager will find it useful, and in some

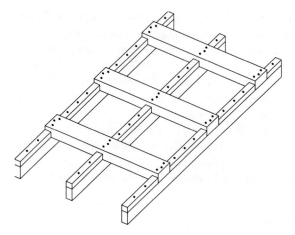

FIGURE 18.5

Double-cleat ladder for simultaneous two-way traffic

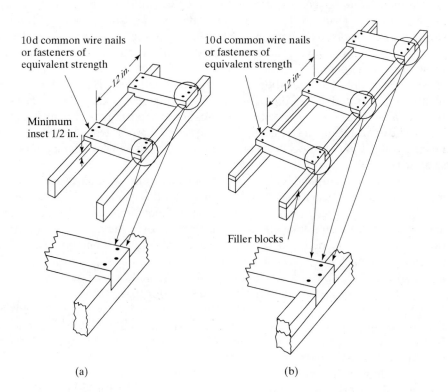

10d common wire nails
or fasteners of
equivalent strength

12 in.

Minimum
inset 1/2 in.

10d common wire nails
or fasteners of
equivalent strength

12 in.

Filler blocks

(a)   (b)

FIGURE 18.6

Two acceptable ways of setting cleats in construction job-made ladders: (a) cleats inset into
side rails; (b) cleats braced by filler blocks.

cases imperative, to obtain the services of a registered professional engineer. This is one area in which the credential as well as the knowledge can be quite useful.

One of the technical aspects of scaffolds is safety factor. Design safety factor for scaffolds and their components is a factor of four. This factor increases to a factor of six for the suspension ropes supporting the suspended type of scaffolding. The application of counterbalances, tie-downs, footings, and the allowance for wind loading all can be quite technical, and an engineering evaluation is advisable.

The safety and health manager may be frustrated by the many bewildering names of scaffolds listed in applicable construction standards. But the majority of the scaffolds with unfamiliar names, such as "window-jack scaffolds," "outrigger scaffolds," and "chicken ladders," are rarely seen. The most popular scaffolds are the following types:

- Welded frame (or "bedstead" scaffolds)
- Manually propelled mobile scaffolds (on casters)
- Two-point suspension (or "swinging" scaffolds)
- Tube and coupler scaffolds

Some scaffolds, such as tube and coupler scaffolds and welded frame scaffolds, are supported by structure on the ground and must have sound footings. If the ground slopes, scaffold jacks may be necessary to assure that the footings are level. Certain engineered "cribbing" may be acceptable, but such unstable objects as barrels, boxes, loose brick, or concrete blocks are criticized. Concrete blocks are a real problem because most people feel that they are very strong and rigid. But scaffolds direct very highly concentrated loads on their relatively tiny feet, and such loads can break through a molded concrete block. Once a scaffold support breaks through its footing, a major shift can occur aloft, and the consequences can be extremely serious. Such a mishap is most likely to occur at the worst time (such as when personnel are on the scaffold).

For scaffolds suspended from above, such as from two-point suspension (swinging) scaffolds, the security of the attachment on the roof is of obvious importance. Since rooftops vary in structure and design, an engineer is very useful in ensuring a safe anchor point. Cornice hooks are designed to hook over the edge, not into it. In addition, tiebacks are needed as a secondary means of support. Sometimes a sound structure for the tieback is not available on the rooftop, and the only solution is to cross the entire roof and go down to the ground on the other side of the building. Tying a scaffold to an ordinary vent pipe on the roof is asking for trouble.

Safety belts and lifelines for personnel on suspended swinging scaffolds must be tied to the building, not to the scaffold. Thus, if the scaffold falls, the personnel can still be saved. For guidance on the attachment of the lanyard to the lifeline, refer back to the earlier discussion of fall protection.

The floor of the scaffold is also important. Loose planks can be especially hazardous if the overhang beyond the support is insufficient for security. But too much overhang can also be dangerous because a worker might step beyond the support and cause the plank to tip like a seesaw. Figure 18.7 illustrates minimums and maximums for plank overhang. Figure 18.8 illustrates the minimum for overlap, unless planks are secured from movement.

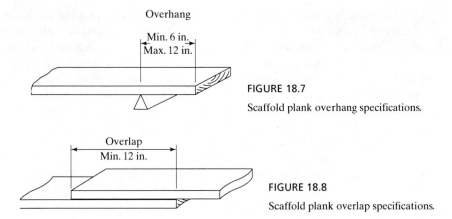

FIGURE 18.7

Scaffold plank overhang specifications.

FIGURE 18.8

Scaffold plank overlap specifications.

FLOORS AND STAIRWAYS

As in general industry, the standard for guarding of open-sided floors and platforms is one of the most frequently cited standards in construction. Curiously, though, instead of setting the vertical fall distance at 4 feet as in general industry, the specification for construction is *6 feet*. Thus, an open-sided floor or platform 6 feet or more above the adjacent floor level is required to be guarded by a standard railing. Runways 4 feet high or more must be guarded.

During construction of buildings with stairways, construction employees use the new stairways during finishing operations for the building. If the building's stairways are properly designed, the safety and health manager for the construction company has little to worry about.

A pitfall needs mentioning on the subject of use of new building stairways during construction. Many stairways and landings today are of steel construction with hollow pan-type treads that are filled on-site with concrete or other materials. Contractors often save until last the job of pouring the treads. Meanwhile, during building construction, workers are walking on the unfilled treads and are subject to the trip hazard created by the steel nosing along the leading edge of the riser. Of course, exposure to the hazard is unavoidable during the actual construction of the stairway itself. But after the stairways have been installed, lumber or other temporary material can be used to fill the hollow space and eliminate the trip hazard during completion of the building.

CRANES AND HOISTS

Cranes, hoists, and other material- or personnel-handling equipment are essential tools of the construction industry. Chapter 15 investigated the hazards of these machines in detail. This chapter discusses the subject from the viewpoint of the construction industry, the most important user of these machines.

One of the hazards addressed in Chapter 15 was two-blocking. Although two-blocking can be a hazard with any crane or hoist, most of the fatalities resulting from this hazard have occurred in the construction industry. A crane can be two-blocked in many ways. Hoisting the load, extending the boom, or even *lowering* the boom on a crane with a stationary winch mounted to the rear of the boom hinge can lead to two-blocking. It is difficult for the crane operator to avoid all of the ways in which a crane can be two-blocked, and consequently fatalities have occurred even when experienced crane operators are at the controls. In 1973, the ANSI standard[2] for mobile hydraulic cranes incorporated a requirement for a "two-blocking damage prevention feature" on telescoping boom cranes with less than 60 feet of extended boom. Safety and health managers should beware of the temptation to purchase old equipment that might not be built to safe standards. And for equipment that has been purchased, the feasibility for retrofit should be considered.

On construction sites, the simultaneous execution of many parts of the overall project means that personnel will often be working around or near a crane in operation. The crane operator will avoid moving the bucket or other load over personnel and will attempt to keep the cab from striking personnel, but it is impossible for the crane operator to watch all moving parts at all times. Particularly hazardous is the rear of the cab, which on many models swings outside the crawler or other substructure when the cab and boom rotate, as shown in Figure 18.9. This motion generally occurs on every cycle of a crane's operation and is a constant threat to personnel on the ground. The hazard is a very serious one, and accidents carry a high likelihood of fatality. The employee may be either struck or crushed between the cab and some other object, such as a building wall, stack of materials, or another vehicle.

Another serious hazard with construction cranes is the possibility of contact with exposed live overhead utility lines. Crane boom contact with high-voltage transmission

FIGURE 18.9

Rear of crane cab is a hazardous area due to swing radius (*Source*: courtesy of the Construction Safety Association of Ontario).

---

[2]ANSI B30.15–1973.

lines results in fatalities every year. The higher the voltage, the greater must be the clearance between the crane and the electric transmission line, to prevent arcing. Federal standards recognize this physical reality by setting up formulas for calculating the minimum clearance required for various voltages. Recognizing that during transit it may be more difficult to maintain clearances, OSHA standards are a little more lenient for cranes in transit. Further complicating the problem is that requirements for cranes in general industry are different from requirements in construction, resulting in a very complicated set of requirements. These requirements are summarized in Figure 18.10.

A common worker practice is "riding the headache ball." Figure 18.11 identifies the headache ball as the ball-shaped weight used to keep a necessary tension on the wire rope when the hook is not loaded. It is possible for workers to stand on this ball and take a ride, using the crane as an elevator, a practice that usually horrifies passers-by. Riding the headache ball is not explicitly addressed in the OSHA standards, but is generally considered a dangerous practice. OSHA can turn to the General Duty Clause to cite dangerous practices likely to cause death or serious physical harm. Also, lack of fall protection can be cited in cases where persons are riding the headache ball without fall protection. The practice is so highly visible to the public from the street that it easily can trigger an OSHA inspection. If persons are to be elevated using a crane, the recommended practice is to use a lift cage attached to the crane hook.

Hammerhead tower cranes are large structures that take advantage of counter-weights on the end of the jib opposite the work. (See Figure 18.12.) This crane is often used for large building construction. Sometimes construction workers will have duties

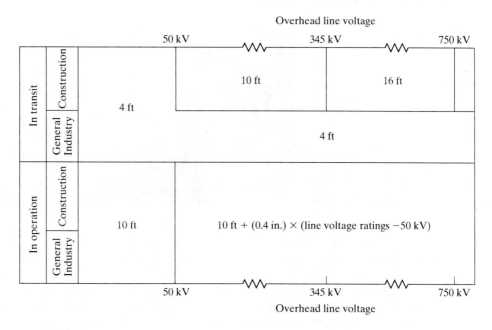

FIGURE 18.10

Clearance for cranes from electric transmission lines.

FIGURE 18.11

Headache ball. These balls range in weight from less than 100 pounds to 1 ton or more. The weight of the ball overcomes the friction of the sheaves for the running rope of the crane. The headache ball should not be confused with the much heavier wrecking ball.

FIGURE 18.12

Hammerhead tower crane.

on the horizontal jib of a hammerhead tower crane. This presents a fatal fall hazard, and guardrails or safety belts, lanyards, and lifelines are needed to protect the worker.

Helicopters are sometimes used in construction for such operations as the placement of a steeple. Although the use of helicopters in construction is rare, the nature of the hazards of the operation is somewhat strange and therefore deserves some mention. Ordinary tag lines, used with all cranes to control the load from below, can be a hazard to helicopters because the lines can be drawn up into the rotors, resulting in a tragedy. Tag lines must be of a length that will not permit their being drawn up into the rotors.

Cargo hooks are another problem with helicopters used as cranes. With ordinary cranes, the sole concern is that the hook will hold and not release at the wrong time. With helicopters, there is this concern and the additional concern that the hook might *not* release at the right time. Cargo hooks for helicopter cranes need to have an emergency mechanical control to release the load in case the electrical release fails.

Another unusual effect that can represent a hazard is the generation of a static electrical charge on the load. This charge is developed by the friction of the air on the rotor and other moving parts. To deal with this hazard, a grounding device can be used to dissipate the charge before ground personnel touch the load, or protective rubber gloves can be worn. Once the load actually touches down, the static charge is generally dissipated through the load itself directly into the ground.

An indirect hazard that can develop from the use of helicopters is fire on the ground. The rotating blades generate such a wind on the ground that it is considered unsafe to have open fires in the path of a low-flying helicopter.

Material and Personnel Hoists

Temporary external elevators are often used on construction sites to move workers and materials and must be designed, maintained, and used properly to avoid a serious hazard. The seriousness of this hazard is quite personal to me because my brother narrowly escaped a fatal accident on such a hoist when two of five members of his engineering inspection section were killed when a personnel hoist failed in an oil refinery. Two others were totally and permanently disabled, and the fifth, my brother, was uninjured because he had been asked to remain in the office that fateful day to complete an engineering drawing.

The design requirements for personnel hoists and material hoists are different, and one of the principal safety factors is maintaining the distinction between the two hoists during use. Material hoists must be conspicuously marked "No riders allowed." On the other hand, it is permissible to move material on a personnel hoist provided that rated capacities are not exceeded.

Latched gates are needed to guard the full width of the landing entrance for both material and personnel hoists. In the case of personnel hoists, an electrical interlock must not allow movement of the hoist when the door or gate is open. Furthermore, on personnel hoists, the hoistway doors or gates must have mechanical locks that are accessible only to persons in the car.

Aerial Lifts

An alternative to scaffolds, ladders, and hoists is needed for high and awkward locations on a construction site. The use of vehicle-mounted boom platforms or aerial "buckets" is becoming increasingly popular. The boom is usually *articulating* (capable of bending in the middle) or is *hydraulically extensible* (telescoping) or both.

The biggest problem with aerial lifts is not their construction, but the way they are used. Anyone in an aerial bucket needs to recognize the difference between his or her perch and terra firma. The floor of the bucket is the only place to stand—not on a ladder or plank carried aloft. Sitting on the bucket's edge is also dangerous. Even if the worker *does* stand properly in the bucket, a body belt with lanyard tied to the boom or bucket is needed to protect against a hazard such as a surprise encounter with a tree limb or a dip in terrain that can toss the operator from the basket.

HEAVY VEHICLES AND EQUIPMENT

Next to falls and electrocutions, more construction fatalities involve vehicles, tractors, and earthmoving equipment than any other hazard source. The fatality hazard is both to drivers of the equipment and to their coworkers. Vehicle *rollovers* are the principal cause of driver fatalities, whereas vehicle *runovers* are the problem for coworkers. Not to be excluded, however, is a significant number of fatalities from repairing tires for these vehicles.

ROPS

The acronym ROPS (rhymes with "hops") represents the term *rollover protective structures* and is a major change in construction vehicle design brought about by federal safety standards. The purpose of the ROPS, illustrated in Figure 18.13, is to protect the operator from serious injury or death in the event the vehicle rolls over. The following kinds of construction equipment require ROPS:

- Rubber-tired, self-propelled scrapers
- Rubber-tired, front-end loaders
- Rubber-tired dozers
- Wheel-type agricultural and industrial tractors
- Crawler tractors
- Crawler-type loaders
- Motor graders

Exempted are sideboom pipelaying tractors.

To be effective, the ROPS system must be able to withstand tremendous shock loads, which increase as the weight of the vehicle increases. The standards are quite specific regarding the structural tests to which ROPS systems must be subjected in order to qualify. For all wheel-type agricultural and industrial tractors used in construction, either a laboratory test or a field test is required to determine whether performance requirements are met. The laboratory test may be either static or dynamic. In

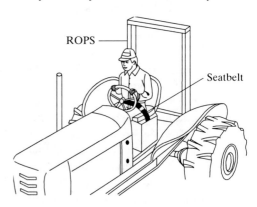

FIGURE 18.13

Rollover protective structures for construction vehicles prevent fatalities when used with seatbelts.

the static test, the stationary tractor chassis is gradually loaded while strain is measured by deflection instruments. The required input energy is a function of tractor weight, which in turn is required to be a function of tractor horsepower. In other words, the tractor's gross weight cannot be lightened below rated horsepower limits in order to meet ROPS tests.

The dynamic test, an alternative to the static test, uses a 2-ton pendulum that provides an impact load on the rear and side of the ROPS in successive tests. The height from which the pendulum is dropped is dependent on the calculated tractor weight based on horsepower, as in the static test just described. Deflection limits must not be exceeded.

If the field test is used, the tractor is actually rolled over, both rearward and sideways, as both types of accidents can easily occur. If the actual weight of the tractor is less than specified for its horsepower, ballast must be added for the tests.

For all ROPS tests, it is a good idea to remove protective glass and weather shields, which would probably be destroyed during the test. If there is any question whether such shields may absorb some of the energy, thereby assisting ROPS to pass the test, the shields *must* be removed.

Having read thus far, one can see that retrofitting an old tractor to meet current requirements for ROPS is not an easy task. The safety and health manager is cautioned against taking the tractor to a local welder and requesting a ROPS system to be fabricated. Unless the tractor is actually going to be subjected to the standard ROPS test, the frame should be of a design identical to a frame actually tested for the model tractor in question. Very old or rare model tractors are obviously a problem. If a qualified ROPS system is removed for any reason, it must be remounted with bolts or welding of equal or better quality than those required for the original. The ROPS must be permanently labeled with manufacturer's or fabricator's name and address and the machine make, model, or series number that the structure is designed to fit. This labeling requirement is a sobering thought for the welder or fabricator who is asked to retrofit an old tractor with a ROPS system. All told, it is easy to see why most companies dump the old equipment on the used-equipment market, and many are shipped to foreign countries that do not require ROPS.

After the safety and health manager has ensured that all appropriate construction equipment has been equipped with ROPS systems, the next task is to ensure that the equipment is used properly. Essential to the effectiveness of the ROPS system is that the operator wear a seat belt. If the operator is thrown out of the vehicle, the ROPS will afford no protection at all and may actually contribute to a fatality. Passengers are another hazard unless the vehicle is equipped with seat belts for passengers. Hitchhiking on heavy equipment at construction sites is a dangerous practice.

Runover Protection

Most of the balance of fatalities with heavy construction equipment is due to personnel being run over by the equipment. Confrontation of this major fatality category has two main thrusts: operator visibility and pedestrian awareness.

Operator visibility as good as the visibility in a private automobile is simply not feasible for a huge piece of earthmoving machinery. It is no wonder that runovers occur frequently on construction sites. The operator needs all the help affordable, but ironically, some of the poorest windshield conditions occur on construction equipment.

In the morning, the operator, foreman, and everyone concerned is anxious to get equipment rolling, but if the morning is cold, defrosting and defogging are essential. Often, the defrosting or defogging equipment is ineffective. Dirty or cracked windshields are also a common sight in the harsh environment of the construction job.

The second link in the hazard-prevention chain for runovers is the horn used by the operator to warn personnel when visibility *is* good enough to notice the endangered worker on the ground. Personnel are generally distributed all over a construction site, and the operator needs a good operable horn to warn them when they are dangerously close.

Besides the ordinary horn, many construction vehicles also need "backup alarms." Earthmoving equipment and construction vehicles that have an obstructed view to the rear need these backup alarms if they are used in reverse gear. The term *obstructed view* may be somewhat vague, but most safety and health professionals are taking the position that earthmoving machines of all types need these backup alarms. Too many people have been killed by machines backing over them to take this requirement lightly. This is said although it is acknowledged that the steady beep-beep-beep of the backup alarms can be very monotonous on a construction site and perhaps even lead to a certain complacency on the part of the personnel endangered. An alternative to the beeping backup alarms is the use of an observer standing behind the machine to alert others every time the machine backs up. This is expensive, though, and has the disadvantage of being an *administrative* or *work-practice control*, instead of the preferred *engineering control* represented by the backup alarm.

Dump Trucks

One more hazard with construction vehicles and equipment needs emphasis. Dump trucks can cause a terrible accident if the raised dump body falls while the driver or some other worker has crawled into the exposed area for maintenance or inspection work. Sometimes all that holds the dump body aloft is the pressure in a hydraulic line, which can be suddenly lost due to any of a variety of failure modes. For this reason, the safety of the maintenance or inspection worker inside the exposed area demands that the truck be equipped with some positive means of support, permanently attached and capable of being locked into position.

TRENCHING AND EXCAVATIONS

A major cause of construction fatalities is the sudden collapse of the wall of a trench or excavation. It is difficult to imagine the drama of digging for a coworker who has been literally buried alive in such a cave-in. Before becoming involved in the field of occupational safety and health, I coincidentally became an eyewitness to such a drama in Tempe, Arizona. The trench was located directly below a public stairway landing on which I happened to be standing, and thus my vantage point was directly over the scene of the cave-in. The impression was unforgettable, and its memory would motivate anyone to try to prevent such accidents in the future, a point supporting the principles of hazard avoidance. Recognizing the seriousness of this hazard, OSHA has undertaken several special-emphasis programs on trenching and excavation cave-ins.

Joseph Dear, in the mid-1990s (ref. Dear), cited a dramatic result of such emphasis in the State of Indiana where trenching and excavation fatalities decreased from six per year to one per year after conducting special trenching programs.

All trenches are excavations, but not all excavations are trenches. Trenches are narrow, deep excavations; the depth is greater than the width, but the width is no greater than 15 feet, according to the standard definition. A trench is more confined and generally more dangerous than other excavations, especially because both walls can collapse, trapping the worker. However, the walls of a trench are easier to shore than the walls of an excavation. Both are dangerous if over 5 feet deep and will easily snuff out the life of anyone who stands in the path of a collapsing wall. The hazard is not simply one of suffocation. A cave-in generally represents tons of falling earth, which can crush the body and lungs of the worker even if the face and breathing passages are left clear.

The *angle of repose* is defined as the greatest angle above the horizontal plane at which a material will lie without sliding. The angle naturally varies with the material, and approximate angles are shown in Figure 18.14. The science of soil slides is not exact, and the uncertainty thwarts attempts to control the hazard. It is difficult to say whether a particular soil type is "typical" or "compacted angular gravels," or something between the two. The specifications for trench shoring are more detailed, as can be seen in Table 18.2.

Adding to the uncertainty of the cave-in hazard are certain hazard-increasing factors, such as

- Rainstorms, which soften the earth and promote slides
- Vibrations from heavy equipment or street traffic nearby
- Previous disturbances of the soil, as from previous construction or other excavations
- Alternate freezing and thawing of the soil
- Large static loads, as from nearby building foundations or stacked material

Although judgment is required in deciding whether to employ shoring, the hazard is so serious that it is wise to adopt a conservative policy, well clear of the marginal

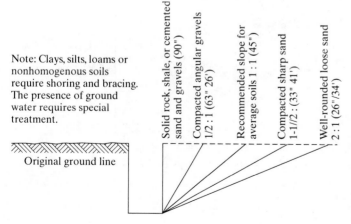

Note: Clays, silts, loams or nonhomogenous soils require shoring and bracing. The presence of ground water requires special treatment.

Original ground line

Solid rock, shale, or cemented sand and gravels (90")
Compacted angular gravels 1/2 : 1 (63" 26')
Recommended slope for average soils 1 : 1 (45")
Compacted sharp sand 1-1/2 : (33" 41')
Well-rounded loose sand 2 : 1 (26"/34')

FIGURE 18.14

Approximate angle of repose for sloping the sides of excavations.

TABLE 18.2 Trench Shoring—Minimum Requirements

Depth of trench (ft)	Kind or condition of earth	Uprights Minimum dimension (in.)	Uprights Maximum spacing (ft)	Stringers Minimum dimension (in.)	Stringers Maximum spacing (ft)	Cross braces[a] Width of trench (ft) Up to 3	3–6	6–9	9–12	12–15	Maximum spacing (ft) Vertical	Horizontal
5–10	Hard, compact	3 × 4 or 2 × 6	6			2 × 6	4 × 4	4 × 6	6 × 6	6 × 8	4	6
	Likely to crack	3 × 4 or 2 × 6	3	4 × 6	4	2 × 6	4 × 4	4 × 6	6 × 6	6 × 8	4	6
	Soft, sandy, or filled	3 × 4 or 2 × 6	Close sheeting	4 × 6	4	4 × 4	4 × 6	6 × 6	6 × 6	8 × 8	4	6
	Hydrostatic pressure	3 × 4 or 2 × 6	Close sheeting	6 × 8	4	4 × 4	4 × 6	6 × 6	6 × 8	8 × 8	4	6
10–15	Hard	3 × 4 or 2 × 6	4	4 × 6	4	4 × 4	4 × 6	6 × 6	6 × 8	8 × 8	4	6
	Likely to crack	3 × 4 or 2 × 6	2	4 × 6	4	4 × 4	4 × 6	6 × 6	6 × 8	8 × 8	4	6
	Soft, sandy, or filled	3 × 4 or 2 × 6	Close sheeting	4 × 6	4	4 × 6	6 × 6	6 × 8	8 × 8	8 × 10	4	6
	Hydrostatic pressure	3 × 6	Close sheeting	8 × 10	4	4 × 6	6 × 6	6 × 8	8 × 8	8 × 10	4	6
15–20	All kinds or conditions	3 × 6	Close sheeting	4 × 12	4	4 × 12	6 × 8	8 × 8	8 × 10	10 × 10	4	6
Over 20	All kinds or conditions	3 × 6	Close sheeting	6 × 8	4	4 × 12	8 × 8	8 × 10	10 × 10	10 × 12	4	6

[a]Trench jacks may be used in lieu of, or in combination with, cross braces. Shoring is not required in solid rock, hard shale, or hard slag. Where desirable, steel sheet piling and bracing of equal strength may be substituted for wood.

Source: Code of Federal Regulations 29 CFR 1926.652.

area where a cave-in might or might not occur. One thing is certain: *After* the cave-in *does* occur, and there is a fatality, the OSHA officer will come to the scene, and everyone (including the OSHA officer) will conclude that the shoring or cave-in protection was insufficient.

A trench shoring system is shown in Figure 18.15. The trench jacks may be either screw-type or hydraulically operated. They need to be secured to prevent falling or sliding if they loosen as the sidewalls adjust slightly. Care must be taken to level the jacks and also to be sure that they are below the plane of the surface of the surrounding earth. A trench jack placed too high can be subjected to bending stresses, as shown in Figure 18.16. This can damage or even ruin the trench jack. The shoring system should be removed slowly and carefully. It is sometimes necessary to remove braces or jacks by means of ropes from above after everyone has cleared the trench.

A cave-in is not the only hazard to working in trenches and excavations. All workers in the ditch are subject to the hazards of falling rocks, tools, timbers, or pipes. Head protection is needed for workers below, and good housekeeping is important along the edges of the excavation.

Even when personnel are not inside the excavation and machines do all the work, another hazard presents itself. Utility lines are often broken, resulting in fire, explosion, or inhalation hazards. Such accidents are not only dangerous, but are always costly and require additional coordination with the utility company—coordination that would have been better handled in advance of the excavation. The safety and health

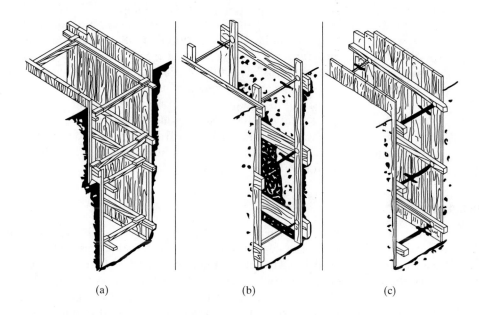

(a)   (b)   (c)

FIGURE 18.15

Trench shoring system: (a) bracing used with two lengths of sheet piling; (b) bracing with screw jacks, hard soil; (c) screw jacks used with complete sheet piling (*Source*: courtesy of the National Safety Council, Chicago; used with permission).

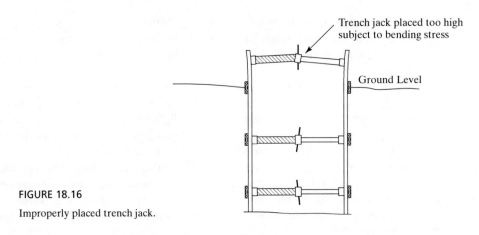

FIGURE 18.16

Improperly placed trench jack.

manager should install a procedure that ensures that someone stops and checks with utility companies before proceeding "blind" into an excavation project. Excavation contractors are generally familiar with the information system for dye marking underground utilities. Signs often post warnings: "DO NOT DIG; BURIED UTILITIES." Most communities have a toll-free number accessing a free service for dye marking underground utilities to warn excavation contractors before proceeding.

Signs of an imminent cave-in, rupture of a utility line, dangerous accumulations of toxic gases in deep excavations, or other possible emergency situations dictate the need for quick and easy exit. A ladder, steps, or other adequate means of exit should be located so as to require no more than 25 feet of lateral travel for escape.

It was stated at the beginning of this section that OSHA has undertaken several "special-emphasis" programs for enforcement of trenching and excavation hazards. Just how much "special emphasis" does OSHA place on this type of hazard? Some insight is provided in a 1997 news release (ref. Fleming, 1997) in which OSHA stated that in the previous 5-year period the agency and state agencies having enforcement jurisdiction had conducted a total of 9400 trenching inspections. Of these, almost 200 inspections were investigations of fatal accidents. Trenching and excavations remain as one of the principal hazards of the construction industry, and it is likely that OSHA will continue its emphasis well into the 21st century.

CONCRETE WORK

Perhaps the most dramatic industrial accident in history was the partial collapse of a vertical wall of concrete. The year was 1978, and the location was Willow Island, West Virginia, where a huge cooling tower was under construction for a nuclear power plant. The continuously poured concrete walls of the structure supported scaffolds for workers 170 feet above the ground. At the time of the accident the "green" concrete wall was insufficiently cured to accept the load. The wall failed, dropping the scaffold; 51 workers fell to their deaths.

The pressure to keep a construction project on schedule is antagonistic to the careful curing of concrete. But the consequences of rushing the job are serious even if no one is injured. The memory of the tragic Willow Island accident serves to remind concrete project managers of these consequences. Concrete curing time is a function of both time and temperature. About 70°F is ideal, and temperatures either too hot or too cold can delay curing.

Even before the concrete is poured there are hazards to the placement of the reinforcing steel *rebars*. For vertical structures, rebars need guys or other support to prevent collapse. Another hazard is the protruding points of exposed vertical rebars. It may seem farfetched, but workers have actually been *impaled* by falling on these bars. The most serious hazards are for workers on ladders when these ladders are placed over protruding rebars. But even at floor or ground level, a trip and fall on an exposed rebar can be fatal. In one case, a worker stumbled at ground level and fell on an exposed rebar, which impaled his neck and ruptured his jugular vein. The life of the worker was saved by the quick action of a trained first-aid person. The answer to the exposed rebar problem is to bend down the ends, cover them with plywood, or wrap them with canvas until ready for pouring.

Concrete forms need carefully designed shoring systems to prevent collapse together with hazards reminiscent of the excavation cave-in hazards discussed earlier. The hydrostatic pressure of wet concrete can be very great just after it is poured. Then, at a time when the forms' stress is greatest, vibrating equipment is often applied to ensure even distribution, adding to the stresses on the forms. Overdesign is necessary to prevent the hazard of forms "kickout."

Concrete is often poured by buckets handled by cranes. Unfortunately, vibrator crews have to work with the freshly poured concrete in close proximity to the moving bucket. The pouring strategy should be to keep the vibrator crews away from the overhead path of the bucket. Riding the concrete bucket is prohibited.

STEEL ERECTION

Who has not marveled at the daring of the highrise steelworker "walking the beam" hundreds of feet up the steel superstructure of a new building under construction? Perhaps this work will always be dangerous, but the hazard has been mollified somewhat by requiring safety nets to be installed whenever the fall distance exceeds two stories or 25 feet. An alternative is to use scaffolds or temporary floors. Case Study 18.1 is a classic example of the benefits of using safety nets in steel erection.

CASE STUDY 18.1

SAFETY NETS ON THE GOLDEN GATE BRIDGE

The construction of San Francisco's Golden Gate Bridge in the 1930s was a dramatic engineering feat made even more perilous by the wind, rain, and ocean tides. Many workers lost their lives due to falls into the treacherous water. After the death toll reached, 23 workers refused to continue without increased safety protection. Work was resumed after safety nets were installed. An additional 10 workers fell from the bridge, but all 10 were saved by the safety nets (ref. Avers).

A safety railing around the perimeters of temporary floors is now required for tier buildings and other multifloored structures. During structural steel assembly, however, the use of $\frac{1}{2}$-inch wire rope approximately 42 inches high is permitted for the safety railing. To be effective, the wire rope should be checked frequently to be sure that it remains taut.

To maintain structural integrity on the way up, the permanent floors should follow the structural steel as the work progresses. The general rule is no more than eight stories between the erection floor and the uppermost permanent floor. No more than four floors or 48 feet of unfinished bolting or welding is permitted above the foundation or uppermost permanently secured floor.

Structural steel erection sites are subject to constant hazards of falling objects. Rivets, bolts, and drift pins are required to be stored in secured containers, and if all else fails, there is the hard hat to protect the worker below. For some objects at the steel erection site, the hard hat is no protection, however. I am reminded of an instance in Chicago in which a falling steel beam flattened a parked car from left taillight to right headlight. The car was parked next to a sidewalk along which I walked to and from a meeting. The accident occurred during the meeting; luckily, no one was injured.

DEMOLITION

Some would say that the subject of demolition does not belong in this chapter, but demolition and construction are actually closely related. If the construction site is not clear, demolition of previous structures may be the first step in construction of a new building. Many of the tools and equipment, such as cranes and bulldozers, are the same.

People identify skill, knowledge, and quality as important to construction jobs, but most people do not think of demolition as requiring skill and knowledge. But often the engineering expertise required of a demolition job far exceeds the engineering for the original construction. Buildings to be demolished have often been previously damaged by fire or may have been condemned for some serious reason, such as structural damage. Required for every demolition operation is a written report of an engineering survey conducted in advance.

A demolition operation begins with manual operations, such as disassembly of salvage items, and then proceeds to material teardown and dumping to street level. Dangers exist in the debris dumping operation. The area below needs protection if it is outside the walls of the structure. Well-designed chutes capable of withstanding impact loads, together with substantial discharge gates, are needed to control the dropping material. One hazard is that personnel can fall down the chute while dumping debris. A substantial guardrail about 42 inches high is needed to protect against this hazard. A toeboard or bumper is also needed, if wheelbarrows are used, to prevent losing the wheelbarrow down the chute.

Once light teardown operations are completed, heavier demolition equipment such as cranes with wrecking balls are used. Most walls are unstable without lateral support, so they should not be allowed to stand alone at heights greater than one story. No unstable standing wall should be left at the end of a shift.

One sensational demolition technique that is gaining in popularity is controlled explosive demolition, illustrated in Figure 18.17. In this method, carefully engineered

FIGURE 18.17

Building collapses under controlled explosive demolition (*Source*: courtesy of
Jim Wolfe Photo, Tulsa, Oklahoma).

explosive charges are detonated to precipitate a catastrophic failure of the building
structure, resulting in an immediate and total collapse. The operation has been carried out successfully on many downtown buildings in U.S. cities, typically triggered at
the quiet time of dawn on Sunday mornings. Although the operation is dramatic and
seems dangerous, it is really quite safe and avoids many of the hazards of a slow teardown process.

EXPLOSIVE BLASTING

Demolition is only one application for blasting; the construction industry has others.
The preparation of roadway cuts is the most important. The chief concern with

construction blasting is the safe handling, storage, and transportation of the explosives themselves.

Almost everyone has witnessed the familiar warning to "turn off two-way radio" when in a blasting area. The chance is remote, but an electrically fired blasting cap could be detonated by a small stray current induced by a radio transmitter. Lightning is even more of a hazard, and all blasting operations should cease when an electrical storm is near. Radar, nearby power lines, and even dust storms can also be sources of stray currents.

Good visibility reduces many hazards, and explosive blasting hazards are in this category. Aboveground blasting should be conducted in the daytime only. Black powder blasting has been replaced by safer modern methods, and black powder blasting is now prohibited in construction.

The transportation of explosive materials is subject to Department of Transportation (DOT) regulations familiar to suppliers and most construction operators who use explosives. Signs saying **EXPLOSIVES** in large (4-inch) red letters are required on all four sides of the vehicle. Blasting caps should be transported in a separate vehicle from the vehicle transporting other explosives, and both should be transported separate from other cargoes.

Vehicles for explosives need a good fire extinguisher rated at least 10-ABC on board. It would be foolhardy to attempt to control a fire in the cargo compartment of a vehicle transporting explosives. However, most vehicle fires begin in the engine compartment or outside but adjacent to the vehicle. Such fires can sometimes be controlled with a good fire extinguisher wielded by a trained operator, thereby averting a major explosives catastrophe.

ELECTRIC UTILITIES

A specialized type of construction is the erection and modification of electric transmission and distribution lines and equipment. The efficient transmission of usable levels of electrical power necessitates very high voltages. The rules for handling high voltages are quite different from the rules for handling ordinary household and industrial and commercial voltages. For instance, with ordinary voltages, a danger is the contact with exposed live parts. With high voltages, it can be dangerous even to approach the *vicinity* of live parts, as is reflected in Table 18.3 based on the OSHA standard. For voltages in the kilovolt range, the atmosphere may not be an effective insulator, and arcing becomes a hazard. Therefore, safety distances must be maintained. Of course, the distances shown in Table 18.3 apply safety factors. The actual physical arcing distances are much smaller, but there is an element of uncertainty due to such factors as humidity and barometric pressure. Furthermore, the electric-utility lineman may not be able to estimate precisely his distance from the high-voltage line or equipment, making safety factors essential.

Personal protective equipment for high-voltage work takes on a new dimension, that of *degree* of protection. Ordinary insulators on tools, protective gloves, and other insulating equipment that are effective insulators for ordinary applications might completely break down in high-voltage exposures. The whole business of working with energized high-voltage lines is a strange world to the uninitiated—a world fraught with

TABLE 18.3 Minimum Clearance Distances for Live-Line Bare-Hand Work (Alternating Current)

| Voltage range (phase to phase) (kV) | Distance (feet and inches) for maximum voltage | |
	Phase to ground	Phase to phase
2.1–15	2–0	2–0
15.1–35	2–4	2–4
35.1–46	2–6	2–6
46.1–72.5	3–0	3–0
72.6–121	3–4	4–6
138–45	3–6	5–0
161–169	3–8	5–6
230–242	5–0	8–4
345–362	7–0[a]	13–4[a]
500–552	11–0[a]	20–0[a]
700–765	15–0[a]	31–0[a]

[a] For 345–362, 500–552, and 700–765 kV, the minimum clearance distance may be reduced provided that the distances are not made less than the shortest distance between the energized part and a grounded surface.

Source: Code of Federal Regulations 29 CFR 1926.955.

curious physical effects. The electric-utility industry offers a prime example of an industry in which training in awareness and understanding of hazards is the key to a safe workplace.

SUMMARY

The construction industry deserves special consideration because it is so dangerous and also because OSHA has watched construction more closely than general industries. The safety and health manager for construction jobs should remember that the principal task is to avoid *fatalities*. The top five categories of fatalities in the construction industry are

- Falls
- Electrocutions
- Vehicle rollover
- Personnel runover by vehicle
- Excavation cave-ins

If the safety and health manager keeps these fatality categories in mind, it will help to place overall efforts in proper perspective on the construction site.

This complete chapter has represented somewhat a summary of the entire book. The construction industry displays virtually every hazard presented by general industry, but in construction, the hazard is usually worse. Compounding the problem is the transitory nature of the problems that are encountered. It is difficult to pursue costly safeguarding procedures such as trench shoring when the exposure to the hazard will consist of only a few days or even hours. Construction schedules are always demanding for several reasons. High-stakes investments are on the line, costly interruptions to facilities and street traffic are often present, and unplanned chance events are always popping up to ensure that the construction project manager will always struggle to stay on schedule. In this environment, there will always be room for improvements to the safety and health program. What is true for construction is also true of general industry, although perhaps to a lesser degree. The reader should recognize the challenge that this reality represents.

It is hoped that this book has cast some light on the challenges that face the safety and health manager in today's industrial and regulatory environment and some insights for dealing with these challenges. The field is certain to present new challenges in the coming years. Each new challenge ushers in new opportunities for safety and health managers to have an impact on the lives of their co-workers and on the health and financial well-being of their companies.

EXERCISES AND STUDY QUESTIONS

18.1 What is the minimum illumination level permitted for general construction areas? In what areas may lighting be reduced to 3 foot candles?

18.2 How are lasers used in construction?

18.3 What tensile strength is specified for safety belt hardware? Give two reasons that the specification is so much higher than the weight of any human being.

18.4 What is a safety belt lanyard? What nominal breaking strength is specified for lanyards?

18.5 What is a triple rolling hitch?

18.6 Compare hydraulic versus pneumatic power tools from a safety and health standpoint.

18.7 How are construction cranes particularly hazardous to persons on the ground?

18.8 Why are helicopter hooks (for load attachment) more complicated than those for ordinary construction cranes?

18.9 What does the acronym *ROPS* represent?

18.10 What are the two principal strategies for preventing personnel from being run over by construction equipment?

18.11 What is the difference between a trench and an excavation?

18.12 How can trench jacks be damaged by improper placements?

18.13 What is a rebar? Why is it dangerous?

18.14 When must steel erection workers be protected against falls with safety nets?

18.15 What type of safety rail construction is permitted during steel erection?

18.16 Why is an engineering survey required prior to demolition of a building?

18.17 Is it a good idea to carry a fire extinguisher aboard a truck that transports explosives? Why or why not?

18.18 A crawler-type construction crane is operating near a 550-kilovolt power line. What is the minimum distance the boom should approach the line?

18.19 The crawler-type construction crane in Exercise 18.18 finishes its job and travels to the next job, passing under the same 550-kilovolt power line where the power line crosses over a city street at a different location in the neighborhood. What minimum distance is specified for this situation?

18.20 Suppose in Exercise 18.18 that the crawler crane had been employed in general industry instead of construction. What minimum distance would be permitted in general industry?

18.21 For the crane of Exercise 18.20, what is the minimum clearance from the 550-kV power line if the crane is in transit?

18.22 A painter is standing on a work platform that is 27 feet above ground level. For fall protection, the worker's safety belt is attached to a 12-foot safety line, which serves as a lanyard and is securely fastened to the structure at a point 40 feet above ground level. Does this arrangement violate standards for fall protection? Explain.

18.23 A convenient and secure attachment point for fall protection lines is located 35 feet above ground level on the exterior wall of a building. A 20-foot safety line, which can be used as a belt lanyard, is available for connection to this attachment point. What is the lowest and highest level at which a work platform can be safely positioned for workers to be protected by a 20-foot belt lanyard fastened to this attachment point? State any assumptions necessary to your solution.

18.24 Explain the hazard of mushroomed heads on chisels.

18.25 What provisions are specified by federal standards to protect workers from drowning?

18.26 Explain the coding system for identifying the power level for cased power loads for powder-actuated tools.

18.27 To comply with standards, how often should material handling rigging on a construction site be checked?

18.28 What is the standard method of disposing of scrap materials from higher than ground level during construction? What special precaution is required when the material to be discarded is at a height greater than 20 feet?

18.29 What is the principal fire hazard on construction sites?

18.30 What personnel hazard arises when a pneumatic power hose is severed? What device is specified by federal standards to deal with this hazard? What problems have been encountered in the field with the use of this device?

18.31 Describe several ways in which a crane can be maneuvered into a two-blocking situation. Prove your point using diagrams to clarify your reasoning.

18.32 What hazard takes priority in the selection of the type of hydraulic fluid to be used for general construction tools? How does this priority change when the hydraulic tools are used in the public utility industry?

18.33 Compare the hazards of handguns and powder-actuated tools.

18.34 Explain the controversy behind the requirement for GFCIs in the construction industry.

18.35 What is a cornice hook? What additional precautions are needed when cornice hooks are used?

18.36 What is the principal hazard of using concrete blocks for scaffold "cribbing"?

18.37 What are hollow, pan-type treads, and what hazard do they represent?

18.38 **Case Study.** A construction crane is resting with no load, and the headache ball is close to, but not touching, the nose of the crane boom, which is in an almost erect position. The running rope of the crane is mounted on a stationary winch to the rear of the boom hinge. While the operator is in the process of lowering the boom, the wire rope breaks and the headache ball and hook assembly falls to the ground. Explain the most likely cause of this accident. Use a diagram to show how the hazard would develop. What precaution could have prevented it?

18.39 How many lives were lost due to falls during the construction of the Golden Gate Bridge? How many additional falls occurred after the erection of safety nets? How many of these additional falls were fatalities?

18.40 At what time in a building's life is the floor likely to be subjected to its heaviest load?

18.41 What is "two-blocking," and under what conditions do ANSI standards require "two-blocking damage prevention features?"

18.42 How often must rigging for construction material handling be inspected for damage or wear?

18.43 What characteristic of artificial fiber ropes besides strength and weight make them especially favorable for selection as lanyard ropes?

18.44 What is "spalling" and what has it to do with the need for eye protection?

18.45 Is it okay to splice flexible extension cords on construction sites? Explain.

18.46 What is a "headache ball" and what is its purpose?

18.47 What is the principal advantage of a hammerhead tower crane over a conventional crawler crane?

18.48 Cargo hooks for helicopters used in construction have an additional hazard that is not present for cargo hooks for construction cranes. What is this additional hazard?

18.49 Is it okay to use a material hoist for personnel? What about vice versa? Explain.

18.50 Explain the terms *articulating* and *hydraulically extensible* with respect to vehicle-mounted boom platforms.

18.51 Identify an example "engineering control" versus an example "administrative or work-practice control" for the hazard of personnel being run over by heavy construction equipment.

18.52 Explain the concept of "angle of repose" with respect to construction hazards.

18.53 Identify the two types of extraordinary stress on concrete forms that creates a need for overdesign to prevent forms kickout.

18.54 Identify the top five fatality hazards to construction workers.

RESEARCH EXERCISES

18.55 Construction and agriculture share many common hazards. Examine available data on agriculture hazards. Specifically, attempt to identify the single most common fatal farm accident. How many fatalities are estimated to occur each year due to this cause?

18.56 Less than 10 years after the Willow Island, West Virginia, tragedy that took the lives of 51 construction workers, another accident of the same type occurred. Use the Internet or other sources to look up details of this second tragedy of the same type resulting in the highest number of construction fatalities since Willow Island.

18.57 **Research Case Study.** In an actual accident,[3] a construction worker was installing steel channel for a roof of a new building. He was using a fall protection system, by attaching his standard 6-foot lanyard to a line that ultimately connected to a rigid structure. However, the attachment line was an extra 10 feet of line looped between the lanyard and the rigid attachment. Since the 10-foot line was looped, its working length was half that: 5 feet. The worker was standing on a 10″ beam, which was 20 feet off the concrete slab floor. This beam served as the rigid attachment for the worker's lifeline system. The worker lost his balance and accidentally fell. How far do you estimate that he fell? (*Hint: The answer is not 11 feet.*)

---

[3]The source of the information surrounding this accident has been withheld upon request.

Index

A

Abrasive, 318
  wheel, 347
Accident:
  analyses, 76, 83
  courses traced back to management
    responsibilities, 4
  reports, 75
  accidental motion, 313
Accidental in–process damage or loss, 28
Accident Investigation Form (Department of
    Labor), 62
Accident investigations, 60
  accident reports, 66
  completed products, loss of, 69
  conduct of, 64
  conducting, 65
  contributing personnel, 63
  corrective actions, 68
  costs, certifying/evaluating, 68
  emergencies, labor costs in combating, 69
  equipment, 65, 69
  initiation of, 65
  insurance adjuster, 69
  insurance claims, 68
  investigating board chairman's responsibilities,
    63
  investigating board members/professionals, 64
  lost claim, preparing, 69
  materials in process, loss of, 69
  methods of, 66

  raw materials, losses of, 69
  reason for, 60
  statements, 65
  temporary facilities, erection/use of, 69
Acetone, 231–232
Acetylene, 231–233
Acoustics, 381
Adjustable barriers, 326
Administrative controls, 76, 408
Aerial baskets, 273
Aerial lifts, 405
Aeroembolism, 186
Aggravating factors, 88
Air:
  compressors, 354,
  conditioners, 221
Aisles, 263–266
  blockage, 280
  marking, 265
  standards for, 265
  trip hazards, 264–265
  water on the floor, 264
  widths, 260, 265
Alarms:
  audible, 80
  backup, 408
  filter, 365
  visible, 80
Alert mode, 77
Aluminum extrusions, 353
American Gas Association, 172
  Standard Z16.1, 48